ECHOES FROM THE SKY

Richard N. Scarth

First edition published by the Hythe Civic Society 1999
Second edition 2014

Revised and expanded edition published in 2017 by:

Independent Books
3 Leaves Green Crescent
Keston
Bromley
BR2 6DN
United Kingdom

Tel: 01959 573360

e-mail: mail@indbooks.co.uk

web site: www.indbooks.co.uk

Jacket design and page layout by Peter Osborne

Printed and bound in Malta by Melita Press

ISBN (13):   978-1-872836-17-1

Front cover illustration by Tony Crowhurst
Back cover illustrations by Peter Osborne

In memory of
Dr William Sansome Tucker O.B.E.
1877 - 1955
and his scientific colleagues.

ECHOES FROM THE SKY

RICHARD N SCARTH

CONTENTS

PHOTOGRAPHS AND ILLUSTRATIONS

INTRODUCTION

The first edition of 'Echoes from the Sky' was published in 1999. After that Richard commenced further research, made more contacts and found previously unknown sources. The last piece of this jigsaw was the rediscovery of the mirrors at Fan Bay, near Dover, which we visited in October 2014; tragically, Richard died two weeks later, following an accident.

A chance contact in 2015 offered the opportunity of seeing this legacy, the much expanded and revised work, published. It also offered the chance to have it brought right up to date with the addition of material on the Fan Bay mirrors, written by two of the people who discovered the mirrors and our publisher. I hope you enjoy this account of a unique piece of scientific history which without Richard's interest and tenacious research might have remained largely forgotten. I am, therefore, extremely grateful to all those who have made this revised edition of 'Echoes from the Sky' possible.

HPS – 2017.

FOREWORD

THE ACOUSTIC YEARS

Some years ago I wrote a small book on acoustic early warning systems. I had little idea at the time that there would be such public and media interest in the subject. "*Mirrors by the Sea*" was followed by a more comprehensive account in a second book "*Echoes from the Sky*". In writing the present volume, I have made use of the original material together with the results of further research in the intervening years.

Aircraft detection based on listening for distant engines is not an exact science. Weather conditions affect the transmission of sound waves through the atmosphere, and extraneous noise in the local environment creates problems for the listener. Nevertheless, in the first half of the twentieth century before the advent of radar, great efforts were made over many years to develop early warning systems against hostile aircraft using acoustic methods. This book is about those acoustic years. The story begins in the First World War of 1914 - 18 when listeners were at work on the Western Front plotting the positions of enemy guns. By the end of that war, experiments in the acoustic detection of aircraft were taking place both in France and on the Home Front in England. The development of listening systems continued throughout the inter-war period and into the early years of the Second World War.

There was considerable overlapping of the various lines of acoustic research, and following a strictly chronological plan would make the story too complex. For greater simplicity, I have chosen to base this account on three main themes, each related to a type of equipment used in acoustic detection. The first theme begins with a description of the work of pioneers engaged in gun sound ranging on the Western Front in the First World War. Some of those people went on to develop acoustical methods of aircraft detection, in particular the use of sound mirrors, until such devices were rendered obsolete in the late 1930s by the advent of radar. A second theme is related to experiments with acoustic disks which ended in the middle 1930s. The third main theme covers the development of mobile sound locators using trumpet-type collectors, beginning in the First World War and continuing into the early years of the Second World War.

Many of the documents studied during a long period of research give an insight into the largely forgotten work of members of the Air Defence Experimental Establishment under the leadership of Dr W. S. Tucker. I make no apology for the frequent quotations which are a feature of the book. The account is based for the most part on primary sources in the form of letters, personal papers, and archive documents. It seems important to tell the story whenever possible in the words of those who took part, attempting to bring to life dusty records of efforts to design acoustic aerial defence systems in the years before radar.

RNS

CHAPTER ONE

SOUND RANGING

The world famous narrow gauge Romney Hythe and Dymchurch Railway on the Kent coast in South East England has carried many thousands of passengers since its inception in 1927. No tourist trains ever traversed a little known section of line constructed in the following year. That short branch, leaving the main line between New Romney and Dungeness, was built to carry materials for the construction of an acoustic aerial defence system. There are few visible remains of the line which was abandoned in the 1950s, and for much of its length, the track bed is under water or covered by housing developments.

Part of the route survives as a footpath leading towards an area of the Dungeness peninsula known as Denge. Walkers along the path join a shingle causeway to the shores of a lake where they cross a swing bridge to an island, the site of three impressive concrete objects dominating the landscape at this point. Two of the devices are circular dishes of 20 and 30 feet in diameter (6.1 and 9.1m) and the third is a great curved wall, 200 feet long and 26 feet high (61m and 7.9m). These structures, known as sound mirrors, are acoustic devices, built between 1928 and 1930 for the detection of engine sounds from distant aircraft.

On a cold November day in 2004, a group of people stood on the forecourt before the great curved wall of the 200 foot sound mirror at Denge. Most of those present looked towards the sky, but a small team of scientists watched instruments set up on the forecourt. They became animated as graphs on their visual displays responded to signals from a microphone placed in the focal area of the mirror and a similar microphone standing on the open shingle nearby.

Soon, the distant beat of an aero engine could be heard, and a speck against the wintry sky grew into the outline of an approaching biplane. As it passed overhead, the Tiger Moth flew along the centre line of the sound mirror and then turned back over the sea. After several passes at different heights, the old biplane built in the 1930s and contemporary with the mirror, departed for base leaving the listeners to discuss the results of the experiment. There seemed no doubt that although the mirror had stood unused for almost 70 years and was in a state of partial decay, there was a response from the microphone placed at the focal point of the curved wall before the aircraft was in sight or sound of the listeners. Perhaps the ghosts of the men who created the 200 foot mirror were around somewhere on that day when the sound mirror was briefly re-activated, probably for the first time since abandonment.

Allowing for the ravages of time on the structure of the Denge 200 foot sound mirror, the main difference in operational method in 2004 compared with the 1930s was in the type of microphone used. In 2004, a single microphone of contemporary design was placed at the central focus of the mirror, whereas in the 1930s, a group of specially designed hot-wire microphones were spaced in a radial pattern along the focal area of the forecourt of the mirror. Those hot-wire microphones were a link back to the early days of acoustic experiments, as they were originally invented for use in gun sound ranging on the Western Front in the First World War.

Attacks on enemy trenches in that war were often preceded by tremendous artillery barrages. Great efforts were made to detect the positions of guns on the opposing side, and to plot the fall of shot from friendly guns. At first, this activity depended on visual observations from forward ground positions, and later on spotting from balloons and aeroplanes. But other methods were soon adopted.

In the early months of the war, both the French and the British experimented at the front line with methods of fixing the position of enemy batteries by plotting the sounds of gunfire. This activity was known as sound ranging, and in the early stages, the system depended upon observers sending in reports from various listening posts. These observations were collated to give some idea of the positions of enemy gun batteries. Success in this activity depended to a great extent on the use of maps and surveying techniques, and many of the people involved were selected for their particular skills as technicians, surveyors, and draftsmen. They became members of Field Survey Battalions, and their work in gun sound ranging is described in the historical record of the Royal Engineers. According to the record, these men "were not soldiers at all, but specially enlisted for their skill as craftsmen." Despite that statement, the very nature of the work ensured that members of gun sound ranging units were frequently exposed to the dangers of the front line. Some of the officers were peacetime academics, and such men play a key role in this account.

A manual of sound ranging in the Royal Artillery archives contains a description in general terms of the use of microphones in sound ranging.

"For the purpose of locating a gun by measurements made on the sound wave set up when it fires, it is necessary to know the intervals between the times of arrival of the sound wave at 3 or more points whose positions are known. The sound ranging instrument consists of 2 distinct parts:-

(i) At each of the fixed points, a microphone (i.e. an instrument capable of receiving the sound wave and of transmitting a signal instantaneously to a central headquarters)

(ii) At the headquarters an instrument capable of recording the signals from the various microphones and of registering accurately the instant at which each arrives.

It has been found in practice that the microphones should not normally be spread over a distance greater than 5 or 6 miles (8 or 9.7km). In order to obtain good results with a microphone base of this length, measurements of the time intervals to an accuracy of 1/100th of a second are necessary. This degree of accuracy cannot be obtained from any system of observation based on the use of stop watches. The personal errors in measurements with stop watches are comparatively large, so that an instrumental method of recording the time intervals is necessary in order to transmit a current to the recording instrument without appreciable lag."

In 1914, the War Office appointed Lieutenant, later Major W.L.Bragg to take charge of sound ranging in the British Army. This officer won the Nobel Prize for physics in 1915, sharing the distinction with his father W.H.Bragg. Major W.L.Bragg subsequently became famous as Sir Lawrence Bragg, Professor of Physics at Manchester University, and later at Cambridge, where he succeeded Rutherford. Bragg collected a small staff of physicists around him and began experiments to improve the system[1]. In June 1916, a Royal Engineer officer and scientist in his team, Lieutenant W.S.Tucker, invented a type of microphone which was named after him. According to a report in the Royal Engineers Journal, the Tucker microphone made British sound ranging "an exact method of locating guns."

Writing after the war, W.L.Bragg described events leading to Lieutenant Tucker's invention. Gun sound ranging observers were experiencing two shock waves after the firing of an enemy gun. One was a result of the explosion as the gun fired, the other was caused by the shell, travelling through the air at high velocity. The 'shell-wave' tended to mask the sound of the preceding 'gun-wave'. For the purpose of locating the position of the gun, the gun-wave was the important sound. Bragg explained that the shell-wave was very noisy, but made up of high frequency sounds. In contrast "the gun-wave is a low 'boom' not easy to hear, but which has a much bigger pressure behind it, and rattles windows etc." Referring to the gun-wave, Bragg pointed out that "there was a good deal of energy in the pressure-wave, and if only we could use it, our difficulty was solved."

"The next step was made by Tucker, of Tucker microphone fame. Just beside his camp-bed were two small holes (mice?) and he noticed that the pressure caused a freezing jet of air to play on his face whenever the report arrived. He had been making experiments on the cooling of a hot thin wire by an air jet, and he had the inspiration to make a microphone which embodied this principle. A thin wire was stretched over a small hole in a container (empty rum jars were very convenient and easily obtainable) and heated electrically. The gun-waves cooled it as explained above, and so lessened its electrical resistance, and the galvanometer recorded the effect.

Directly we had got the right wire from England, we rigged up a rough apparatus to try out the idea at Kemmel in 1916. I will never forget the thrill of seeing the first record, in which the shell-wave hardly made the galvanometer string quiver, while the gun-wave gave an enormous kick. The real success of our Sound Ranging dated from that day, because not only shell-waves, but other unwanted sounds of high pitch, such as rifle fire, traffic, and bad language in the neighbourhood of the microphone, were equally well eliminated. A curious difficulty with the first microphones was that small insects so enjoyed the warmth of the hot wire that they used to creep into the holes and break the wires. We made an issue of small grids to the Sections to stop this, and 'Protectors, Earwig Mark I' duly appeared in the Army list of stores."

Further details of the use of hot-wire microphones in sound ranging are given in a post war document in the archives of the Royal Artillery.

"The instruments used in locating a source of sound consist of a number of hot-wire microphones and a recording instrument. In practice it has been found that from four to six microphones are required. These microphones are connected electrically to the recording instrument at Headquarters. In addition, two advanced posts are joined to the instrument." The document includes a sketch showing the layout of the system with advanced posts and microphones spaced out roughly in an arc facing the enemy. Wires led back from the field positions to Headquarters were they were connected to the recording instrument which consisted of "a multiple-string Einthoven Galvanometer [2], an optical projection system, a timing control and a moving film camera."

"The instrument is started by an observer at the advanced post. Each string of the galvanometer is in a circuit containing one of the microphones. When the sound reaches the corresponding microphone the current in this circuit is increased so that the string is deflected momentarily. Such a deflection is known as a 'kick'. A small lamp shining through a narrow horizontal slit, the string being vertical, provides illumination which is projected on to the lens of a camera. A strip of film is drawn past the lens of the camera. When a sound-wave reaches a microphone the corresponding 'kick' is photographed on the film as a sharp bend."

The use of photographic methods in gun sound ranging described above is graphically illustrated in W.S.Tucker's surviving personal papers. A small piece of film attached to a card is headed "One of the first records of German Howitzers obtained with a Tucker microphone. Taken by the Kemmel Section on 26 June 1916. Two 10.5 cm. Howitzers of the same battery, firing with an interval of 1/10 second." The film is a photograph of traces made by a recording instrument, and the 'blips' marking the explosions of guns are clearly visible. The inscription ends with map references to enemy gun positions, a reminder that there would have been no shortage of sound ranging targets around Kemmel, near Ypres and the Messines ridge, an area much fought over during the 1914 - 1918 war at great cost to both sides.

Lieutenant Tucker described subsequent developments. "The hot-wire microphone was introduced into immediate use throughout the whole of the English Army Front, part of the French Army front, and later employed entirely by the American Armies till the end of the war."

[1] Amongst the team was also Lieutenant (later Captain) Percy Rothwell who had been wounded twice (on both occasions in the hands) whilst serving with the Royal Horse Artillery. Rothwell had read physics at Leeds University pre-war and was a gifted scientist, becoming a key member of the team. Tucker and Rothwell were to become lifetime friends.

[2] The Einthoven Galvanometer was named after Willem Einthoven 1860 - 1927 a Dutch physiologist and Professor at Leiden University. He was awarded a Nobel Prize in 1924 for physiology, medicine and his work on the string Galvanometer, the forerunner of the electrocardiograph.

CHAPTER TWO

SOUND MIRRORS IN THE EARLY DAYS

Acoustical methods were soon applied in the growing field of aviation. Lieutenant Tucker became involved, probably as a result of his work in gun sound ranging with microphones. "In October 1917 by General Straubensee's suggestion, I devoted my attention to the possible application of electrical methods to aeroplane detection. By arrangement of Colonel Hedley, War office, I was transferred to the Munitions Inventions Department, and empowered to form an Acoustical Research Section under the controller Admiral Bacon." This posting was to lead to a life-long search by Tucker for a successful method of detecting aircraft by acoustic methods. Physical laws dictated that for effective detection of aircraft sounds, the collecting surface of the listening device should be related in size to the long waves of low frequency emitted by aircraft engines. Such considerations pointed the way to the eventual development in the 1930s of very large sound mirrors.

A report by a French experimenter R. Baillaud described a sound collector used in the First World War in 1916. In October of that year, "a small paraboloid was constructed of wood, 60cms in diameter, with a focal length of 18cm. The receiver consisted of a copper tube arranged so that the cross section of one end was perpendicular to the axis of the mirror and passed through the focus. The other end of the tube was connected by two india-rubber tubes to the observer's ears. With this apparatus, sound sources of high pitch were located with great precision; there was no indication at all of low notes." Later, a paraboloid two metres in diameter was constructed; this was the first to give accurate bearings on an aircraft. Shortly afterwards, a larger mirror, three metres in diameter, was tested with an aircraft in October 1917.

Some definitions may be useful at this point. Listening devices were defined by shape. A collector with a parabolic cross section was often referred to as a "paraboloid". It was most effective when incoming sound rays were parallel to its axis, therefore it had to be movable. The other main type of listening device was a fixed structure in the form of a concave dish known as a 'sound mirror', where the collecting surface was part of a sphere. The most effective sound mirrors were fixed structures possessing the useful property of focusing incoming sound waves both oblique and parallel to the axis. The sounds were concentrated in a focal area in front of the mirror. A movable sound collector was used to search the focal area. As will be seen at a later point, sound mirrors played a major part in the story of acoustic defence.

Baillaud listed some conclusions from the trials. He reported that sounds were considerably amplified by the mirror. "A man 100m distant, reading a newspaper in a low voice was heard perfectly. Aeroplanes were heard up to distances of 8 kilometres." Although it was not the experience of later experimenters, he asserted that "the device was uninfluenced by wind," and that "the device was not affected by sounds occurring in directions greater than 30 degrees away. It is necessary that the rolling of traffic along the road should not prevent the device giving good indications." Other points in Baillaud's report included statements that "the device is able to distinguish between two aircraft in the air together" and that "the accuracy obtained does not vary sensibly with distance." He ended on a confident note. "We will content ourselves by remarking that at night, under calm conditions suitable for air raids on big towns, the device has attained 12 and even 15 kilometres. Practically all the anti-aircraft batteries of the Paris Command were equipped with paraboloids for night flying, the effectiveness of which was without doubt. Of the 483 planes despatched by the enemy during 1918, 13 were brought down by the AA defence, and only 37 managed to fly over

Paris."

A "Report of the Battery at Ecouen, relating to a raid on 15.9.18" states that "the paraboloid at Ecouen allowed each wave of aeroplanes to be picked up, that which was heard best to be followed. Even during the firing of other local batteries and of the Ecouen battery, the paraboloid has a marked superiority over all the trumpet sound devices for use in conjunction with artillery." The battery brought down a German machine during this raid by a direct hit.

Tests of the Baillaud type of sound collector were also carried out in England at the experimental station at Imber Court near Thames Ditton. Particulars are to be found in a report of January 1918. "The Baillaud paraboloid was a device employed in the French service for the location of enemy aeroplanes. One of these instruments was installed at Imber Court and full use was made of it in testing its reflecting properties. The whole instrument consisted of a plaster of Paris mirror mounted on a heavy girder, capable of rotation about a vertical axis, the mirror itself being able to rotate about a horizontal axis. The sound focus was located by a system of 8 trumpets forming a hollow square about a central aperture."

In addition to trials with paraboloidal and mirror-type sound collectors in France during the First World War, parallel experimental work with such devices was also carried out by various researchers and government establishments in England. Some of these experiments took place in Kent, a county which was to become much associated with acoustic research. On 29 June 1915, the Superintendent, Royal Aircraft Factory, South Farnborough wrote to the War Office "with reference to the subject of listening for aeroplanes by means of acoustic arrangements".

The Superintendent continued: "I got in touch with Professor Mather F.R.S. of City and Guilds (Engineering) College, Exhibition Road, South Kensington, and one of his assistants Mr Irwin, who is very keen on this subject and has made with him a large sound mirror about 4 feet in diameter and brought it down here. We made a certain number of tests, and gave him certain recommendations in connection with this. The outcome was that to be useful, this mirror must be of very much greater size to deal with the long wavelengths of low sounds. Thereupon, Professor Mather has had a large reflector, 16 feet in diameter of paraboloid shape, cut into the face of a chalk cliff between Maidstone and Sittingbourne on the farm of Mr Murray, Binbury Manor (Map 1- p. 23). This reflector is expected to sweep out as much as 30 degrees of the horizon, and each reflector could be made for the sum of about £10."

Sound Mirror at Binbury Manor, Kent, 1915

The Superintendent's letter ended with a request. "As this device would appear to have the possibility of being useful, I would like to suggest that arrangements be made for a flyer to go over the site from Dover to Folkestone aerodrome. Could this be arranged to assist the experiment?"

The Deputy Director of Military Aeronautics responded in a letter to the Officer Commanding Administration Wing, Royal Flying Corps, South Farnborough, on 11 July 1915. "I am directed to forward to you the enclosed copy of a letter from the Superintendent, Royal Aircraft Factory. I am to ask

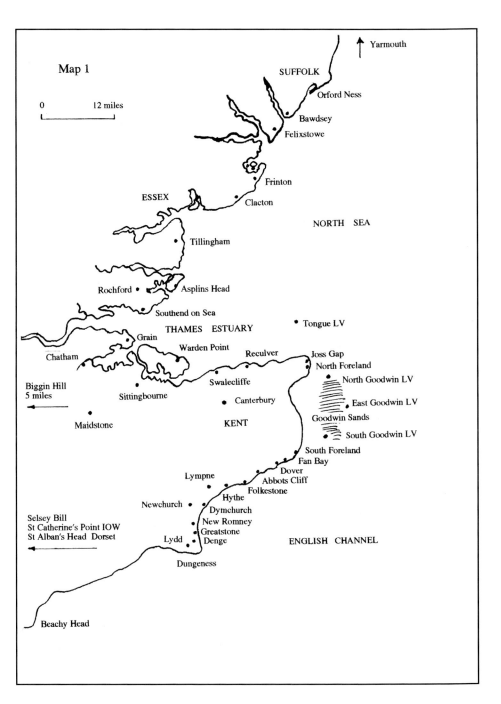

Map 1

0   12 miles

Yarmouth

SUFFOLK

Orford Ness

Bawdsey

Felixstowe

Frinton

ESSEX

Clacton

NORTH   SEA

Tillingham

Rochford •   • Asplins Head

Southend on Sea

THAMES   ESTUARY   • Tongue LV

Grain

Warden Point   Joss Gap

Chatham   Reculver   North Foreland

                                            ≋ North Goodwin LV

Biggin Hill   Swalecliffe   ≋ East Goodwin LV
5 miles
←   Sittingbourne   • Canterbury   Goodwin Sands

                                         KENT   ≋ South Goodwin LV
Maidstone

                                            South Foreland
                                            Fan Bay
                         Lympne   Dover
                                       Abbots Cliff
                                    Folkestone
                              Hythe
              Newchurch •   Dymchurch
Selsey Bill   New Romney
St Catherine's Point IOW   Greatstone
St Alban's Head Dorset   Lydd • Denge   ENGLISH   CHANNEL
←

                          Dungeness

Beachy Head

you to arrange for an aeroplane from Dover to assist Professor Mather in carrying out experiments. Arrangements should be made direct with Professor Mather and the Superintendent, Royal Aircraft Factory."

Trials with an aircraft evidently took place, as described in a letter from an officer in the Royal Flying Corps on 15 July 1915. "About the experiment at Binbury with concave mirror for detection of approaching aircraft - I sent an aeroplane over yesterday but it did not come within the radius of action of the mirror. I paid a visit to the place myself on Sunday, and suggest that either I send a pilot and observer, with lamp, and a lamp ground station for a fortnight or so to the naval aerodrome at Detling, or that the Navy carry out the experiments altogether. As you know I can little spare the pilot necessary but I am sure that unless the experiments are carried out methodically, no useful data will be obtainable."

Professor Mather and his colleagues produced a report on the 1915 Binbury Manor experiments, which also made reference to tests carried out by the Army at Upavon in Wiltshire. The scientists claimed that as a result of the experiments "it is extremely probable that a Zeppelin with its very large engines and gearing would be easily heard at a distance of 20 miles. (32 km) We think a concrete reflector of 16 feet (4.9m) diameter would be superior to one of chalk as the reflecting surface would be harder. If made 20 to 30 feet in diameter (6.1 to 9.1m) there would be a safe margin of power. The reflector, if mounted on gimbals, and made, say, 25 feet (7.6m) in diameter, would weigh about 12 tons (12.2 tonnes), but made in reinforced concrete on the spot, it need not be very expensive, and two of these worked on a known base could locate the position of a machine in space."

"The position chosen for a reflector should be the flat top of a low hill since such a position is fairly free from local sounds. An absence of trees is also an advantage since the rustling of leaves interferes with the hearing. If mounted near the coast, say on cliffs, the reflector should be kept back say 200 to 300 yards (183 to 274m) from the edge of the cliffs so as to eliminate the noise of the waves. A reflector of this size could also be used to detect at night the presence of submarines when they came to the surface or petrol driven motor boats up to a distance of 12 mile (19km). Signed: F. Mather,

J.T.Irwin, W.H.Cable, H.C. Gibson, City and Guilds College, South Kensington."

Subsequent tests at Upavon in Wiltshire were disappointing due to the "ineptness of army personnel", and the Army proposed taking no further action, much to Professor Mather's disappointment.

The suggestion in this report to construct concrete mirrors, following on from early experiments with mirrors cut in the chalk in Kent, implies that the chalk mirrors were pioneering structures, preceding the construction of concrete mirrors. This gives some indication of the dates of early concrete mirrors on the north-east coast of England, sited in areas subject to attacks by Zeppelins. No documentary evidence has been found for the precise dates of these mirrors, but by inference, and anecdotal evidence, it seems probable that they were constructed during the First World War at about the time of

The sound mirror at Marske near Redcar was of the same design as those at Fulwell and Boulby and now lies in the midst of a housing estate. In this 2016 view, the top of the concrete base of the receiving instrument can be seen

The sound mirror on Namey Hill in Fulwell, north of Sunderland,
was the subject of a 2015 restoration project that included
the provision of interpretation boards

Professor Mather's experiments. The four surviving mirrors on the north-east coast are at Marske, Fulwell, Boulby, Kilnsea.

The Fulwell mirror carries a plaque which reads: "City of Sunderland, World War I Defences, Coastal Watch Mirror. This concrete dish detected German Zeppelins sent to bomb north-east ports. Their course could be judged from engine sounds focused onto a receiver, giving 15 minutes warning for anti-aircraft defences to be directed onto them."

Although there are no specific references to sound mirrors in the reports, the National Archive contains detailed accounts of attacks on the East Coast by airships during the First World War. Zeppelin raids on 2 May 1916 are described in a typical report. "Enemy aircraft in the neighbourhood of Spurn Head...during the evening the first intimation of the approach of a Zeppelin was the explosion of bombs dropped in the neighbourhood of Skinningrove

*At Fulwell the provision of interpretation boards
and landscaped presentation have made the
mirror a more popular heritage visit*

..the Zeppelin was caught in searchlights at 7000 feet (2133m) and fired on from Loftus after dropping further bombs on Skinningrove at 10.50 p.m. One plane went in pursuit but did not locate the Zeppelin. On landing, it collided with a small searchlight "which had gone out." The plane was wrecked but the pilot was unhurt. There was no damage to Skinningrove. Another report of activities on 28 - 29 July 1916 refers to "L24" crossing the coast at Spurn Head. At 12.40 the airship was east of Withernsea "She was seen from Kilnsea." Other airship sightings at Hartlepool, Redcar and Saltburn are mentioned in the report, with the detail "bombs dropped at Skinningrove."

The sound mirror at Kilnsea has the same technical specification as the other sound mirrors in the north east of England, but differs in design by omitting the side walls. Unusually it retains part of the pole that supported the receiver instrument in front of it, as can be seen in this 2016 view

The airship raids described in these reports were aimed at industries around the estuaries of the Rivers Humber and Tees, and it is significant that places named in the reports coincide with sound mirror sites, for example the Kilnsea mirror on Spurn Head, and the Boulby mirror which is sited about two miles east of Skinningrove.

The Boulby mirror, in company with the mirrors at Marske and Sunderland, has side walls projecting forwards, and it seems likely that these features would have impaired its acoustic properties. The Kilnsea mirror has no side walls, and is similar in design to the later sound mirrors built in the 1920s.

The Boulby sound mirror lies in fields on a hill behind the remains of old alum workings which is private property; land owner's permission is therefore required to visit it. It is of the same size and design as those at Fulwell and Marske, but no longer has any remains of the receiver instrument. This view was taken in summer 2016

As in the case of the East Coast mirrors, there is a scarcity of information about another early sound mirror at Warden Point on the Isle of Sheppey in Kent, which subsequently collapsed in a land slip. There is a similar lack of documentary evidence about a sound mirror at Selsey on the Sussex coast.

Reports by local historians suggest the mirror dates from 1916, and its layout with two side walls projecting forwards is similar to mirrors on the East Coast at Boulby, Marske and Sunderland which appear to date from that period. Subsequently, at the time of abortive plans for a housing estate, the Selsey mirror was converted into an estate office by incorporating the side walls and adding a fourth wall and roof; it later became part of a dwelling.

The sound mirror at Warden Point on the Isle of Sheppey
has been the victim of coastal erosion and in 2016 lay in
pieces below the high tide mark

A War Office publication, written at a later date, contains references to the Binbury Manor mirror: "The magnification of sounds of high pitch was very marked, and trials upon aircraft gave fair results. This mirror was fixed and hence unless the sound sources were close to the axis of the mirror, little magnification could be obtained." Professor Mather recommended the use of concrete as a suitable material for the construction of sound mirrors. According to a document of December 1916, "one of his concrete parabolic sound reflectors detected an aeroplane at a distance of 10 miles." That particular mirror was later sent to Capel Air Station near Dover "for operational use."

In addition to the mirror at Binbury Manor, a mirror constructed by Mr Cowper-Coles is described. This mirror was "6 feet (1.8m) in diameter, with a focal length of 2 feet (61cm). The mirror was made of plaster 3/8 inch (9.5mm) thick, supported upon a wooden frame which was mounted between 2 wooden pillars so as to swing on a horizontal axis. The two pillars were fixed to a wooden under-frame which rotated on castors running on wooden rails. The weight of the mirror and stand was 10 cwt (508kg). The receiver was a sheet metal cone of fair size, to which was attached a piece of 3/4 inch (19mm) gas barrel, fixed in the centre of the mirror. The listener stood at the back of the mirror, the stethoscope tube being attached to the gas pipe after the latter had passed through the mirror. It was particularly noticed that the thickness of this mirror was not nearly sufficient to prevent

The sound mirror at Selsey was unusually converted into a dwelling in the 1930s. This photograph of the rear of the mirror was taken in summer 2016, when work was being done that involved some restoration work on the structure. The wooden board covers a hole that had been punched through the mirror in order to create a window

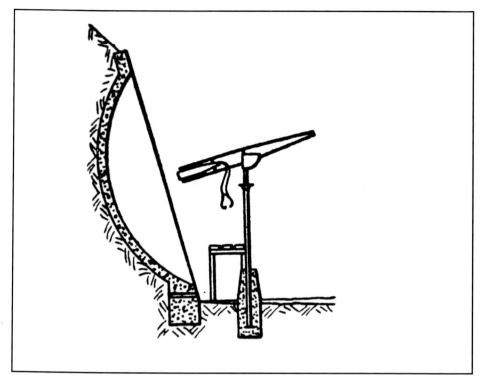

Section through a 'spherical' mirror showing the position of the listening equipment

the reception of sound from the back; talking in a low voice behind the mirror seriously interfered with observations upon a sound in front."

Experience with the mirror at Binbury Manor led to the construction of a smaller type, mounted on a stand, and capable of movement. "One of these was tested at Dover upon aircraft and fixed sounds. This mirror was of concrete, 6 inches thick (15 cm) and four feet in diameter (1.2m), and had a focal length of two feet six inches (76cm). It was mounted upon a cast-iron stand of U shape, giving motion about horizontal trunnions, the whole stand rotating in azimuth. The weight of the mirror was 6 cwt (305kg) without the frame and stand. The collector used at the focus consisted of a brass receiver 3 inches in diameter (7.6cm), gradually tapering to 3/8 inch (9.5mm) in a length of 5 inches (12.7cm). The whole was surrounded by a block of concrete 7 inches (18cm) in diameter and 5 inches (12.7cm) long, the outside of the concrete being wrapped in sacking. This was found the most efficient." The method of listening to the sounds received is described. "The narrow end of the receiver was connected to rubber tubes leading to the stethoscope. Adjustments in elevation and azimuth (i.e. in a horizontal plane) were made by a single observer, the correct direction being determined by the position of maximum intensity. Trials upon aircraft proved, as would be expected, that the low notes were not well received by the mirror, and there was considerable alteration in the quality of the sound."

The principles governing the design of sound mirrors are also explained in War Office publications. "When a solid on which a wave impinges does not exceed about one quarter of a wave-length in diameter, the wave passes round it with little interruption. When the diameter of the barrier exceeds one wave-length, appreciable reflection should occur, and therefore a certain amount of concentration should be obtained by making the surface concave. The concentration in the focal region might perhaps be twice that of the direct radiation, in the case of a mirror of diameter one wave-length. As the mirror increases in size, the concentration should improve, and up to a total diameter of a few wave-lengths it should vary as the area of the mirror. In all these cases, the focus will not be a point, but an area in the focal plane of quite considerable size. It is only by increasing the dimensions of the reflecting surface relative to the wave-length that any approach to a point focus can be obtained."

This matter of size in relation to sound mirrors occupied the Department of Scientific and Industrial Research in 1915. A document in its files dated November 1915 is headed "Advisory Committee for Aeronautics. The Detection of Aircraft by Sound. Note by F.W.Lanchester."

Lanchester commented "The trouble seems to be that the acoustical mirrors so far tried have been totally inadequate in size. It would seem to me likely that if, instead of a parabolic mirror on gimbals of a few feet in diameter, a cup-shaped depression were made in the ground, say 160 feet diameter (49m) by 40 feet (12m) deep, there would be an area about 30 or 40 feet diameter about on a level with the surrounding ground in the centre of the "cup" where some kind of sound picture would be formed of the region above, a region probably subtending about a 60 degree angle. The depression would of course be spherical. Before however anything of the kind is done, I think some really good work should be put in on the theoretical side. The experiment should be more in the nature of a confirmation of a theory than a venture into the unknown. I feel sure however that the matter is only one of the size of the excavation i.e. whether it needs to be 80 feet (24m) or 300 feet (91m) diameter, and after that the question whether the execution of the scheme would be of service commensurate with the cost. With immobile mirrors of this kind, evidently a chain of stations about one mile apart would be necessary."

Although such a scheme may not have been very practical, the ideas expressed are a reminder of the important relationship between the pitch or note of an aircraft engine, and the size of the device designed to detect the sounds of that engine.

Raids by enemy aircraft during the First World War brought a sense of reality to such theoretical matters. The low pitched sound waves of their engines were often heard in the skies, pointing to the need for larger sound mirrors.

CHAPTER THREE

AERIAL THREAT

A brief consideration of the forces involved in aerial warfare during the First World War demonstrates why researchers in the period were trying to find ways of detecting aircraft by acoustic means. In 1913, immediately before the war, there was a considerable disparity in strength between the British and German air forces. A paper by R.W.Burns in the Science Museum Library provides details. "In 1913-14, just before the outbreak of the First World War, the German air force consisted of five battalions of aircraft totalling 232 machines, and a military airship organization, also of five battalions. This was set against the total effective strength of 63 aeroplanes in the Royal Flying Corps, and 41 aircraft and 52 seaplanes in the Royal Naval Air Service. In 1914 the means to detect and locate enemy aircraft were limited to unaided visual sighting by day, search-light aided sighting at night, and initially, unaided listening by day and night. The inadequacy of these measures, especially for night attacks by Zeppelins, is exemplified by a few statistics from 1915: there were 37 airship journeys in 20 separate raids; the defending aircraft made 81 sorties; they sighted the enemy 3 times and failed to engage them at all."

The east and south-east coastal areas of England were in range of German bases across the North Sea, and the first bomb on Dover was dropped from a seaplane in December 1914. By early 1915, Zeppelin airships were raiding the Humber and Thames Estuaries, and industries in the North-East were attacked in May 1916.

The Royal Flying Corps formed in 1912, was given the task of defending important targets such as ports. The responsibility for air defence in the early part of the Great War was shared between the War Office and the Admiralty, and in late 1914, the Admiralty set up bases for defending aircraft in a system of airfields ringing London. In May 1915, the Kaiser approved raids on London, but gave orders that historic buildings should not be bombed. The first air raid on the city was on 31 May 1915, and from that date London was attacked frequently, causing many casualties.

Raids on London by German aircraft stimulated the development of a defence system for the city which demonstrated, in embryo, the way towards the control and reporting system used by Fighter Command in the Second World War, particularly in the Battle of Britain. In the later stages of the war, a central control room with a map table and plotters was in communication with a number of outlying control centres by telephone. These centres received information from gun and searchlight units, sound locators and observation posts. The officers directing operations were connected by telephone to the fighter stations, and early in 1916, experiments were made in radio communication between ground stations and Royal Flying Corps aircraft, using simple Morse messages to indicate the map positions of raiding aircraft. In addition, coastal wireless direction finding stations were able to indicate the tracks of raiders by plotting the transmissions from Zeppelins.

Apart from the use of airships, the Germans developed efficient types of bomber aeroplanes during the war, in particular the twin engined Gotha. It is a salutary thought that when late in 1917, a large new German bomber was introduced nicknamed 'Giant', its dimensions and loaded weight approached those of bombers used in the Second World War. Gotha aircraft made daylight attacks on London in 1917, and the bombing offensive against England was not abandoned until August 1918.

The Kent coast, which was soon to become the scene of much research in acoustic early warning systems, suffered frequent aerial attacks during the First World War. On 25 May 1917, a force of Gothas attacked Folkestone, killing 95 people and injuring 195. A vivid description of a typical raid by German bombers in 1917 appears in The Air Defence of Great Britain 1914-1918, by Cole and Cheesman.

"On Monday 24 September, the sinister, undulating hum of Gotha engines off the North Foreland barely 15 minutes after sunset, signalled the start of the most intensive night bombing phase which England had experienced during the entire war. Zeppelins also bombed that night, confining their activities to Northern England. During the next seven nights of the harvest moon period there were five more aeroplane raids, with 60 of the 97 bombers despatched attacking London and South Eastern England. Despite relatively few casualties - 95 killed and 260 injured - these raids, sometimes dragging on for several hours with a succession of unseen raiders, interminably within earshot, caused long-lasting feelings of anger and revulsion in the population comparable with those produced by the 1940 - 41 'blitz'."

Cole and Cheesman pointed out that night attacks by German aircraft stimulated research into the use of trumpet type sound locators, and also that a spherical, 15 foot (4.6m) diameter sound mirror at Fan Bay east of Dover, saw operational use against enemy planes. Like the mirror at Binbury Manor, the Fan Bay mirror was cut in the side of a chalk cliff, and it was faced with a thin layer of concrete. It was in action during a raid on 1-2 October 1917, when sounds of enemy aircraft flying down the Channel some 12 - 15 miles (19 - 24km) out to sea, and inaudible to the gun crews, were detected by the mirror. (Map 1 - p.23)

A line drawing in a 1932 War Office publication shows the listening gear at the Fan Bay mirror mounted on a vertical tube protruding from a small concrete pillar just above ground level in front of the mirror. In the 1990s, the remains of such an arrangement could be seen in front of the 15 foot mirror (4.5m) at Kilnsea in East Yorkshire, and it is possible that the mirror was erected in the latter part of the First World War, in roughly the same period as the mirror at Fan Bay.

The Fan Bay mirror was not the only acoustic device in the area used in anger against enemy aircraft. A Munitions Inventions Department Report, dating from January and February 1918 mentioned the setting up of an acoustic station at Joss Bay, on the Thanet Coast of Kent, near the North

Foreland. The date of the report implies that the station must have been established at least as early as 1917. The site was often referred to in contemporary documents as the Joss Gap station, named after a feature in the cliffs overlooking Joss Bay. One of the leaders of experimental work at Joss Gap, already a familiar figure in this account, was former Lieutenant, now Captain W. S. Tucker.

CHAPTER FOUR

ACOUSTIC STATION THANET

The North Foreland on the Thanet coast has long been a familiar sight to mariners entering the Thames Estuary from the English Channel. A beam of light, at first coal fired, and later powered by oil lamps and electricity, has shone out as an aid to navigation from various towers on the North Foreland since the 16th century. Within sight of the lighthouse, experiments with a different type of beam were carried out during the First World War. Just below the lighthouse is a sandy bay, bordered by chalk cliffs, known as Joss Bay or Joss Gap, which was the site of an acoustic research station, established by 1918.   (Map 1 - p.23)

In the closing months of the First World War, Captain Tucker wrote about acoustic activities on the coast of South East England. In a paper dated 10 October 1918, headed "Munitions Inventions Department, Imber Court Experimental Ground, Acoustical Research Section, Report on Sound Mirrors" he provides an illuminating account of operations at that time. "Two spherical mirrors are in action on the Kentish coast, one at Joss Gap, and the other at Fan Bay near Dover. These mirrors have a range of observation from the direction of Zeebrugge down to that of Calais."

Captain Tucker's report includes detailed descriptions of the method of listening and the site at Joss Gap. He described it as "a cutting in the chalk cliffs on the headland occupied by Kingsgate Castle. The opening is about 30 feet square, (9.1m) and is bevelled back with its hinder face about 20 feet square (6.1m). On this face a concrete mirror is formed. Its diameter is 15 feet (4.6m) and its radius of curvature 9½ feet (2.9m) and its axis is inclined upwards 15 degrees. The sound is received by two trumpets about 3 feet (91cm) long and shaped internally so as to give a curved throat and an easy gradation in width to the receiving tube. Its (i.e. the trumpet's) mouth is extended by a wire frame covered with green baize. The trumpet itself is carved out of two blocks of yellow pine each 6" by 3" by 3" (15cm by 7.6 by 7.6cm), and the resonant note, which is very pronounced, happens to be about that of the Gotha, although this point was not considered when the trumpets were made. The baize aperture is elliptical, and the two trumpet mouths lie side by side."

The report continues with an explanation of the method used to locate aircraft. "The trumpet pair is mounted on a counterpoised iron rod, pivoted at the centre of the mirror on an iron upright. A horizontal circular scale is mounted at a convenient height and graduated in degrees reading '0' towards the geographical north. A pointer attached to the trumpet arm and travelling over this scale gives the bearing. Another scale graduated in degrees but with its face vertical enables one to read altitude. This scale rotates with the trumpets and a pointer moves over it as the trumpets are elevated or depressed. The reading zero is of course the horizontal. The observer stands on a wooden platform whose level is slightly above the lower edge of the mirror. The mirror is especially good on the higher pitch notes, and for the lower notes, in my opinion, its success is due to the trumpet resonance note nearly coinciding with that of the aeroplane. It is possible, however, that in view of the recently discovered properties of the mirror, the position of the trumpets is unsuitable for low pitch sounds. In the hands of highly trained observers, such as those constantly on duty there, it is a highly efficient instrument for giving early warning and getting bearing of the incoming enemy 'plane. The elevation obtained by intensity is not quite so accurate but is nevertheless surprisingly good. The mirror at Fan Bay is of precisely similar construction. It is manned in the same way and its indications, coupled with that of Joss Gap, give a good indication of the distance of the marauding 'plane. Both mirrors were designed and installed by Major Mather, RE., and Lieutenant Rogers RE., of the Dover Anti-Aircraft

Defences."

Could 'Major Mather' be the former Professor Mather, designer of the early chalk mirror at Binbury Manor? Many academics were called into the armed services and given military rank. Good use was made of their particular skills to assist the war effort, a process which was to continue into the post war years and assume even greater importance in the Second World War.

Further reference to Captain Tucker's activities at the Joss Gap station occur in a letter he wrote to the Scientific Attaché to the American Embassy in December 1918 concerning arrangements for a visit by the Attaché to the Joss Gap Station. In his letter, Captain Tucker mentions that he will be working at the station from 30 December 1918 to 6 January 1919, and he suggests that the visit should be arranged in that period (Map 1 - p.23).

The importance of the acoustic station at Joss Gap is indicated by contemporary reports that it was set up "at the suggestion of Major-General Ashmore, Commanding Officer of the London Air Defence Area, and the GHQ (General Headquarters) authorities." Reasons were given for the choice of the site. "This station was chosen, since it was specially adapted for listening purposes, in view of the fact that it lay on the recognized route of the German raiding aeroplanes. The station was already equipped with listening apparatus for long distance detection and for giving early warning of the approach of enemy aircraft, and in a great many cases it was the first to report enemy activity."

At least two sound mirrors were in use at Joss Gap station. A 12 foot 6 inches (3.8m) diameter movable mirror was sited on the cliff top. Details are provided by a Munitions Inventions Department report. The mirror was erected at a cost of £130, and "it occupied a position on the ground above the cliffs, and its purpose was to test the properties of sound mirrors generally with a view to obtaining useful information for employment in coast defence. The surface of the mirror was built up on a strong wooden framework with a reinforcement of expanded metal and its thickness at the thinnest part was about 3 inches (7.6cm)." The report contains a small sketch, showing that windlasses were used to elevate the mirror, and there is a statement that it was "capable of rotation about a horizontal axis." This

Sound mirror in the chalk cliffs at Joss Gap on the Kent coast c.1918.
Note acoustic sound collecting trumpet, and stethoscope worn by the listener.

mirror was also used in experiments to find the best position for a more permanent mirror.

The main mirror at Joss Gap, mentioned previously in Captain Tucker's report, was aligned "with an aspect about ESE, 100 degrees geographical." It consisted of a large dish, cut into the face of a chalk cliff overlooking Joss

Bay, in a similar fashion to the mirror in the chalk cliffs east of Dover at Fan Bay. Both mirrors were faced with a coating of smooth concrete. A sentence in the Proceedings of the Board of Invention and Research provides some evidence that the Joss Gap mirror may have been the earliest of its type used to detect enemy aircraft during the First World War.

Joss Gap sound mirror, acoustic operation, listener wearing stethoscope. Note focusing equipment on top of the sound collector.

"The first of the fixed concrete mirrors which were operation during the later stage of the war was the 15 foot (4.6m) mirror at Joss Gap, North Foreland, run by the Signals Experimental Establishment, Woolwich." However, other references suggest that the Fan Bay mirror was the first of its type. What seems certain is that both were in operation in the later stages of the First World War.

A report from Major G. H. Boreham, Royal Garrison Artillery,

Commander of the Dover Anti-Aircraft Defences, included references to the performance of the mirrors at Joss Gap and Fan Bay during attacks on London by German aircraft in the Spring of 1918. Listeners at the mirrors were able to give early warning of the approach of the enemy aircraft several

The mirror at Joss Gap in operation with electrical sound collector and listener wearing earphones. The quadrants indicating vertical and horizontal bearings can be seen attached to the equipment.

minutes before the sounds of their engines could be heard with unaided ears. Included with Major Boreham's papers, which make no specific reference to the acoustic devices on the Kent coast, is a photograph of a sound mirror in the face of a chalk cliff.

Although there is no caption, comparison with other contemporary photographs, and the fact that a sub-control of the Dover Defences was based at Cliffsend, Ramsgate, not far from Joss Bay, makes it almost certain that this is a view of the Joss Gap mirror.

The picture demonstrates clearly the method of operation at a fixed sound mirror as described in Captain Tucker's reports. A soldier is standing on a wooden platform in front of the mirror face, wearing a stethoscope connected by flexible tubing to a trumpet shaped sound collector. The collector is mounted on a frame which enables the listener to move it over the focal area of the mirror, searching for the point at which the loudest sounds are heard in his ear pieces. Pointers, attached to the arm of the sound collector move over marked quadrants which enable the listener to give bearings, related to the sounds heard in the mirror, in both horizontal and vertical planes, thus giving an indication of the position of an approaching aircraft. This type of listening depended entirely on acoustic principles, using no electrical equipment.

Documents dating from 1919 contain references to new sound collecting apparatus at the Joss Gap mirror, and a report by recently promoted Major Tucker, in April 1920 describes tests of a "listening trumpet collector" for use at the mirror. "This instrument is intended to give the bearing and altitude of a 'plane in conjunction with the 15 foot (4.6m) concrete mirror which was part of the Anti-Aircraft Listening Post. The apparatus has been tested and has proved to be satisfactory so far as experiments have proceeded. Three flights with a 'Flying Boat' and a 'Bristol Fighter' aeroplane have been conducted, and the position as indicated by the mirror scales has been given. The focusing device, which has not been accurately tested yet, seems to a very important one requiring a nice adjustment. The range is about that anticipated, being twice that given by the unaided ear."

The chief feature of the new collector was the focusing arrangement "which enables the trumpet pair to be brought nearer to, or further from, the mirror surface." The pulleys and wires of the focusing mechanism can be seen on a contemporary photograph of the mirror.

Tests of the mirror with an aircraft flying at 6000 feet (1828m) were carried out in March 1920, and reports indicate that "on occasions, the sound was picked up over 10 or 11 miles (16 or 18km)."

The trumpet shaped acoustic listening device described by Captain Tucker was not the only means used to detect sounds in the Joss Gap mirror.

A contemporary photograph shows a box shaped device mounted in front of the mirror. The listener is wearing earphones rather than a stethoscope, and this suggests the device is a microphone, which would have been a logical step in the light of successes with Tucker hot-wire microphones in France for gun sound ranging.

Reports from March 1920 mention that some of the apparatus was in the "Acoustical Hut" in charge of "Sergeant Player and one Royal Engineer Sapper." Wireless installation for communication with aircraft was in the charge of "technical assistant Reading". These people were involved in tests with a Flying Boat. The first trial was on 19 March 1920.

"Flight 1 was followed by electrical apparatus. A strong adverse wind rendered the noise of the Flying Boat inaudible to the unaided ear at less than 1 mile (1.6km). With the telephones, the aircraft was heard at 10 or 11 miles (16 or 18km) despite "jamming" due to sea noise and wind. "A trained observer should be able to give 10 minutes warning of approach." 'Telephones' here probably means a telephonist's headset wired to the receiving microphone mounted at the mirror.

Flight 2 used listening apparatus with "trumpet collectors." This system gave "2 or 3 times the range of the unaided ear, despite the inaccurate mounting of the trumpet, since remedied." "The operation of getting definite bearings was confined to a very short interval owing to the high speed of travel of the 'plane. A zig zag course may overcome this."

A second trial took place on 23 March 1920. The Flying Boat was not available, and wireless communication was not possible with the replacement aircraft, a Bristol Fighter. The sound of the 'plane was heard at a range of "over 10 or 11 miles (16 or 18km)," though the single engined Bristol aircraft produced different results from those expected from the twin-engined Flying Boat. Another trial was planned for 29 March 1920, using Morse signals from land to aircraft. An application for a signalling lamp was sent to the Air Ministry.

Major Tucker reported that "on April 22nd, members of the Naval Anti-Aircraft Committee and Colonel Warrington Morris inspected the mirror and the devices described for obtaining a bearing for the sound. The details of the flight are not yet to hand. During the inspection, observation was made almost entirely by members of the committee. Some disturbance was caused by the wind being gusty and blowing into the mirror face - a very unusual condition for that situation. The gustiness of the wind would also tend to cause dissipation of the sound for long range - a condition which is more noticeable by day than by night. No data as to range of listening can be quoted under the circumstances, since this operation requires the continuous listening of one observer. When the 'Flying Boat' is employed, the small wireless installation at Joss Gap is available for communicating instructions. On this occasion, when a 'Bristol Fighter ' was employed, lamp signalling was used. Provision has been made for the maintenance of Joss Gap as a long distance station, having the peculiar advantage of a long stretch of open sea in which no similar sounds are likely to interfere with those generated by a 'plane. The mirror however is not an ideal collector for long sound waves of aeroplane frequency." This implies that a mirror of only 15 feet (4.6m) in diameter was not proving ideal for listening to aircraft sounds. Nevertheless, Major Tucker described the value of the site at Joss Gap. He pointed out that " a number of experiments can be conducted at Joss Gap which could not be carried on at other stations, notably a falling off in intensity of sound at long ranges under different atmospheric conditions."

Experiments with the Joss Gap mirror continued in the summer of 1920. A June report mentioned that the microphone had been altered and "tested by a flight with a Flying Boat on June 3rd." The day was calm, but poor for sound. The *Royal Sovereign*, a pleasure steamer, which could normally be heard was "quite inaudible." This steamer normally "drowns out listening at the mirror." The North Goodwin Fog Horn "which also makes listening very difficult, was nearly inaudible on this occasion. Observations with the electrical listening apparatus gave audible aircraft engine sounds 15 minutes before the Flying Boat came into view. With an east wind at Joss Gap, the range of course would be greatly increased." The sound of the aircraft was difficult to locate, but it was "unmistakable", even though it did not "increase in audibility."

The observers, including Captain Darwin of the Butley Acoustic Section RAF, noted distinct properties of the sounds in this experiment. "A strong characteristic aeroplane sound which gradually diminishes until at a certain range it disappears very rapidly, its place being taken by the low, faintly audible hum which persists for a considerable time afterwards. The whole effect is analogous to the direct rays of the sun before sunset, followed by a long period of twilight in the latter case giving also some difficulty in location of the original source."

One of the problems faced by researchers attempting to develop acoustic early warning systems was the shortage of target aircraft, especially in peacetime. Throughout the early years of experiment, acoustic work was undertaken by War Office scientists and army personnel from the Royal Engineers. It was necessary to request co-operation from the Royal Air Force if military aircraft were to take part, and such aircraft were not readily available. Furthermore, few civil aircraft passed over Joss Gap, and researchers at that site sought to alleviate the problem by adopting other ways of testing the sound mirror.

CHAPTER FIVE

BEAMS

Although tracking aircraft was the best way of testing the efficiency of a sound mirror, in the frequent absence of such targets, much use was made at Joss Gap of a reverse technique in which the mirror was used to project a sound beam. The principle was described at the time: "This is the converse process to that of listening, and observation of the beam enables one to speak authoritatively on the properties of a mirror for listening. Such a beam was produced, the source of sound being placed at the appropriate focus of the mirror, and the observers being stationed half a mile from the mirror."

The method of operation is outlined in a Signals Experimental Establishment Report of 14 June 1920. "A number of observations have been made with the 15 foot (4.6m) concrete mirror at Joss Gap with the object of ascertaining the character of the sound beam which is produced when a source of sound is placed at the focus of the mirror, and of determining the sort of accuracy with which the sound beam could be projected in a given direction under various weather conditions. It may be noted that the observations will also serve to show the accuracy with which a sound can be located by the mirror."

The sound beam was produced by placing a Klaxon Horn at the focus of the mirror. An observer was stationed on the cliff near North Foreland at a distance of 550 yards (503m) from the mirror, and the beam was trained on him. The path of the beam was across Joss Bay, from the top of the cliff on the Kingsgate side in a south easterly direction, to the cliff under the North Foreland and back, so that it was never less than 50 feet (15m) from the ground immediately below it. "

The beam was then swung from side to side so as to pass backwards and forwards over the observer. The latter indicated by signals where the edges of the beam were passing over him i.e. when the sound was coming in or out. These edges were found to be fairly well defined. The operator at the mirror recorded the azimuth readings (compass bearings) corresponding to the edges of the beam. The intensity of the sound of the beam was found in general to be fairly uniform. Indications of a central maximum of intensity could be heard, but it was found to be extremely difficult to keep this maximum trained on the observer, showing that the angular width of this maximum must be very small."

When the klaxon is sounded for a short time 1 to1½ seconds an echo is heard some 3 seconds after the klaxon has ceased. On good days the echo may be heard 2 or 3 times by repeated reflections off the cliff. The observers first arrange the direction of the sound-beam so as to get the best effect. This direction of course depends on the strength and direction of the wind. They then sound the klaxon and note the strength of the echo, recording it as good, very good, bad etc. on an arbitrary scale based on their own experience. The sound after reflection travels back over approximately the same path, the effect of wind being thus eliminated, and the difference in the loudness of the echo on different days must be due only to the variations in the 'acoustical transparency' of the atmosphere.

The conclusion to be drawn from these observations is that when the beam is well focused, most of its energy is confined within a cone of semi-vertical angle of 3 degrees, which under normal weather conditions is not deflected from its mean position to any considerable extent. The centre of this beam can be located within 1 or 2 degrees and this again defines the probable error in location of a sound beam received by the mirror."

Further experiments were carried out to test the relationship between reception or projection of sound and atmospheric conditions. Regarding weather conditions, "it is well known that there is great variation from day to day, and that conditions are much better at night than in the daytime. Bad conditions are probably due to the heterogeneous state of the atmosphere and consequent scattering of sound." One of the main purposes of the experiments was to explore the relationship between weather and acoustical conditions, and a table of events covering the period 10 May to 5 June gives some idea of the problems encountered.

Acoustical conditions ranged from good to very bad 'within 24 hours', and the visibility conditions displayed the same range. Weather varied from "south west gale on the 18th with fair acoustic conditions and bad visibility" to" excellent acoustics and visibility, with a calm haze on 20th." On 1 June, the acoustical conditions were poor, the visibility was bad with overcast skies and a light north west wind. On 4 and 5 June, the conditions were reported as "bad acoustics with excellent visibility and half a gale from the north."

Experiments in the projection and reception of sound beams using the Joss Gap mirror were extended to involve light ships and passing vessels. A demonstration was arranged on 22 June 1920 for visitors, named in a report as " the Commandant of Biggin Hill Aerodrome, Dr Robinson, and Major Erskine Murray."

The sounds of the *Royal Sovereign* paddle steamer had already been detected at Joss Gap as the ship passed along the coast in front of the mirror. The reverse process is described in reports dealing with the reception of sound beams on the vessel. "On two occasions, observations of a sound beam produced in the mirror have been made on the *Royal Sovereign* which passes at a distance of about a mile from the coast. The beam of sound was set at a given bearing - well ahead of the steamer - and an observer on the ship listened for the moment of entering and leaving the beam. A well defined entrance into the beam was observed, but the observations so far obtained are not reliable enough to enable an estimate of the width of the beam to be given, since the operator at the mirror cut off the sound before the steamer was out of the beam. The power of the source used in this experiment was 60 watts. This could be heard as a distinct beam above the local sounds incidental to a steamer of this class steaming at 16 knots. The result promises well for the high power sources of sound which it is decided to install."

It is evident from various reports that normal use of the mirror as an acoustic device for tracking aircraft was resumed whenever there was an opportunity. A flying boat was available for the purpose in the summer of 1920. The aircraft appears not only to have acted as a target for listeners, but was also required to land on the sea in connection with sound beam experiments, although these are not specified. "A detailed programme of work with sound beams has been drawn up for the Flying Boat if conditions permit it to surface on the water. The Flying Boat lacks certain wireless accessories to make intercommunication possible."

Although noise from the foghorn on the North Goodwin Lightship had previously been described as a nuisance during tests of the Joss Gap mirror, at this point, the lightship was brought into the experiments as a listening post for beams projected from the mirror. "Trinity House has been communicated with and has given permission for Regimental Sergeant Major Player to observe sound beams on the North Goodwin Lightship. He will be equipped with a Sterling Wireless Set for communications. The Elder Brethren of Trinity House have expressed a desire to witness some of the experiments." (Map 1- p.23)

A report from the Signals Experimental Establishment on 22 September 1920 contains a description of the mirror, followed by further details of the sound beam experiments at Joss Gap. "There are two small huts about 10' by 12' (3 by 3.6m) which give accommodation for instruments used in conjunction with acoustical experiments. The chief purpose of the station is to try new apparatus designed at Woolwich for long distance reception of aeroplane sounds by electrical methods, and to this programme has been added long distance transmission of sound in the form of sound beams." According to this report, the limited number of staff of the station, in charge of a senior NCO (non-commissioned officer), was supplemented by officers from Woolwich when important experiments were in progress.

"In addition to the mirror, the station has a complete installation for getting early warning of approach and obtaining the bearing of aircraft flying in from the sea by listening methods." This must refer to the use of purely acoustical trumpet type collectors and listeners with stethoscopes at the mirror, as the next statement in the report describes "performing the same operation by electrical methods using microphones and telephones." There is also reference to "projection apparatus consisting of sources of sound and the gear for swinging them in front of the mirror so that a definite sound beam may be produced."

Under "subsidiary apparatus" the report describes two wireless installations, for communication with the flying boat and the North Goodwin Lightship, and Aldis signalling lamps for communication "where wireless is impracticable, and for communication between the man operating the mirror gear and the distant observer for local tests ."

The problem of unwanted noise, a common factor in all acoustic experiments, is addressed in this report, where there is a reference to the need for selective listening equipment. "Listening apparatus designed to magnify sound and lead it into the ear has one universal failing. It magnifies all sounds without discrimination, if properly designed, and the degree of magnification increases as the pitch rises. Thus, while straining to hear and locate aeroplane sounds, the ear is conscious of the drowning effect of wind and sea noises or any local disturbances."

It appears from this report that Tucker hot-wire microphones were used as a means of making the mirror more selective. "The electrical apparatus is so designed as to eliminate the unwanted sound and then magnify up that which it is desired to observe. The apparatus therefore, includes specially tuned microphones and a suitable amplifier. This installation is quite effective with a Flying Boat and has observed at ranges of 12 to 15 miles (19 - 24km). Progress is now being sought along the lines of getting accurate direction, and for long ranges, this is not very easy to do owing to the faintness of the sound. It is proposed to add to the amplifier a tuner similar to the wireless tuner, so that by varying an inductance, we can further select our aeroplane sound to the exclusion of others - thus using the principle of electrical resonance in addition to the acoustical resonance at present employed."

The Trinity House yacht *Patricia* assisted the sound beam experiments on the occasion of a visit to the acoustic station by people from Trinity House on 6 September 1920. The yacht took part in observations of the sound beam at sea when ranges up to 2½ miles (4km) were achieved. The

Elder Brethren of Trinity House agreed to further experiments using the North Goodwin Lightship, which was moored at a point 6 miles (9.7km) east south-east from Joss Gap. "Signals to be given by the North Goodwin siren at 3.30 p.m. on Tuesdays, Wednesdays, Thursdays and Fridays throughout October."

Regimental Sergeant Major Player appears in various reports, and he was to continue to play a part in acoustic experiments during this period. He was posted to the North Goodwin Lightship in October 1920. Details of the experiments are recorded in a report on "Special Acoustical Experiments conducted between the Acoustical Station at Joss Gap and the North Goodwin Light Vessel" from the Signals Experimental Establishment.

The ideas behind the experiments are listed, including "the possible employment of sound for long distance signalling, or as a means of directing navigation on the sea or in the air. The experiments were initiated as part of a programme put forward for directing aircraft."

"The home station was manned by Sappers of the Royal Engineers, and supervised by officers at intervals. Assistance was given by a Chief Petty Officer from the Navy, and Ramsgate Coastguards, commanded by Commander Williams, R.N. The observations on the Light Vessel were made by Regimental Sergeant Major Player at the North Goodwin Light Vessel, who occupied this station continuously for a month."

The report goes on to describe the source of sound used throughout the experiments. This was a "Manual Horn, employing an air compressor worked by hand and requiring about 2/3 h.p. (500w) when sounding, an instrument lent by the Elder Brethren of Trinity House. It was fitted with a steel reed at the throat of a metal trumpet 7'6" (229cm) long, and gave a note of 512 vibrations a second. The trumpet is bent at right angles near the mouth, its diameter at the mouth being 15 inches (38cm) which at a distance of 10 inches (25cm) from the opening reduces to 7 inches (17cm)." From various references, it appears that this apparatus consisted of an air compressor on the cliff top, piped to a horn at the focus of the mirror on the cliff face. The report gives details of the experiments, including the fact that the horn had a range of about 7 miles (11km). As could be expected, the best results were obtained in very calm conditions.

The experiments involved a two way process. The observers at Joss Gap listened for a siren on the lightship, and those aboard the lightship listened for the Joss Gap horn. One conclusion reached was that observers on ships, or flying boats, could use a focused sound beam to obtain bearings.

Some of the documentary evidence from this period leaves an impression that the experimental work at Joss Gap was not entirely satisfactory, and that it was time for a change of direction. In fact, events were moving towards the abandonment of the site.

CHAPTER SIX

A MOVE FROM THE NORTH FORELAND

At the end of September 1920, there are the first references in contemporary documents to the possibility of moving the acoustic station to another site near Joss Gap.

"The Commander Royal Engineers is in communication with us relative to the cost of transfer of the existing huts and instruments, and provision is to be made for a new 60 foot (18m) hut to be employed as a laboratory on the new site. A specification for a new 20 foot (6.1m) mirror is being drawn up." A "Programme of Research for the Air Ministry" outlined the aim of the acoustic experiments as "the production of sound beams of great intensity for possible aid in aerial navigation, especially applicable to fog conditions. In this connection, our equipment includes the new 20 foot mirror in altitude mounting, a compressed air installation, and certain effective sources of sound, all of which await test and suitable accommodation."

The new 20 foot (6.1m) mirror mentioned was in fact a proposal, it had not been constructed at this point. A contemporary map shows that the new station was to be further south "situated on the North Foreland on ground hitherto occupied by the Royal Marine Artillery." (Map 1 - p.23)

The matter was raised again in a report of January 1921 under the heading 'Joss Gap Station.' "The future of this station requires further consideration. A letter has been received from the agents of Lady Avebury, on whose property the Station is situated, asking for the ground to be vacated. This would involve closing the station, or moving it to a suitable adjacent site."

According to the report, there would be no difficulty in moving to a site nearby, but it was stressed that the large mirror in the chalk cliff face should be retained. Various points were made about the importance of the mirror, for example that "it is necessary for long distance detection of aeroplanes or seaplanes and for use with the instruments we are now designing both for the Navy and Army. It is immediately available for sound transmission work as required by the Air Force, and it is of great tactical value for defence purposes, and has special equipment rendering it available for active service immediately. A further need of the station, as a whole, is the co-ordination of acoustical observations and the meteorological conditions. This is work of importance to the whole of our anti-aircraft experiments and cannot be done elsewhere without a considerable outlay of money and materials. The station is fully equipped for all meteorological observations."

On the 23 February 1921, the President of the Royal Engineers Board and the Chief Experimental Officer visited Joss Gap "with a view to settling the question of the site. An alternative site 600 yards (549m)south of the present one was inspected and approved."

Early in 1921, there were proposals to make use of a tower in the vicinity. "A sound receiving station should be installed in a disused tower on the North Foreland. This would merely consist of a tuned microphone of high sensitivity. The source of sound should be the blasts from two Light Vessels, Tongue and North Goodwin, situated respectively at distances of 9 miles and 7 miles (14km and 11km) from the Station. Each gives characteristic blasts on the same note and with the same intensity. These sounds, received by the microphone, would be recorded photographically by apparatus in the headquarters and, at the same time, observations of the upper wind etc. would be made by the apparatus supplied for the purpose. Comparison of photographic records from day to day and with accompanying weather conditions, would yield information hitherto unobtainable, and be of service to every branch of acoustical work. The Chief Engineer of Trinity House recommends our application for daily working of the sirens when there is no fog and thinks that the Elder Brethren of Trinity House would afford necessary facilities."

Further references to the tower appear in reports of this period. "The owner has given formal permission for us to install the necessary apparatus, subject to our non-interference with the structure of the tower. An official application for its use is desirable, but no rent is asked for. Application has been made to the Superintending Engineer of the Post Office, Canterbury Division, for permission to make use of their telephone poles for carrying our connecting wires. Such has been refused, but they would undertake to connect us up and maintain the line themselves for 27/- (£1.35p) per annum, the route of the line being about 500 yards (457m). Authority for this sum is asked for from the Committee."

Regimental Sergeant Major Player continued to play an important part in the activities at Joss Gap. To assist him in his work, he was sent to Croydon Aerodrome to receive instruction "from the meteorological personnel on upper wind measurements by arrangement with Colonel Gold of the Air Ministry." Meanwhile, in early 1921 at Joss Gap, bad weather and "the absence of men on leave" prevented any further work with the 'Flying Boat'. Nevertheless "a programme of experiments is being considered, so that the motions of the 'Flying Boat' could be controlled in a Sound Beam while surfacing on the sea."

Apparently, up to this time, the air horn used to create the sound beam at the mirror was manually operated. This probably involved someone in the labour of turning a hand wheel for considerable periods, hardly a popular task. In March 1921, the Chief Engineer of Trinity House agreed to lend a manual horn for an extended period, but some method of working it by power was under consideration to avoid the necessity of obtaining "extra assistance when the station is carrying out experiments." Eventually a "petrol motor for driving the manual" was delivered from Woolwich, presumably to power an air compressor. The records contain further references to practical matters. "A derrick and block and tackle have been rigged so that the manual horn can be removed and replaced quickly in position on the swinging arm in the mirror."

In reports from April 1921, the tower adjacent to the Joss Gap station is named as the "Harley Tower", which had been acquired as a "Listening Post", and as a position for erecting an electrical anemometer for measuring wind pressures. The name of this tower is a reminder that the Joss Gap station occupied a historic site, once owned by Henry Fox, Paymaster General and Leader of the House of Commons in 1762. He became Baron Holland of Foxley, and lived in Holland House overlooking the sea. One of his hobbies was building follies, which included a castle, modified but still surviving at the time of writing as Kingsgate Castle, and various towers, including the Harley Tower. This tower was named after a contemporary Lord Mayor of London.

An application was made to the Post Office for "the connection of this tower with the Joss Gap station by wires, and the Post Office would undertake this on receipt of proper authority." By May, the Post Office had provided the wiring, but in June, it was reported that the installation of microphones and the anemometer would require the construction of a wooden platform, and this work was awaiting the necessary timber and transport.

Communications were not all that could be desired at this time, and there is a plaintive note in one of the reports. "In anticipation of the resumption of experiments with Flying Boats sent from Sheerness, the installation of a telephone at Joss Gap is highly desirable. This would also enable the observer to communicate with the North Goodwin Lightship. Several of last year's Flying Boat experiments suffered badly from lack of communication with Sheerness. We are advised locally that a spare line exists to within a 100 yds of the Station."

Experiments using the Joss Gap mirror and various lightships continued in the summer and autumn of 1921. A summary of this work appears in the Proceedings of the Royal Engineers Board.

"Experiments are being carried out to obtain the curve of reception for the mirror, thereby connecting intensity of received sound, as measured by electric current, with bearing. The experiment is devised to answer criticism offered, that sounds transmitted through fog suffer abnormal changes in direction. A photographic recorder was reported to have been installed as an accessory to the mirror, so that records might be obtained whenever the siren of the North Goodwin Light Vessel is in operation. The Elder Brethren, Trinity House, kindly intimated their willingness to afford facilities by systematic working of the sirens of the Tongue and North Goodwin Light Vessels, and a programme of work has been put into operation - June 1921. A manual horn used in conjunction with the mirror on the North Foreland is in daily communication with the North Goodwin Light Vessel, and evidence is being obtained of the penetrability and sharpness of the sound-beam under varying atmospheric conditions."

Reports from the Signals Experimental Establishment also relate to experiments with sound beams. "North Goodwin Experiments. The third series of these experiments commenced on October 4th, the siren being blown at 3.30 p.m. on Tuesdays, Wednesdays, Thursdays and Fridays each week during the month. There were sixteen of these experiments, of these, on ten occasions the siren was inaudible, on six occasions siren was audible. Records for the first time, have been obtained of the East Goodwin Light-ship, although the North Foreland is between this vessel and the station, and when on its bearing, the apparatus is swung almost to the extreme edge of the mirror. When an opportunity occurs it is hoped to obtain records of the Tongue Light Vessel." The experiments included recordings of sounds from the "Kentish Knock Lightship 19 miles away" (31km) and the "Tongue Lightship 9 miles away" (14.km) obtained by "a microphone in the open."

A sketch map of the Thanet coast is included in reports of this period. It shows the positions of the Joss Gap station, and nearby, the 'Black Tower', which may well be the Harley Tower. Lines representing the central focal line of the mirror are drawn from the station to some of the lightships. The positions of the lightships form an arc of 180 degrees, taking the Joss Gap station as the centre. Reading the map clockwise from the north, the light-ships marked are Tongue, Kentish Knock, North Goodwin, East Goodwin, Gull, and South Goodwin. The promontory of Thanet would cause an inter-ference to sound waves from some of the lightships, and it is obvious why the North Goodwin vessel was frequently used, as its bearing from Joss Gap was more favourable to sound reception (Map 1- p.23).

Late in 1921, there are more references to the proposed move of the acoustic station to a site nearby. There was a plan to equip the new station with a 20 foot (6.1m) sound mirror. A blueprint headed "Proposed New 20 foot mirror for the North Foreland" and dated 1 November 1921 shows details of the design. A slim concrete column, to be mounted in front of the mirror and marked "about 10 feet (3m) in height and 1 foot (30cm) square" has four bolts protruding from the top. In the blueprint, the top of the column is opposite the centre of the mirror, and presumably, the bolts were for securing listening gear to be attached to the column. This column is unlike any columns or pillars subsequently fitted to mirrors at a later date. In the event, this design was never put into practice, as the proposed move to another site at Joss Gap did not take place.

Major Tucker must have had the proposed move in mind. In a letter of 16 December 1921 he used a new name for the site. "I shall be doing a week's experimental work at the North Foreland Station from January 16th to 23rd."

Despite uncertainties about the site, the listening tower was in operation by the summer of 1922, as detailed in several reports. "Sound Reception at Joss Gap, Harley Tower. The three drainpipe resonators and microphones have been placed in the tower and give collectively a pitch range of from 60 - 100. To eliminate oscillations due to wind, the resonator stands have been screwed to the floor, and the resonators themselves braced to brickwork A test of an aircraft from Manston on 9 June picked it up 3 minutes before it reached Harley Tower and 5 minutes after. The aircraft was a DH3 at 6000 feet (1828m) at 110 mph(177kmph), pitch of note 90."

The pitch numbers in this description represent cycles per second. These units usually bear the name of a 19th century German scientist Hertz, abbreviated 'Hz'. The figures indicate the pitch of the notes concerned in terms of frequency. Using the piano as an illustration, the bass note 'G', almost at the bottom of the keyboard, has a frequency of 49Hz, and the 'G' one octave above has a frequency of 98Hz. Thus it can be seen that in musical terms, the microphones in the Harley Tower, tuned to a pitch range of 60 - 100 Hz, were receptive to aircraft engine notes in the bass register.

The reference to drain pipe resonators relates to the physical fact that the size of a cavity is related to its responsiveness to sounds of various frequencies. A long cylindrical vessel, for example, shaped like a drain pipe, would give a good response to low frequency sounds, such as those produced by an aircraft engine. It is clear from these reports that microphones were mounted in such resonators in the Harley Tower.

By the time of the tower experiments the days of the Joss Gap station were numbered. Proposals to move to a completely new site appear in documents dating from the summer of 1922. On 1 July, under "Anticipated Removal from Joss Gap" there is the following statement:

"The present site has to be vacated in the near future. It was thought desirable to choose a new site where there was prospect of continuous flying. The best position on the west (sic) coast is at Lympne on the cross channel route, and after inspection of the neighbourhood, a very good position was discovered on an escarpment, with S.E. aspect, and about half a mile from Hythe School of Musketry. The site is on War Department ground and could probably be secured without difficulty. There is a good place for a 20 foot mirror facing the route of the 'planes. A scheme has been submitted for the building of a laboratory, workshop and stores, and includes provision for a technical assistant to live on the site. Authority to proceed is awaited. A map showing the position of the site will be available."

Although largely forgotten, the station at Joss Gap played an important part in the development of acoustic defence systems. It deserves a small place in history for its association with attempts to track enemy aircraft during the Great War, using a vertical disc and a sound mirror. Experimental work continued into the post war years, but the site was becoming unsatisfactory in some respects, not least because of the scarcity of aircraft targets. The station was finally abandoned during the first week of August 1922, and the apparatus transferred to a new site at Hythe.

CHAPTER SEVEN

HYTHE ACOUSTIC RESEARCH STATION

The old town of Hythe, situated on a hillside on the Kent coast overlooking the English Channel, has a long association with defence works of various kinds. As one of the medieval Cinque Ports, in return for certain privileges, the town was required by the King to provide ships and men to defend the country against invasion. At the time of the Napoleonic Wars, Colonel Twiss, Commander Royal Engineers under Sir John Moore, was much involved in the building of fortifications at Hythe. Between the years 1805 and 1809 the Royal Military Canal, passing through the town, was constructed as part of a defence system which included coastal guns, mounted in a chain of Martello Towers. Subsequently, the British Army had a presence in Hythe until the late 1960's. Barracks in the town housed a School of Musketry, later to become the Small Arms School, and the associated firing ranges which were established on a nearby stretch of coast are still in regular use at the time of writing.

During the Napoleonic Wars, troops were stationed in Shorncliffe barracks, situated on the hills to the east of Hythe. In a later period, Royal Engineer officers stationed at Shorncliffe were involved from time to time in constructional work related to acoustic experiments in the vicinity. A few miles further along the coast in a north easterly direction are the towns of Folkestone and Dover, the latter also a Cinque Port, and a centre for much military activity over the centuries. Members of the Royal Engineers from

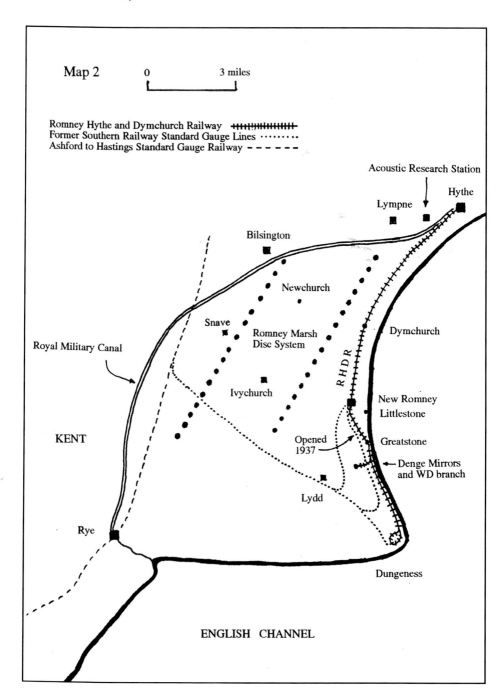

Map 2   0 |⎯⎯⎯⎯| 3 miles

Romney Hythe and Dymchurch Railway ++++!++++++++++++
Former Southern Railway Standard Gauge Lines ·········
Ashford to Hastings Standard Gauge Railway − − − − − −

Acoustic Research Station

Hythe

Lympne

Bilsington

Newchurch

Snave

Romney Marsh
Disc System

Dymchurch

Royal Military Canal

R H D R

Ivychurch

New Romney
Littlestone

KENT

Opened
1937

Greatstone

←⎯ Denge Mirrors
and WD branch

Lydd

Rye

Dungeness

ENGLISH   CHANNEL

Dover were occupied from time to time in work connected with acoustic experiments in Kent.

Dymchurch, and New Romney another Cinque Port, lie to the south west of Hythe. A short distance from New Romney is Lydd, where officers from the Royal Engineers were based at the army camp. The coastal road south of New Romney, passing through Littlestone and Greatstone, eventually leads to the immense shingle headland of Dungeness. These places are the setting for further developments in the acoustic story. (Maps 1 and 2)

By late 1922, there had been considerable progress in establishing an acoustic research station on the hills to the west of Hythe, on an area known as The Roughs. From the site of the station, there is a fine view of the Romney Marshes towards Dungeness. The Royal Military Canal runs along the foot of the hills, and on the stretch of coast below The Roughs can be seen some of the surviving Martello Towers, standing on the Ministry of Defence firing ranges. The towers and canal are reminders of a former defence system.

According to a report headed "New Station at Hythe" dating from December 1922, building operations were in progress at the Hythe station at that time. "The 20 ft concrete mirror and the living quarter for Mr Player are nearing completion, while one laboratory in the hut next to the mirror has been finished, and a certain amount of apparatus can be placed there temporarily. Application has been made for a storage battery of 120-150 AH (ampere hour) capacity. As regards the wiring of the huts for power and lighting, this will be done by the CRE (Commander, Royal Engineers) if suitable cable is supplied for the mains. The class of cable required is now being decided upon. It is proposed to obtain water from a spring which has been discovered near the buildings, but in order to get sufficient head of water a small rotary pump is necessary and this will be electrically driven. The installation of this will be proceeded with as soon as information is received as to the power and output of the pump. New listening apparatus for use with the mirror has been designed and will be made at the Signal Experimental Establishment. It is hoped that this will be complete for the night flying which may take place in January 1923."

Early days at the Acoustic Research Station on The Roughs at West Hythe c.1923

"Mr Player" mentioned above was one of the people actively involved at Joss Gap, particularly in the lightship experiments, who moved to the new station at Hythe. When serving in the army, he appears in the records with the rank of RSM. (Regimental Sergeant Major). He had apparently become a civilian by the time of this report, and it seems likely that he was housed on the site at Hythe to act as caretaker. Subsequently, in the years 1935 to 1937, Mr Player got into difficulties in his business affairs and suffered much ill health. Major Tucker made considerable efforts to help him and his family, evidently regarding it as a responsibility to a former colleague. During 1996, a past resident of Hythe, quoting from his memoirs, mentioned that "at the top of The Roughs, immediately behind Martello Cottages, a wooden bungalow was occupied by Mr and Mrs Player with their son and daughter."

Hythe Acoustic Research Station from the approach road. 1924

Major Tucker was much involved with the new station at Hythe. Important events were taking place in his life at the time. His papers include a letter from the great physicist Ernest Rutherford, inviting him to the Cavendish Laboratory at Cambridge in 1922 to discuss his experimental work. In August 1922, he was demobilized from the Royal Engineers, and appointed Experimental Officer at the Signals Experimental Establishment, soon to be transferred to the Air Defence Experimental Establishment. Although from time to time, documents of the period still describe Major Tucker by his Army rank, it seems appropriate from this period onwards to refer to him by his Doctorate in Science, which he had achieved in 1915 at the time of his enlistment in the Royal Engineers.

It is apparent that the new 20 foot (6.1m) concrete mirror was in position at Hythe by the latter part of 1922. Soon after the completion of the mirror, there was a huge explosion at Oldebroek in Holland, when an ammunition dump was blown up as part of scientific experiments to study the propagation of sound waves in the atmosphere. According to a contemporary source, the sound was heard "in an E.S.E. direction for 850 kilometres, in a S. direction for 600 kilometres, and in a N.W. direction for 750 kilometres." A report relating to the new mirror stated that "observations on the explosion at Oldebroek failed at Hythe because of the absence of the concrete pillar for the support of the apparatus. It was only possible to put in a temporary installation."

One of Dr Tucker's colleagues from the First World War joined his team in January 1923. Like Dr Tucker, physicist Percy Rothwell possessed both scientific qualifications and battlefield experience of the First World War. He was wounded twice whilst serving as a Lieutenant, later Captain, in command of a Gun Sound Ranging Section. Dr Tucker wrote that Rothwell's first duties in 1923 included "control of my outstation at Hythe." He was destined to play a considerable part in acoustic developments in the 1920s and 30s.

A Signals Experimental Establishment report of 28 February 1923 gives a detailed description of the building of the 20 foot (6.1m) mirror at the new station. "The mirror was built up against a steep bank on the escarpment abutting on to the Romney Marshes and overlooking the Channel between Hythe and Dungeness. It consists of concrete with an umbrella shaped reinforcement of iron rod. Great care was taken to face the mirror with a smooth cement surface. The listener is accommodated on a platform about six feet (1.8m) above the ground, and the sound reaches his ears by means of stethoscopes." The report mentions that "this mirror is now complete and has been fitted with listening apparatus." Included in the report are photographs of the completed mirror and associated huts. Unlike the mirror at Joss Gap which was cut in the face of a chalk cliff, the 20 foot (6.1m) mirror at Hythe was formed in a solid slab of concrete, erected in front of the escarpment.

Details of tests of the 20 foot (6.1m) mirror carried out in September 1923, plotting flights by RAF Vickers Vimy aircraft, occur in a report of 16 January 1924. The results of the test flights were tabulated with comments. For example, a test flight took place between 17.00 and 19.15 hours on 11

September at heights from 5000 to 8,500 feet (1524 to 2590m). The comments on this flight were:- "OUT:- Lost to ear at six and a half miles; (10km) lost to mirror at eight and a half miles; (14km) IN:- First heard by mirror at twelve miles (19km)."

New 20 foot sound mirror at Hythe Acoustic Research Station, 1923

Under "Conclusions from Listening Tests" the report states:- "It may be concluded that the 20 foot mirror is an efficient device for anti-aircraft work at a coast station. It appeared to give early warning of presence of aeroplanes at times which would enable anti-aircraft defence units a few miles back to get into effective operation, without requiring them to be continuously on the alert." The report claimed that experiments with the mirror proved it to be "at least ten times more effective than the unaided ear."

Some insight into the more mundane problems of establishing the new station can be gained from Percy Rothwell's various reports and letters to Dr Tucker. In December 1923 he refers to a road over the fields and down the cliff to the site. "Work on the roadway has now commenced. A gang is digging at the cliff end. I have seen nothing of any responsible person on the job." On 8 March 1924, he was concerned with the fencing of the site. "Farmer Chittenden came yesterday to point out that owing to the state of our fence, his cattle can now go right over the top unhindered....we have ceased chasing the animals out. We should be at it all the time if we did."

Photographs of the Hythe station in September 1924 survive with Percy Rothwell's papers. Compared with earlier photographs, these pictures show that the trumpet collector of the 20 foot mirror (6.1m) had been modified. It is larger in size, and appears to have been fitted with padding, possibly to reduce wind interference. In one photograph Dr Paris, another of Dr Tucker's colleagues, is seated in a deck chair in front of a bell tent, with the mirror in the background, suggesting that members of the team camped at the site in the summer months. In another scene, there is a curious dome shaped object on the ground a few yards in front of the 20 foot (6.1m) mirror. This looks like a former for the bowl shape of the mirror, possibly used during construction. Other scenes show that the approach road, footpaths, and steps linking the different levels around the site were well established by this time. Rothwell and Paris are to be seen on one of the paths.

A 1924 document confirms the reasons for the choice of The Roughs as the site for the acoustic research station. In order to test the mirror, it was necessary to plot movements of aircraft, and military machines were not regularly available. An aerodrome had been established on the top of the

*Percy Rothwell, on the left with Talbot Paris, scientists and members of the
Air Defence Experimental Establishment, Biggin Hill.
Pictured here at the Hythe Acoustic Research Station in 1924*

escarpment at Lympne, just behind the acoustic research station. Civil aircraft of the period frequently used the airfield as a turning point when setting course across the Channel for France, and it was also used by military aircraft. These facts influenced the choice of an adjacent coastal site for the acoustic research station. "Continuous observation could only be made by working on some estimated air route, and it appeared obvious that only in the Hythe region, on the Commercial Air Route, could such observations be made. For this reason, the Hythe Acoustical Station occupies its present position, and the axis of the new mirror is made parallel to the main air route." (Map 2 - p.64)

Further details relating to the Hythe 20 foot (6.1m) mirror appear in a Signals Experimental Establishment Report of May 1925. "The new gear forming the equipment of the 20 foot mirror at Hythe has now been completed. It includes an improved receiving trumpet and stethoscopes, and a pointer which travels over the mirror surface. The surface is covered with a grid giving by inspection the altitude and bearing of the source of sound, which will greatly facilitate the operation of discovering and following an aeroplane" Although it seems a practical method of operation, in fact no further references or illustrations have been found relating to the pointer and grid mentioned in this report. "The swinging gear is also capable of carrying special microphones for which an insulated frame has been made, thus the operation of listening in the mirror by electrical means will be investigated. Special flights will be organized for range trials under the new conditions." This reference to microphones suggests that operating methods at the new 20 foot Hythe mirror were to be similar to those at the earlier mirror at Joss Gap, where both an acoustic trumpet and an electrical microphone were used in listening experiments. However, no further documentary references to electrical listening at the Hythe 20 foot (6.1m) mirror have been found, and early photographs of the mirror show only trumpets and stethoscopes in use.

A Royal Engineers Board Memorandum of 20 July 1925 records the setting up of the Air Defence Experimental Establishment. "Sanction has been received on War Office Authority for the formation of the Air Defence Experimental Establishment...All correspondence in connection with the former Searchlight Experimental Establishment and the Acoustic Section of the SEE will be addressed to ADEE, Signals Experimental Establishment, Woolwich until further orders." On a personal note, 1925 was a good year for Dr Tucker. On 1 July he was appointed Director of Acoustical Research at the Air Defence Experimental Establishment which was eventually based at Biggin Hill.

The 20 foot (6.1m) mirror at Hythe was in use in August 1925, when in a report involving flights by a Vickers Vimy aircraft, there is a mention that "observations were made from the 20 foot concrete mirror at Hythe, and the approach of the aircraft to the coast and its approximate position were telephoned to Uxbridge" the RAF control centre at that time. A letter of 3 February 1927 hinted at further developments. The Commanding Officer of the Air Defence of Great Britain, writing to the Air Ministry remarked: "During 1926, experiments were carried out by the Royal Engineers Board in the neighbourhood of Hythe with a 20 foot acoustical mirror." This letter went on to suggest that "three similar 20 foot mirrors be erected along the coast for use in 1928." Other correspondence referred to the possibility of extending the mirror system. A letter to the Air Council, dated 19 April 1927 suggested that "it may be necessary to install a line of 20 foot mirrors along the south east coast."

Despite plans for a coastal chain of 20 foot (6.1m) mirrors, documentary evidence indicates that only two were built at this period in addition to the existing mirror at Hythe. A letter of 6 May 1927 from the Superintendent, Air Defence Experimental Establishment to the Commander, Royal Engineers, Shorncliffe, refers to "proposals to erect two acoustical mirrors, one near New Romney, the other on the cliffs between Hythe and Folkestone." (Map 1 - p.23)

In fact this latter mirror was eventually erected at Abbots Cliff, between Folkestone and Dover. Later in this letter, there is a statement that the design will be "similar to that now at The Roughs," a reference to the existing 20 foot (6.1m) mirror at Hythe. Although the quality of the image is not perfect, a surviving archive photograph of the Abbots Cliff mirror is a rarity in that it shows a listener at work on a 20 foot mirror. The concrete pillar in front of the mirror supports a platform on which the listener is standing facing

*The 20 foot sound mirror at Abbots Cliff on the Kent coast,
newly completed in the Summer of 1928*

the mirror. He is holding a bar connected to the sound collecting trumpet as he directs it over the focal area. The flexible tubes connecting the trumpet to the stethoscope worn by the listener are not very visible in this picture.

On 14 May 1927, the Superintendent gave more details: "Reference our visits to the proposed sites near New Romney and Abbots Cliff on 12 May 1927. I estimate the cost of erecting the mirrors and accessories at approximately £650 in each case. This includes:- a) erection of a concrete mirror similar in design to that at the Acoustical Station, Hythe; b) Erection of a corrugated iron hut, inside dimensions 15 feet by 10 feet (4.6m by 3m); c) erection of a 50 (15m) by 50 foot enclosure fence and gate." A letter of 16 August 1927 from the Superintendent, to the Commander, Royal Engineers, Dover, discussed the orientation of the two new mirrors: "Abbots Cliff - true bearing of axis 165 degrees, and Great Stone 100 degrees." The site of the mirror at "Great Stone" is usually referred to by the name "Denge," describing an area of shingle on the Dungeness peninsula. (Map 2 - p.64)

A letter of 24 August 1927 from the Air Defence Experimental Establishment, Biggin Hill, to the Commander, Royal Engineers, Dover, refers to the "20 foot mirrors for Hythe." As often in documents of this period, the term 'Hythe' here means the Hythe system, and not that all the mirrors were actually to be erected at the Hythe site. The letter requests "will you please therefore proceed with the construction of the mirrors. It is desired to have them completed by 31 March 1928."

Two letters, both dated 25 June 1928 refer to work on the new mirrors. The first is headed to "D. of Ac. (Hythe)" (i.e. Director of Acoustical Research Station, Hythe), from the Superintendent, Air Defence Experimental Establishment. In this letter, which is part of a group referring to the Abbots Cliff mirror, the Superintendent remarks: "I gather that work on the mirror is progressing and that they are starting to concrete the foundations. I therefore thought it as well to send the ironwork down early to avoid the risk of delay." The second letter is addressed to the Royal Engineers Office, Lydd, and is again from the Superintendent: "I have arranged to send the ironwork for the mirror to The Roughs, Hythe on Wednesday 27th inst. and not to Lydd tomorrow as arranged over the telephone. Will you please communicate with Major Tucker at The Roughs, Hythe, tel. Hythe 277 regarding arrangements for delivery of the gear." It is evident that the acoustic station at Hythe was the collecting point for equipment for the new mirrors.

The mirror at Abbots Cliff was the first of the two new 20 foot (6.1m) mirrors to be completed. A plan of the site exists, signed by a draughtsman "A. S. Edwards, Cpl. RE, Dover, 13 October 1927" and headed "Dover, Lydden Spout, Proposed Concrete Mirror for Air Defence Experimental Establishment." (The site of the Abbots Cliff mirror was sometimes described as 'Lydden Spout'.) The drawing is initialled by an officer: "Major, R.E., Dover, October 1927." The mirror was completed in the Summer of 1928. A letter of June in that year not only helps to fix this date, but also gives a brief insight into the human problems involved. The men at this mirror were in a very exposed cliff top position, and a hut was built near the mirror to act as a control room and shelter. It is evident that, at the time of completion, one officer at least had given some thought to the comfort of those manning the mirror. A Lieutenant of the Royal Engineers, writing to the Superintendent, Air Defence Experimental Establishment on 12 June 1928, headed his letter: "Subject: Acoustical Mirror, Abbots Cliff, Stove for Hut." According to the letter, "the stove has now arrived, and the installation of same will be completed today."

The 20 foot (6.1) sound mirror at Denge, near Dungeness, Kent

The site of the second new 20 foot (6.1m) mirror at Denge is established in a memorandum of 14 October 1927, which refers to discussions between Major R.E. Shakespeare, Deputy Commander, Royal Engineers, Shorn-cliffe, and a representative of the Littlestone Estate. One point under discussion was the plan to run the "small gauge New Romney Railway about 150 yards (137m) from the shore in front of the proposed site for the 20 foot mirror." There is further reference to the Romney Hythe and Dymchurch

Percy Rothwell operating the 20 ft mirror at Dungeness

Railway in a letter from the Royal Engineers to the Air Defence Experimental Establishment on 16 December 1927. The letter enquires "whether the approaching construction of this railway will render the proposal to site the mirrors at Dungeness impracticable." The use of "Dungeness" here refers to the site at Denge. On 21 December 1927, the Superintendent, Air

The 20 foot (6.1m) mirror at Hythe in 1976, before it was toppled forward by a landslip. The concrete base of the receiving instrument can be seen but is now under the horizontal mirror

The Hythe mirror face down in 2015

Defence Experimental Establishment replied that "the construction of the railway will not materially affect the operation of the mirrors at the site selected. It is recognized that we cannot get complete silence anywhere, but this site, even with the railway, gives us the nearest approach to silence that we can expect."

Photographs of the 15 foot (4.6m) mirror built some years previously at Joss Gap show that the mounting for the sound collector was a lightweight structure, but by the time of the construction of the 20 foot (6.1m) mirrors at Hythe, Abbots Cliff and Denge, a more substantial mounting had been developed. This was necessary, because to obtain satisfactory bearings on an aircraft under observation, the movable collecting trumpet or microphone required a rigid mounting to allow it to traverse an accurate path over the mirror surface. The substantial mounting, in the form of a concrete pillar supporting the listener's platform in front of the mirror, is a prominent feature in photographs of the 20 foot (6.1m) mirrors. This pillar is an enlarged version of the small pillars used at the earlier 15 foot (4.6m) mirrors at Fan Bay and Kilnsea. Access to the listener's platform at the Hythe mirror was by a substantial flight of wooden steps. Some re-design of these features was undertaken by the time of the construction of the 20 foot (6.1m) mirrors at Abbots Cliff and Denge, and a slimmer concrete pillar was used, with access to the platform by ladder. Metal components of the Hythe mirror were also modified to bring it in line with the two new mirrors. On 9 February 1928 the Superintendent, Air Defence Experimental Establishment wrote to the Commander, Royal Engineers, Dover on the subject of "steel work for the two 20 foot mirrors." "It is desired to replace the existing pillar at the mirror at The Roughs with this type. Can you please arrange to carry out this work by 15 April." The letter goes on to say that "the whole of the ironwork for the three mirrors will be supplied by me."

The Superintendent of the Air Defence Experimental Establishment, referred to the new group of mirrors on 23 April 1928 when writing about arrangements for the "Summer Programme at Hythe". He mentioned a period from 4 June to 13 August involving "three concrete mirrors" at "Hythe, Abbots Cliff and Denge." The "Summer Programme" depended on the completion of the new 20 foot (6.1m) mirrors, and on 7 June 1928 the Superintendent wrote a further letter on the subject to the Commander, Royal Engineers, Dover. "I have now had an opportunity of discussing the programme for the Denge mirror more fully with Major Tucker. As a result of this conversation, we have come to the conclusion that the 31st July will be too late to enable us to complete the experiments this year. Will you please therefore push on the construction of this mirror with all possible speed. Judging by the time taken to erect the Abbots Cliff mirror, there seems to be no reason why this work should not be completed in 3 to 4 weeks." In his reply, the Commander gave an assurance that "every effort will be made to complete the work as soon as possible, but I do not anticipate this will be much before the end of July."

On 15 June 1928, the Superintendent, Air Defence Experimental Establishment wrote to the Secretary of the Royal Engineers Board as follows:

"I am informed by the Commander, Royal Engineers, Dover, that he has arranged to give the Denge 20 foot mirror priority over other work. He states however that there is no chance of completing it in 3 or 4 weeks, and doubts whether it will be ready much before the end of July. After 1st August, the Night Flying Flight will have to operate from Hawkinge instead of Lympne, consequently, conduct of experiments will not be so facile after that date, and there is considerable risk of the experiments not being brought to any definite conclusion this year."

The Denge 20 foot (6.1m) mirror was completed around July 1928, shortly after the mirror at Abbots Cliff. Both these mirrors were still upright in the early years of the 21st century. In terms of design, the Abbots Cliff mirror is similar to the 20 foot (6.1m) mirror formerly standing on The Roughs at Hythe, being a vertical block of concrete, with the mirror bowl hollowed out of the front face. The 20 foot (6.1m) mirror at Denge is a different shape, being somewhat similar in appearance to the 30 foot (9.1m) mirrors which followed at a later date.

The Hythe 20 foot (6.1m) mirror and its pillar survived until the late 20th century, when land slippage caused the mirror to topple. At the time of writing, it lies face downwards, near the remains of the approach road and foundations of the Acoustical Research Station. During the collapse, the pillar was buried under the fallen mirror. The pillars at Denge and Abbots Cliff have also disappeared in the intervening years. Previous reference has been made to four smaller mirrors of this type which survive on the north-east coast of England including the mirror at Kilnsea near Spurn Head. The concrete pillars exist at three of these mirrors, but the residual part of the vertical metal tube supported by the pillar at Kilnsea is, at the time of writing, a unique part of the equipment of an early sound mirror.

Although Dr Tucker must have been heavily involved in the Hythe Summer Programme in 1928, he was absent for at least one day when on 28 June, he was presented with the O.B.E. by King George V at Bucking-ham Palace.

Matters concerning the three 20 foot mirrors in Kent occupy much of the correspondence of this period, but there are occasional references to ancillary equipment at the research sites. A letter from the Royal Engineers at

Shorncliffe to the Air Defence Experimental Establishment, in relation to the site at Denge, refers to "concrete footings for the instrument panel table in the laboratory." In another letter, the Superintendent of the Air Defence Experimental Establishment mentions: "in the laboratory, a concrete slab in the floor, 6 feet by 4 feet (1.8m by 1.2m), in order to give the instruments a firm mounting."

Acoustic activities on the Kent coast attracted an important visitor in the early years. Professor F. Lindemann came to Hythe in July 1927. He was a person of considerable influence, being from 1932 onwards, scientific adviser to Winston Churchill, particularly in matters of air defence.

CHAPTER EIGHT

MIRROR DEVELOPMENTS

By 1928, a case was being made for more sound mirrors. A reference to the costs involved in constructing a chain of mirrors occurs in an Air Council minute. "The mirrors cost £300 each. It would cost £120,000 to place them at suitable intervals between Felixstowe and Portsmouth." This sort of estimate alarmed Air Marshall Trenchard, as expressed in a memorandum of 23 March 1928. "The Air Ministry should not be saddled with charges which relieve the other services of their legitimate responsibilities." He went on to say that this had happened in the past between the Navy and the Air Force in 1922 which "nearly wrecked" the Air Force. "I must impress upon all concerned the importance of bearing the above in mind. Failing to appreciate its importance may be disastrous. After 10 years' experience I am convinced of the truth of this." The memorandum highlights a problem common to all the Fighting Services in those inter-war years, when, during a period of pacifism, they were caught in a politically imposed financial straight jacket. As a general point, it is also worth remembering that shortly after this period, the attitude of the Treasury towards defence spending must have been affected by the worldwide recession following the stock market crash of 1929 .

Despite Trenchard's worries, there were suggestions that the RAF should become more involved with the sound mirrors. A letter from the Air Ministry to Air Commodore F.V.Holt, Chief Air Staff Officer included a statement that "the War Office has suggested to us the desirability of the RAF taking over the acoustical mirrors and disc systems at present located on the South Coast in the neighbourhood of Hythe."

Further developments were proposed in a letter from Air Commodore Holt to Colonel G.R.Pridham, Royal Engineers Board on 6 November 1928. "With regard to the operational experiments with 20 foot (6.1m) mirrors, I think that this year's work permits us to say definitely that a line of acoustical mirrors will eventually be required along our South East coast for Air Defence purposes." Later in the letter, Air Commodore Holt spoke of "an improved 20 foot mirror as suggested by Dr Tucker." In correspondence with Colonel Pridham on 14 November 1928, Air Commodore Holt referred again to a new type of mirror. He mentioned a "20 foot mirror of new 'bowl' design" to be built at Hythe, and stated that a new "bowl design" of mirror would be constructed at Dungeness "as soon as the one at Hythe has been tested." The mirror site at Dungeness was on an area of the peninsula known as Denge, a place name frequently used in descriptions of the period. The above references to a new "bowl" design of mirror must relate to the two 30 foot mirrors (9.1m) eventually erected at Hythe and Denge alongside the existing 20 foot mirrors (6.1m) at those sites.

The personal papers of Dr Tucker's colleague Percy Rothwell reveal that he put forward proposals for a "30 foot hemispherical mirror" in 1925. Writing at a later date about the importance of Mr Rothwell's work, Dr Tucker stated that "the designs of the standard 30 ft. mirror and the 200 ft. mirror were his own production" and that "the large concrete sound mirrors were developed for long distance detection of aircraft" under Rothwell's supervision. A letter from the Superintendent, Air Defence Experimental Establishment, of 16 November 1928 confirms that practical steps were taken to move ahead with the construction of a new mirror at Hythe. The Superintendent referred to Dr Tucker by his military rank. "Accompanied by Major Tucker, I visited the Commander, Royal Engineers, Dover, on Wednesday 14th instant and discussed the proposed construction of a new Mirror at The Roughs. Two alternative sites were selected, but that on the top of the crest of The Roughs had been ruled out, after obtaining Colonel Pridham's opinion, as being too conspicuous. The site will therefore be approximately 200 yards (183m) west of the Air Defence Experimental Establishment enclosure at The Roughs, just below the crest. This site will probably entail additional cost for repairing the approach road to The Roughs and constructing an approach road to the actual site."

The 30 foot mirror at Hythe, sited "...just below the crest." Taken in 1976 this illustration shows the surviving approach road which was constructed to access the site. At that time the mirrors were in good repair.

A contemporary plan shows the original 1923 station, the approach road, the 20 foot mirror (6.1m), and associated buildings. Sketched on the plan, in a later hand, at a site to the west of the existing station, is "site of proposed mirror." The plan is signed by various officers of the Royal Engineers, Shorncliffe, and the signatures are dated January and March, 1929. The position described in the letter above corresponds to the place for the 'proposed mirror' sketched on the plan; both must be references to the 30 (9.1m) foot bowl mirror which was still standing in a state of advanced decay on The Roughs at Hythe in the early years of the 21st century (Map 2 - p.64)

In correspondence with the Royal Engineers Board on 25 January 1929, Squadron Leader R.Collishaw, on behalf of the Chief Air Staff Officer, discussed problems with the 20 foot (6.1m) mirrors and mentioned a new design: "The three existing mirrors at Dungeness (Denge), Hythe, and Lydden Spout (Abbots Cliff) were not properly oriented when they were laid down. It is now proposed to re-orient two of the mirrors and to re-design them. The layout will be known as the 'bowl type' mirror." In the light of what actually happened, the 're-design' mentioned resulted in two new 30 foot (9.1m) mirrors, not changes in the existing 20 foot (6.1m) mirrors . The 're-orientation' probably refers to the fact that the new 30 foot (9.1m) mirrors were designed with bowls inclined at an angle upwards towards the sky, whereas this was not the case with the older 20 foot (6.1m) mirrors formed in vertical slabs of concrete. The 30 foot (9.1) mirrors featured a major improvement over the 20 foot (6.1m) type in the provision of an enclosed, weather-proof listening chamber under the bowl.

A report of April 1929 refers to proposed operations with the Hythe 30 foot mirror (9.1m). "It is anticipated that during the summer, the 30 ft mirror will be completed and ready for trials. It will be erected on the Hythe Station with a south easterly aspect, and will be capable of comparison with the existing 20 ft mirrors. The following tests will be made:

1) listening range;
2) effective listening arc;
3) accuracy of location.

In addition, attempts will be made to test its capacity for obtaining elevation angles, as it will be capable of dealing with angles of about 70 degrees. At the same time, careful meteorological observations will be taken and the data derived from the mirror correlated with them."

Further information about the new 30 foot (9.1m) mirror at Hythe is given in a memorandum of 24 June 1929 from Squadron Leader Collishaw to the Air Officer, Commander in Chief, Air Defence of Great Britain. The memorandum refers to poor results with the three existing 20 foot mirrors at "Hythe, Dungeness (Denge) and near Dover (Abbots Cliff)." He went on to say: "the two 30 foot 'bowl' type mirrors which were promised by June 1929 have not been built; one is under construction at Hythe, but the Royal Engineers who have the task in hand have not succeeded in reproducing the model. The construction, which should be a concave segment of a sphere, has turned into an ellipse, owing to insufficient support for the top hamper. It is doubtful whether this one will be ready to test in September. Nothing has been done with regard to the second 'bowl' type mirror." (This last point refers to the proposed 30 foot (9.1m) bowl mirror for Denge.) The memorandum suggested that pressure be applied to the Air Ministry and the Royal Engineers Board " for completion of the two 'Bowl' type mirrors by September, 1929." There follows a suggestion that the Air Ministry should be asked to "assume sole responsibility for carrying out all further experiments in acoustics. This will probably mean taking over the Scientific Staff of the Acoustical Section of the Air Defence Experimental Establishment."

Contemporary photographs included in Percy Rothwell's papers show various stages in the construction of the new 30 foot (9.1m) mirror at Hythe. He pencilled dates on the back of some of the views, and these give a clear idea of progress towards completion. An aerial ropeway was constructed to assist in bringing materials from the top of the escarpment to the site of the mirror. A picture dated '1929' shows the first pieces of the lower part of the mirror framework being hoisted into position, and in a view dated 14 June 1929, the skeleton framework is complete. Other photographs show the addition of a metal mesh covering the mirror bowl.

On 3 July 1929 Air Commodore J.D.Boyle, Chief Air Staff Officer, reported: "I met the President and Joint Secretaries of the Royal Engineers Board last week, and ascertained that the first Bowl Mirror will be completed at Hythe by the end of the second week in August. Trials of this Mirror have already been arranged in conjunction with No. 9 Squadron in September. The second 30 foot (9.1m) Bowl Mirror will be completed at Dungeness by 1 November, and I propose to ask Sir John Steel next time I see him whether he would oppose such co-operation as would be possible during November by No 9 Squadron to try them out. I feel it is important that trials of these Mirrors should take place this year, so that we may be in a position to say what further equipment of this nature is required for trial

Assembling the metal skeleton of the 30 foot (9.1m) sound mirror at Hythe.
Annotated by Percy Rothwell: "14 June 1929"

*Coating the metal framework with concrete during
construction of the Hythe 30 foot (9.1m) mirror.
Annotated by Percy Rothwell: "12 August 1929"*

during the operational period of next year."

Air Commodore Boyle expressed some impatience on the part of the RAF with the other services: "The impression I have got during attendances at Royal Engineers Board meetings and various discussions with the Royal Engineers Board, is that they and the War Office have little interest in pressing for rapid progress in the development of the mirrors. We were under the impression the Bowl Mirrors would be completed for trial in September, and we were never informed either by the Royal Engineers Board or by the War Office via the Air Ministry that they were not to be so completed."

The Superintendent of the Air Defence Experimental Establishment had evidently visited the 30 foot (9.1m) mirror at Hythe during the construction stage in July 1929 and noticed some faults in the metal work. He wrote about these to the Director of Acoustical Research, Dr Tucker, on 10 July.

"Regarding phone conversations to Rothwell at Hythe yesterday and yourself today, the correction to the mirror is being made without any trouble. Had I not mentioned it, the work would have been done and nothing said." At this point in the letter, there is a small sketch, showing a general view of the mirror. From the captions on this very rough drawing, it appears that there was a problem with "a warp at the bottom lip," apparently referring to the shape of the lower edge of the bowl. The letter continues: "I don't know whether you will be able to follow the trouble from the enclosed sketch, but it looked most irregular, and I cannot conceive anyone leaving it in such a state."

The newly completed 30 foot sound mirror at Hythe. Note the trumpet shaped sound collector, and window frames for the listening chamber under the bottom edge of the mirror.
Annotated by Percy Rothwell: "30 foot mirror, Hythe 1929."

Percy Rothwell, at that time based at the Hythe Acoustical Station, wrote to Dr Tucker on 17 July 1929. "There is no further development at the mirror, but I hope to let you know tomorrow about the possibility of testing the steelwork and fixing the pillar on Monday. We hope to fix the mirror on the map tomorrow, and I can then send the data for marking out the plotting board." On the 18 July, Rothwell wrote again, reporting that: "Mr Hughes, (Lester Construction Company) tells me that he will be ready on Monday for a test of the steelwork. We shall want to adjust the pillar to the best advantage, and then fix it, and we shall require the Biggin Hill fitters. I can start first thing on Monday doing the test, and then everything will be ready by the time they arrive. If after adjustment of the pillar there are big errors, Hughes will want to do some straining and guying. He has left the gusset plates off the side stanchions and will not fix these till everything has been tuned up. There is a possibility of truing up being a protracted job, in which case, I think we should send the fitters back. According to the Sergeant, Royal Engineers, who was at the mirror this morning, it is a matter of doubt whether it can be finished by August 14th as stated, so we had better cause no delays on our side."

Evidently the adjustments to the metal framework of the mirror were successful, as one of Rothwell's photographs, dated 3 August 1929, shows that by then, a gantry had been erected over the bowl of the mirror, presumably to enable concrete to be lifted and poured. In this picture, the bowl is complete in metal mesh, and the side buttresses of the mirror have been filled with concrete. In another, taken 12 August, the concrete skin has been applied to the bottom section of the bowl. Another scene shows the bowl almost covered with concrete except for a small section near the top. This is followed by pictures of the completed mirror before the gantry was removed. In one view, a workman is directing a jet of water at the mirror from a hose pipe, possibly part of the finishing process. Rothwell's papers include a specification for the surface of a sound mirror. The specification is undated, but it is part of a collection of files from 1934. It is not clear whether such a finish was applied to the new mirror, but the detail is worth quoting to demonstrate the thinking of the time about the importance of a good finish to the surface of what was in fact a scientific instrument.

Tentative Specification of Method Proposed in finishing the surface of Acoustical Mirror Bowl

Render the inside of the bowl with a thickness of 1/8 in. (3.2 mm) or 3/16 in. (4.8mm) granite dust, having the finest of the 'flour' dust previously sifted out, no sand being added. The surface so rendered must be protected from sun and wind and kept sprayed with water for 2 days after being applied to achieve the result desired... When this surface of rendering is dry, it be coated with 2 or 3 solutions of Silicon Ester 'O' the resulting surface would then be smooth and hard.. Note: The solution Silicon Ester 'O' is pure silica dissolved by a special process in Ethyle-Alcohol....its action being that when applied the Ethyle-Alcohol evaporates and leaves the pure silicon combined with the cement surface. It entirely fills the pores of the concrete, and leaves a hard gloss surface on the concrete impervious to weather conditions and permanent.

A workman directing a jet of water at the mirror from a hose pipe, possibly part of the finishing process

In Percy Rothwell's pictures of the new Hythe 30 foot (9.1m) mirror, the trumpet collector is mounted, and the frames for the windows of the listening chamber can be seen under the lower edge of the mirror. Unfortunately, the final scenes are only dated '1929', but taken together, these photographs indicate that the mirror was completed in August of that year.

References to the construction of a 30 foot (9.1m) bowl type mirror at Denge are contained in notes of a meeting of the Royal Engineers Board on 24 October 1929. "A second 30 foot (9.1m) mirror was sanctioned and probably would be completed by the end of the Financial Year." The reference to a second 30 foot mirror is a confirmation that the first 30 foot (9.1m) mirror was already in existence at Hythe. There are also details about the performance of a 30 foot (9.1m) mirror which must have resulted from trials of the mirror at Hythe. "The 30 foot mirror was no advance on the 20 foot as regards range. It has however the great advantage of being able to follow the track of the aircraft, the point of this being to get more accurate cuts nearer the coast and when overhead, instead of following it by estimation as in the case of the 20 foot." The reference to "cuts" probably means the use of two or more mirrors, where by observing on a map the points at which reported bearings cross, an estimation of the position of an aircraft is possible.

The notes of the Royal Engineers Board meeting contain further information about the new 30 foot (9.1m) mirrors at Hythe and Denge. "Major Tucker considers that with two 30 foot mirrors, he would be able to plot the aircraft within a kilometre of its actual position at 10 miles (16km), and within half a kilometre or less at the coast. Colonel Carden and Major Tucker think they will be able to give a demonstration of the value of the two 30 foot mirrors in about May or June. They will be glad to show the Commander in Chief the existing 30 foot mirror with aircraft working in the vicinity at any time convenient to the C. in C." The "existing" mirror must be the 30 foot (9.1m) mirror on The Roughs at Hythe, and it appears from these notes that Dr Tucker was confident he would be able to use both the Hythe and Denge 30 foot (9.1m) mirrors by the Summer of 1930.

Percy Rothwell's photographs are again useful in providing dates for the construction of the 30 foot (9.1m) mirror at Denge. As Dr Tucker wrote elsewhere, Rothwell was responsible for the design of the 30 foot (9.1m) mirrors, and the dates on his photographs are the best evidence available. A picture showing the early stages of the Denge 30 foot (9.1m) mirror bears the pencilled caption 'Commencement of 30 foot mirror at Denge Beach, February 1930." In this view, there are deep excavations in the shingle, with wooden shuttering in position, ready for the concreting of the foundations.

Construction must have been well advanced by April 1930, as on 17th,

Deep excavations in the shingle, with wooden shuttering in position, ready for the concreting of the foundations.

Robert Ferguson of the Air Defence Experimental Establishment, wrote from Hythe to headquarters at Biggin Hill, reporting that he had made frequent visits to Denge Marsh and Shorncliffe in connection with the 30 foot mirror. He explained that he had "supervised the transporting of the 30 foot mirror pillar to Denge from New Romney." Writing again on 23 April 1930, Ferguson reported that the contractors for the 30 foot mirror would "finish on Friday next. The mirror is being rubbed down in order to make the surface smooth, and a light cement wash applied, or at least, I think it is a cement wash. The surface is much improved, and probably compares favourably with the 30 foot mirror at Hythe before the final surface was applied. The pillar is being put in the centre according to the contractor's specification, and this I propose to check." These references make it clear that the Denge 30 foot mirror was completed by the end of April 1930.

Percy Rothwell with the 30 foot (9.1m) mirror at Denge, shortly after completion in April, 1930. Note windows in the listening chamber.

Shortly after the end of construction work at Denge, there were proposals for more mirrors. On 1 October 1930, the Royal Engineers Board asked Dr Tucker to choose sites for two 30 foot (9.1m) mirrors to defend Portsmouth. He suggested sites on the Isle of Wight. In 1931, a Senior Air Staff Officer suggested that "say three mirrors of the 30 foot type should be built for test purposes." In a reply in November of that year, Group Captain E. Gossage wrote: "As regards the 30 foot bowl type mirror, I like your suggestion that we should have a small framework of the mirror system built up, about which the rest of the system could be formed if necessary."

Despite these suggestions, no records have been found of the construction of any other 30 foot (9.1m) mirrors, and it is quite possible that those at Hythe and Denge are unique structures.

Denge 30 foor mirror before the 2003 restoration. The square concrete box below the mirror is the remains of the listening chamber. The space above the box was originally filled by a wooden framework and glass windows. The top of the box was at ground level when the mirror was constructed in 1930.

CHAPTER NINE
THE ULTIMATE MIRROR

Plans to build a new mirror on a scale far larger than anything previously attempted were under consideration as early as 1924. In that year, a report of 11 August from the "Acoustical Station, Hythe" includes references to a "long circular wall of large radius of curvature...distance from end to end of wall 200 feet." Percy Rothwell worked at the Hythe station in those years, and on 18 February 1925 he sent a report to "Major Tucker, Signals Experimental Establishment Woolwich" in which he referred to "a new mirror" including sketches showing it to be a 200 foot wall (61m), 20 feet (6.1m) in height . The names "Fan Hole" and "Langdon Hole" are written on the sketches, referring to sites on the Dover cliffs. The axis of the mirror was to be 130 degrees, giving a bearing "just west of Paris". Later in the report the height of the wall is given as 26 feet (7.9m), a dimension subsequently adopted.

Although Fan Hole had already been a sound mirror site since the First World War, the suggestions on Percy Rothwell's sketches for a 200 foot mirror (61m) there were not pursued. Nevertheless, action was soon to follow, and there is reference in a letter of October 1927 from the Superintendent, Air Defence Experimental Establishment, to the Commander, Royal Engineers, Shorncliffe to the erection of a 200 foot (61m) mirror at "Dungeness" (i.e. Denge). It was to be built on a site "alongside that chosen for the 20 foot mirror. The same telephone line can be used with the necessary extension. Telephone arrangements must be such that the Hythe Acoustical

Station can be in communication with this site for an uninterrupted period of four hours during experiments, mostly at night." (Map 2 - p.64)

Dr Tucker, both in lectures and in writing, described the philosophy leading to the construction of the 200 foot mirror (61m). "It has long been known that the most penetrating sounds for long distance transmission are the lowest pitched sounds with the greatest wavelength. Whereas the 30 ft (9m) mirrors are very efficient for waves up to 3 ft (0.9m) or so, corresponding to the middle of the pianoforte scale, the sounds we wish to deal with have waves of 15 to 18 feet (4.6 to 5.5m), and tend to become inaudible to the ear. This involves extension of mirror surface to about 10 times that hitherto employed. The other dimensions are similarly to be extended 10 fold."

"Since for long distance listening of this type the elevation angles will be small, the vertical mirror dimensions can be reduced." Dealing in particular with the Denge 200 foot mirror (61m), Dr Tucker pointed out that "consideration of these points resulted in the design of a strip mirror of 200 ft. horizontal aperture (61m), 26 ft. high (7.9m), with a radius of curvature of 150 feet (46m) both horizontally and vertically. The focal surface is now at a distance of 75 feet (23m) from the mirror, and of extent 100 feet (30m), so that the use of swinging trumpet and stethoscope has been abandoned. The focal surface is replaced by a forecourt with a gangway for listening sentries, and the ear is employed without any further listening aid.

The magnification depends on the area of the collecting surface, and hence the problem of designing apparatus for long range detection reduces to the constructional problem of making a mirror with a very large collecting surface." In a strip mirror "the surface which reflects the sound is an elongated strip of spherical surface built in the form of a high wall with a smooth cemented reflecting surface. In front of the mirror is a sloping concrete forecourt and a listening trench."

A decision to go ahead with the 200 foot mirror was apparently taken in late 1928, as confirmed by a statement in a letter from the Air Defence of Great Britain to the Royal Engineers that "the 200 foot strip mirror should be built when funds are given."

A letter of 29 January 1929, from the Superintendent, Air Defence Experimental Establishment to the Commander, Royal Engineers, Shorncliffe, refers to the early stages of construction at Denge. "The mirror position is pegged on the ground, and Lieutenant Francis should know its position. It is known to my staff at Hythe, who will give you any assistance you require."

The impressive 200 foot (61m) mirror at Denge, almost surrounded by water in this photograph, taken in the years before the 2003 restoration project

As Garrison Engineer at Shorncliffe, Lieutenant Francis, Royal Engineers, was given the task of making drawings and calculations. During the building of the Denge mirrors, he was stationed at Lydd, from where he supervised the construction work by civilian contractors. Photographs taken during the construction of the Denge mirrors have survived in an album in the possession of his son. There are views of the 20 foot (6.1m) and 200 foot (61m) mirrors under construction, and also pictures of the Hythe 30 foot (9.1m) mirror when new, showing the trumpet sound collector and windows in the front of the listening chamber. Lieutenant Francis finished his service as Lieutenant-Colonel Francis O.B.E., and became Curator of the Royal Engineers Museum at Brompton Barracks, Chatham, Kent from 1968 to 1974. Apparently, he never visited the mirrors in later years, assuming that they were demolished at the start of the Second World War.

The 200 foot (61m) mirror at Denge under construction. At this stage, there has been no progress in building the forecourt. Annotated by Percy Rothwell: "200 foot mirror Denge Beach 1929."

One of Dr Tucker's reports gives details of the method of construction of the 200 foot mirror. "A wall of concrete is built up with shuttering on a reinforcement of vertical rods, so that the overhang at the top is well supported.

Buttresses 10 feet apart form a structure capable of resisting the strongest winds. The surface of the mirror is vertical at the ground, which is finished as a sloping forecourt of concrete, with suitable drainage and sumps to hold the surface water. The forecourt slopes down to a flat platform, bounded by a circular wall concentric with the mirror surface. The vertical cylindrical wall which bounds the listening trench coincides approximately with the focal surface of the mirror."

A view of the rear of the mirror under construction showing the rear buttresses

It appears from photographs taken during the construction stage that concrete was carried from the mixer by barrow up inclined planks and poured into the shuttering.

Progress towards completion of the mirror can be traced from various documents of the time. By April 1929, under the heading "200 foot strip mirror" a memorandum mentions possible use of the mirror "in the summer programme." This was not achieved, and in a memorandum of 24 June 1929, the Chief Air Staff Officer suggested to the Commander in Chief, Air Defence of Great Britain, that the Air Ministry should press for the completion of the 200 foot mirror by September 1929. Writing again to the Commander in Chief on 3 July 1929, the Chief Air Staff Officer reports that he had been informed by the Royal Engineers that "the 200 foot strip mirror will be completed at Dungeness by the 1st of November."

A Royal Engineers Board report of 24 October 1929 states that "the 200 foot strip mirror would be completed this year."

Despite statements in various letters and reports, the 200 foot mirror at Denge was not completed in 1929, although construction was well advanced in that year.

CHAPTER TEN

WAR DEPARTMENT BRANCH LINE

The main line of the Romney Hythe and Dymchurch Railway was opened from New Romney to Dungeness just before the mirror site at Denge was established. The railway proved to be very useful to those building and operating the mirrors. As early as 2 January 1928, a letter from a Royal Engineer officer at Shorncliffe to his Superior at Dover, refers to the railway and the Denge site. "To get to the site will be rather difficult, but possible, by using the Hythe, Dymchurch and New Romney (sic) narrow gauge railway which is being continued from Littlestone to The Jolly Fisherman close to the shore. The representative of that railway told me that they would carry material for us, even if the railway was not open to the public, and could, if required, put in a temporary branch line to the mirror site." Such a line was provided in 1928 and became known as the W.D. or War Department branch.

Eventually the Romney Hythe and Dymchurch Railway made a considerable number of arrangements for the convenience of the War Department. In his book The Romney Hythe and Dymchurch Railway W.J.K.Davies mentions that "a two road wooden shed was erected by the turntable at Hythe, and for the 1929 Season, appears to have been leased to the War Department." Apparently, the War Department had permission to run over the main line and branch from Hythe to the mirror site during the night hours and winter months. "They had a small petrol scooter which was housed by the day in Hythe shed." It was obviously very convenient for people from the Acoustical Research Station at Hythe to be able to travel direct to the Denge mirror site by rail. In 1996, a scientist, who worked at the Hythe acoustical station in the late 1930s, remembered using a petrol driven vehicle to make such a journey (Map 2 - p.64).

It is evident that the War Department branch was an important transport link during the construction of the mirrors.

War Department branch from the Romney Hythe and Dymchurch Railway to the Denge site during the construction of the sound mirrors 1928 - 30.

A letter from Mr R. Hardie, Traffic Manager of the Romney Hythe and Dymchurch Railway to the "Officer in Charge, Acoustical Section, Air Defence Experimental Establishment, Hythe," written on 25 November 1929 illustrates the point. Headed "Spur to Northlade" (another name for the Denge site), the letter continues: "With reference to your communication dated 30 ult., the cost per annum for hire of line from Lade to Northlade would be £24 per annum, providing that you carry out Clause 7 of the existing contract. This clause is as follows:- The Contractor shall, on completion of the work dissemble (sic) the track and load it into Company's trucks and unload at New Romney Station."

Mr Hardie's letter outlined the costs involved, using the Imperial measures for money and weight current at the time. "Should you require a special train from New Romney to the end of the loop, the charge will be £1.10s (£1.50). The single passenger fare from New Romney to the junction of the main loop would be 4d (c.2p). Freight charges between New Romney and this junction, providing that your men do the loading and unloading, would be as follows:

not exceeding 28 lbs 3d (not exceeding c.13kg c.1p)
not exceeding 56 lbs 6d (not exceeding c.25kg c.2p)
not exceeding 1 cwt 9d (not exceeding c.51kg c.4p)
not exceeding 2 cwt 1s 2d (not exceeding c.102kg c.6p)

Above this weight at the rate of 3s (15p) per ton, minimum 1s 9d (9p)."

Two days later, the Director of the Acoustical Section at Hythe wrote to the Secretary of the Royal Engineers Board. "I have communicated with the Romney Hythe and Dymchurch Railway. They have forwarded the enclosed statement of their charges for every kind of requirement. At the present time, and throughout the winter months, the Dungeness site is inaccessible for any transport owing to the marshy conditions of the ground. Moreover, we have no right of way except over half a mile (805m) of shingle following on a very rough beach road from Littlestone. It would be quite impossible to get apparatus to the site that cannot be carried by hand. The programme for the 200 foot (61m) mirror in February necessitates the delivery of several loads of equipment amounting to 2 or 3 tons (2.03 or 3.04 tonnes)in weight."

Further reference to the history of the Romney Hythe and Dymchurch Railway by W.J.K.Davies reveals interesting points relating to the War Department branch line to Denge. There was a sudden and short lived increase in goods traffic on the railway at the time of the work on the mirrors. In 1928 the goods carried amounted to 312 tons (317 tonnes). In 1929, this figure rose to 891 tons (905 tonnes), and in 1931, it fell again to just 314 tons (319 tonnes). It seems obvious that this sudden increase in tonnage was due to the carriage of materials and equipment to the mirror site at Denge during the construction of the mirrors. Letters in December 1929 refer to "retention of access to the mirror site for 12 months" and "necessary adjustments in the contract due to War Department taking over responsibility for dismantling the track." As will become evident at a later point, the branch to the mirror site was not dismantled at this time, and it remained in use for many years. .

RHDR train near Greatstone bound for Dungeness. A passenger looking out over fields to the left of this picture would see the Denge mirrors in the background. The train will shortly pass the site of the former War Department branch to the Denge mirrors, sometimes known as the Greatstone mirrors.

The design work of Dr Tucker's colleague Percy Rothwell relating to the 200 foot (61m) mirror at Denge has already been mentioned, and his papers include photographs taken at the time of construction. As in the case of his pictures of the 30 foot (9.1m) mirrors , he added pencilled captions to some of the photographs. A view of the 200 foot (61m) mirror, completed, but with scaffolding still in position is dated '1929'. In this view, the mirror stands alone on the shingle, with no forecourt. Another view of the completed mirror from the back is also dated 1929. These views show clearly that the mirror was not ready for use when the pictures were taken in 1929, as work on the vital forecourt had not begun at that point. (See p.100)

Dr Tucker, writing on 7 January 1930, hoped that work on the forecourt would be finished by 3 February, but in fact the work was far from complete by that date. The Superintendent of the Air Defence Experimental Establishment wrote to the Secretary of the Royal Engineers Board on the subject on 28 February 1930: "I attach a specification and plan of my requirements for the listening trench and forecourt of the 200 foot mirror. This is required by June 2nd in order to allow time for the installation of the microphone equipment by June 16th when the experiments with aircraft commence. "

The Commander, Royal Engineers, Home Counties East, wrote to his opposite number in Eastern Command in March 1930 about work in progress at Denge, problems with contractors, and the use of the Romney Hythe and Dymchurch Railway and War Department branch to the mirrors. "Messrs. Concrete Structures Ltd, the contractors for the 30 foot mirror, at present have the right of user over the line, and will probably be in possession of the line at the commencement of the contract for the trench and forecourt. If a clause was inserted which required the contractor for the trench and forecourt to arrange to take over the line from the Railway Company, difficulties would probably arise between the contractors for the 30 foot (9m) mirror and the contractor for the forecourt. I am in communication with Messrs. Concrete Structures Ltd., with a view to making an arrangement whereby they agree to the contractors for the forecourt using the line during the period when Messrs. Concrete Structures are completing the 30 foot (9.1m) mirror."

Robert Ferguson of the Air Defence Experimental Establishment, in one of his 1930 reports, mentioned frequent visits to Denge in connection with the construction of the mirrors. He described modifications to the 200 foot (61m) mirror involving "a reduction in the depth of the trench by 8 inches", (20cm) and pointed out that "this necessitates an increase in the height of the outer wall." The use of the word 'trench' suggests a deep hole, but judging by the physical remains of the structure, it was more like a step down in the forward part of the forecourt and a shallow trench just behind the front wall. One purpose of this curved wall, which ran along the outer edge of the forecourt, was to protect listeners or microphones in the forecourt from disturbance from local noises such as traffic, wind or sea. The wall also acted as "the focus of sound waves reflected from the mirror surface." A listener standing near the wall would be in the most favourable position for hearing sounds collected by the mirror.

Difficulties relating to the listening trench also concerned Lieutenant-Colonel S. Pemberton, Commander, Royal Engineers, Home Counties East. In a letter to Major J. D. Inglis, Superintendent Air Defence Experimental Establishment, Biggin Hill, on 7 March 1930, he referred to problems with the trench due to the nature of the site, on shingle, and the proposed depth of the trench. "This would necessitate very costly protective work and pumping during the progress of the construction of the trench which would considerably increase the cost and delay to the completion of the work. It would be quite impossible to complete by June 2nd next."

Further letters passed to and fro on this subject, and on 13 March 1930, Lieutenant-Colonel Pemberton stated "it is more probable that the work will not be completed before 15 August, and no definite guarantee as to this date of completion can be given." This reply was evidently not satisfactory to Major Inglis at the Air Defence Experimental Establishment. Writing to Lieutenant-Colonel Pemberton on 14 March 1930, he suggested that "this estimate of time seems most pessimistic; the listening trench and forecourt cover a large area, and in my opinion, permit a large number of men and several concrete mixers being employed. If a contract is placed which definitely allows 3 months for completion, the 200 foot (61m) mirror will probably not be tested this year."

Lieutenant-Colonel Pemberton was not amused. In a letter to Major Inglis on 20 March 1930, he pointed out that every effort had been made to avoid delays. "My Surveyor of Works Martin, my Chief Draughtsman, and three clerks, have had to shelve all other work for the best part of 6 days at the very busiest time of the year. Martin and my Chief Draughtsman also worked voluntarily on Sunday.

I tell you this merely to show you and Major Tucker how very inconvenient it is to all if we are not given sufficient time to work on your schemes concurrently with others which are equally important. Perhaps this might be obviated in future if I could sometimes be asked to give an estimate of time for completion of a particular work before your dates with the RAF etc. are fixed, and not after." This letter produced a conciliatory reply, explaining that dates for acoustic experiments depended upon the RAF flying programme, which had to be in the Summer months to take advantage of good weather.

By May 1930, a decision had been made to modify and raise the listener's trench in the light of previous suggestions by the Royal Engineers. A photograph dating from the early 1930s shows details of the forecourt area of the 200 foot mirror. The picture was taken from a point in front of the mirror, looking out to sea from the forecourt over an uninterrupted expanse of shingle. A row of microphones can be seen on the forecourt, also the curved concrete wall at the front, and access steps in the left wing wall. The lower part of the forecourt, often described as the 'trench', is clearly visible, and it remains so at the site at the time of writing, although in a ruinous state.

Another archive photograph taken at a later date shows a close-up view of the microphones. Other details are clearly visible in this view including side screens erected to prevent wind interference, and on the front wall, numbers indicating bearings, and switches and marker lights for communication between forecourt observers and the control room.

The mirror site at Denge, in an exposed position on the shingle, was obviously of interest to casual passers by and holiday makers on that part of the coast. Concern about privacy of the site was expressed in letters of the time. As early as November 1928, the Royal Engineers asked the Air Defence Experimental Establishment if boundary stones would be sufficient as markers. The Superintendent of the Establishment replied on 16 November: "I shall be quite satisfied with boundary stones provided that they are clearly visible. If I find that there is any difficulty in keeping sightseers out of the enclosure, I will ask for a fence later."

Forecourt of the 200 foot mirror at Denge with microphones in position c. 1930.
The 20 foot and 30 foot mirrors can be seen in the background

Probably as a result of bitter experience, by early 1930 the Superintendent was thinking very seriously about protecting the Denge site from intruders. He wrote to the Commander Royal Engineers, Dover: "It is considered that the approaching completion of the 200 foot mirror makes it desirable to provide a barbed wire fence round the boundary of the property. The gate should be covered with barbed wire, and provided with a padlock and chain." He referred again to the matter in a letter to the Royal Engineers Board on the 11 June 1930. "Major Tucker reports to me that his staff have already had to turn away trippers from the mirrors, even though the holiday season has scarcely begun. I think it is most important to prevent casual picnic parties, who may include potential journalists, from getting near the focus of the 200 foot mirror and observing its properties. Although it is impossible to keep the mirrors entirely secret, we have hitherto prevented their use by unauthorized persons by removing parts of the listening gear. This means of prevention is not available with the 200 foot mirror, and I therefore regard it as most important to have the fence erected by 11 July, that is, before my staff, who are now quartered there, are withdrawn." A reply from the Royal Engineers indicated that the fencing would be completed by the end of July.

Microphones in position on the 200 foot sound mirror, Denge 1934.
Note bearings marked on front wall.

From the available evidence, it seems that the 200 foot mirror was ready for use by the middle of 1930, and it was reported on the 27 June that "the 200 foot mirror equipment has been used on a few occasions to follow the progress of a single engined aeroplane." The mirrors at Denge were part of what is often referred to in documents of the time as "the Hythe mirror system." The system was tested in October and November 1930, and Air Defence Experimental Establishment reports provide details of the various heights at which the participating aircraft flew, and the effects of wind turbulence on the effectiveness of the mirrors.

The 200 foot (61m) mirror differed from other mirrors in that it involved two types of listening work. In addition to the listeners, or 'sentries' patrolling behind the front forecourt wall, other observers occupied a control room equipped with instruments wired to microphones on the forecourt. At the time of the construction of the mirror, this control room was in a hut nearby.

The newly completed 200 foot mirror at Denge 1930. On the right can be seen the hut used as a control room in the early days.

It is difficult to imagine the work of a 'sentry' or 'outside listener', and in the absence of verbal descriptions by participants, it is necessary to rely on documentary evidence. According to contemporary accounts, each outside listener was given a beat to patrol, over a definite number of 'zones'. A zone was the area covered by one of a row of microphones along the forecourt. On the front wall, there were switches and lamps adjacent to each microphone and wired to the control room, thus allowing two-way signals between outside and inside listeners. The outside listeners were protected from wind disturbance by lateral canvas curtains, and wore rubber shoes so that local sounds were suppressed.

"Bearings marked on the wall at regular intervals help to locate the sentry when he hears the sound at its maximum, and by a system of lights and switches he can communicate his position to the operating room, or reciprocally, can receive indications given from them as to where he should listen. Along the inner surface of this wall is a duck-boarded gangway about 2 feet 6 inches (76cm) high along which listening sentries can patrol. If the sound is focused lower down, corresponding to the aircraft at higher elevation, the sentries can step down to the floor level." (See p.111)

The previous passage poses something of a puzzle in relation to the effectiveness of the "listening sentries" at the Denge 200 foot mirror. (61m) The surviving sections of the front wall are about five feet (c.1.5m) in height. If, as in the previous description, the listener stood on the raised duck-boarded gangway behind the wall, it appears that his head would be above the parapet, devoid of any protection from interfering sounds in the vicinity.

Attention was drawn at this time to the importance of electrical aids to listening. "It has long been realized that with the increased speed of aircraft and need for sustained vigilance, longer ranges for early warning will be essential and that some electrical method capable of extending range beyond the capacity of the ear must be devised, and further that it must be capable of giving clear warning without concentration and continuous effort." This was a reference to the physical problems posed to aural listeners at the smaller mirrors, where extreme concentration was required when wearing stethoscopes attached to a trumpet collector, searching the face of a 20 or 30 foot (6.1 or 9.1m) mirror for elusive sounds.

The 200 foot mirror was found to be effective in collecting long wave aircraft engine sounds. The need for some electrical supplement to purely aural listening was explained by the fact that such long wave sounds of low pitch were not easily picked up by ear alone, and it was necessary to use microphones tuned to detect those sounds.

"On the floor of the forecourt a number of microphones are disposed, 20 in all, 5 feet (c.1.5m) apart, and these are ranged along the focal surface so that indications are given every 5 degrees in bearing, the operation of two giving a 2½ degree accuracy. This takes the place of the moving sentry, and in fact gives earlier warning. When one microphone is operating, the observer can instruct the sentry if necessary to verify if he can, the sound heard. The directional properties of the 200 foot (61m) mirror, even for long wave lengths, are remarkably sharp, and it is found that generally only one microphone is affected at a time by an aeroplane in front of the mirror so that azimuthally bearings (compass bearings) can be given to the nearest 5 degrees." (See p.111)

The performance of Dr Tucker's hot-wire microphone was crucial to the successful operation of the 200 foot (61m) sound mirror. Various details of the instrument have been mentioned previously, particularly in relation to its use in gun sound ranging in the First World War. For a full and definite description of the device, there can be no better source than the writings of the inventor. Dr Tucker's personal papers include the following description, which also appears in War Office publications. The complex accompanying mathematics are excluded.

"The hot-wire microphone has been designed specially for detecting the low-frequency sounds emitted by aircraft. The microphone is composed of two parts, namely (a) a resonator and (b) a hot-wire 'grid'. The function of the former is to collect sound-energy by means of resonance while the latter is a device for converting acoustical effects into electrical effects. A section through a doubly resonant hot-wire microphone is shown in Figure 1. The microphone is said to be 'doubly resonant' since the resonator is a double one consisting of two portions A and B. (Figure 1) The outer resonator (B) is a cylindrical iron casting fitted with two flat end-plates P1 and P2. The lower end-plate P2 has a circular orifice at O through which the sound energy enters.

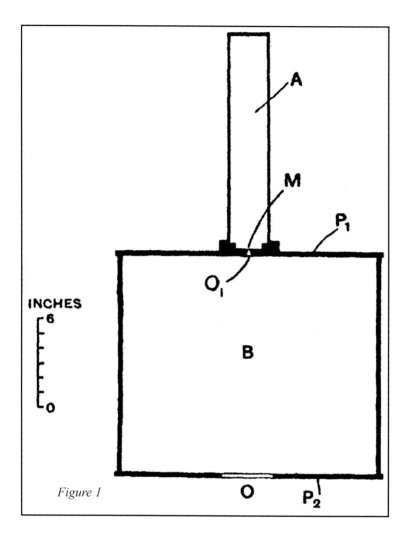

Figure 1

The inner resonator is made of brass and has a small cylindrical orifice at O1 which allows the passage of air between A and B. Both resonators have natural frequencies which are dependent partly on their internal volumes and partly on the dimensions of their orifices. The idea underlying the use of a double resonator is that the sound will be magnified first by the outer resonator and then again by the inner one. The pressures generated in the interior of the outer resonator are many times greater than those in the original sound-wave. These pressures act in turn on the inner resonator which again magnifies the vibrations. The greatest movement of air takes place in the narrow orifice O1 which forms a channel of communication between the outer and the inner resonators, and it is at the inner end of this orifice (at M in Figure 1) that the hot-wire grid is mounted. The amplitude of the vibrations at O1 is sometimes a thousand times as great as the amplitude of the sound waves.

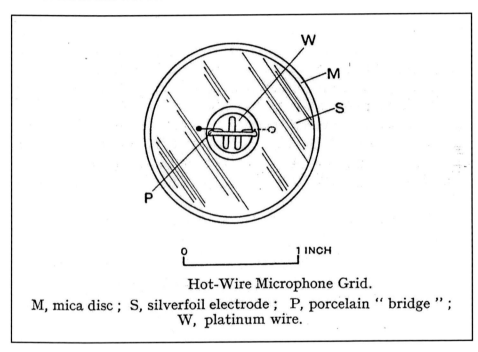

Hot-Wire Microphone Grid.

M, mica disc ; S, silverfoil electrode ; P, porcelain " bridge " ;
W, platinum wire.

Figure 2

The hot-wire grid consists of three loops of very fine platinum wire. The wire is about 0.006 cm in diameter and is supported on a porcelain bridge in a circular hole in a small mica plate. (See Figure 2) The electrodes by which the current is led through the grid are two annular pieces of silver foil cemented to opposite sides of the mica disk. The grid is mounted in a special holder so that it lies in the orifice O1 (Figure 1) and is heated to just below red-heat by a current of about 30 milliamperes. The fine platinum wire has a high temperature coefficient, that is, its electrical resistance changes rapidly with temperature.

When sound of suitable frequency is received by the resonator the oscillatory movement of the air in the orifice O1 cools the hot-wire grid and there is a corresponding reduction in its electrical resistance. It is this change in resistance which is utilized for the detection of sound waves.

The doubly resonant form of microphone is employed for another reason, apart from magnification of the motion in sound-waves. By a suitable choice of dimensions the microphone can be made so that it will respond only to sounds the frequencies of which fall within a certain limited range. Thus a microphone can be designed to respond to the low-frequency sounds of airscrews. The electrical circuit into which a hot-wire microphone is connected in order to record or detect sound is very simple, since it is only necessary to arrange for the change in resistance to produce a movement on some electrical indicating instrument."

Dr Tucker stressed one of the main advantages of his hot wire microphone as used at the 200 foot (61m) mirror. He referred to "its insensitivity to other disturbing noises, as can be shown by substituting a galvanometer so that the response of the microphone is shown visually. Here the magnified alternating current is first made unidirectional by means of a crystal rectifier. A Klaxon horn and other disturbances nearby produce no effect, but the slightest hum on the appropriate note is immediately detected. The microphone may be tuned by altering the volume of the resonator or by altering the dimensions of its neck - thus a larger volume or a longer neck would be employed for a lower note. In general, alteration of volume is the most satisfactory way of tuning."

The mirror and microphone system were obviously quite selective in detecting sounds of a particular pitch, such as the notes of aero engines, and the above passage seems to give the lie to various items of local folklore about the 200 foot (61m) mirror. From Dr Tucker's description, it does not seem likely that listeners at the mirror were troubled by the sounds of a passing milk float, or trains leaving Calais station.

The mirror control room was equipped with a loudspeaker, and the leads from the various microphones on the forecourt ended in jack plugs in a board in the control room. Continuing from a report of the period, "the observer watches the galvanometer, and if there is a movement of the galvanometer, he can at once verify or disprove any suspicion by placing the plug in the appropriate jack, and listening to the loudspeaker. An approximate bearing can be given by noting in which jack the plug must be placed in order to obtain the loudest sound. If the aircraft approaches nearer to the mirror, the galvanometer deflections serve to indicate the bearing."

"Microphones for sensitive listening are very susceptible to wind, and in order to cut out wind disturbance, the opening of the drum is protected by a conical screen of drugget. This stops the wind gusts while giving free passage to the sound. The microphones, like the aerials in a wireless receiver to which these are a complete analogy, are connected with an amplifier and loud speaker, and by interposition of a key board, the listener can discover which microphone is responding, and therefore in what direction the aeroplane is approaching. The microphones are tuned to the lowest notes of the aircraft, and in this way no effect is produced by conversation or the usual disturbing noises associated with a normal listening post. The ranges so far obtained have reached 27 miles (43km) under good conditions, and under all conditions for low flying i.e. below 6000 ft (1829m) an average range of 17 or 18 miles (27 or 29km) including good and bad weather has been realized. It may be of interest to say that the loudspeaker reproducing the aeroplane sound is generally audible outside the operating hut, before the aeroplane can be distinguished by the unaided ear. Roughly speaking, the 30 foot (9.1) mirrors give twice the range of the unaided ear, and the 200 foot (61m) mirror three times that range and sometimes more, with the added advantage of a definite bearing and a capacity to detect and distinguish aircraft when separated 10 degrees apart."

Putting together these various descriptions, the principles of electrical operating methods at the 200 foot (61m) mirror can be summed up briefly. The sound waves of an approaching aircraft were reflected by the mirror onto microphones, tuned to the particular frequencies or notes emitted by aircraft engines. The microphones were arranged along the forecourt, behind the front wall, and connected to visual and aural indicating equipment in the control room. Due to the sensitivity and directional properties of the microphones, arranged in a radial pattern along the forecourt, it was possible to obtain a bearing on the aircraft by observing which microphone was receiving the strongest signals.

The new 30 foot (9m) and 200 (61m) foot mirrors at Denge were completed by the Summer of 1930, and it seems likely that the existing 20 foot mirror (6m) of 1928 became obsolete at that time. Percy Rothwell's collection of photographs includes a view captioned "20 foot mirror at Denge Beach, February 1930." The scene shows the listening apparatus to be incomplete, with the bare vertical shaft of the gear standing on the concrete pillar, with no horizontal arm or trumpet mounted. This suggests that either new gear was to be fitted, or that with the construction of more advanced 30 foot and 200 foot mirrors, the 20 foot mirror was no longer needed.

On 29 July 1930 Major Inglis, Superintendent of the Air Defence Experimental Establishment, wrote to the War Department Chemist at Woolwich Arsenal, asking for a photographer to go New Romney to "photograph the 200 foot, 30 foot and 20 foot sound mirrors there." On the same day, he also wrote to Wing Commander W. V. Strugnell at Manston, asking for aerial photographs of the mirrors. On the 8 August, he was in touch with the Officer in Charge, Hythe Acoustical Station about the arrangements: "Please arrange to meet the 10.30 a.m. with the Trojan at Ashford Station. After the photographs have been taken, please convey the photographer back to the station as necessary." The term 'Trojan' is a reference to a type of motor van of the period.

The ground photographs of the Denge site were taken on 12 August 1930, and on 20 August, Major Inglis wrote a letter of thanks for aerial photographs received from No. 9 Bomber Squadron, Manston. A view looking down on the 200 foot mirror and the wooden control hut could be one of those photographs.

Another aerial photograph survives in the National Archives. It shows the Denge site in 1930 with coastal building development ending just before the track to the mirrors. The Southern Railway branch to New Romney can be seen clearly on its original alignment, passing behind the mirrors.

*Aerial view of the Denge mirror site 1930. At this period, coastal development
ends near the track to the mirrors. The standard gauge branch railway to
New Romney can be seen on its original course behind the mirrors.*

Late in 1933, a decision was made to construct a concrete listening room
behind the 200 foot (61m) mirror at Denge. Up to that point, the control
room at Denge was in one of the huts which can be seen in photographs of
the site taken in the early 1930's. In a letter to the Director of Acoustical

Research, Mr Ferguson of the Air Defence Experimental Establishment, wrote on 3 November 1933: "I have interviewed the Deputy Commander, Royal Engineers re cutting a hole in the centre of the 200 foot (61m) mirror and building a concrete shed 15 feet (4.6m) by 10 feet (3m) - that is the distance between the two buttresses - behind the mirror. The probable cost would be £45, and in any case, not greater than £50. I am preparing a drawing illustrating a scheme for your approval." The new room constructed behind the 200 foot (61m) mirror was a 2 storey building, the ground floor used for stores and batteries, and the second floor housing the listening chamber, which had a window of armoured glass "so that the control room operator has a complete view of the forecourt." The archives of the Royal Artillery contain two pictures of the interior of the listening chamber or control room dating from 1934. In one of the views, an operator sits looking at a wall panel on the left side of the control room with the window to his right. There are three rows of ten dials on the panel, probably galvanometers as mentioned in various reports by Dr Tucker. Under the panel in front of the operator is a desk with an array of switches, laid out in a radial pattern which seems to mimic the layout of microphones on the forecourt. In the second illustration, the desk has been moved to a more logical position in front of the window, through which there is a view of the forecourt with its microphones, and in the distance, the narrow gauge branch line to the mirrors. According to a 1934 Air Defence Experimental Establishment Report, the listening chamber was normally occupied by two people - a listener, and a telephonist.

Rear view of the Denge 200 foot (61m) mirror, showing central listening chamber c.1933

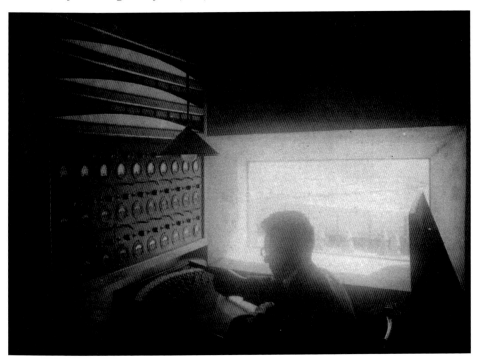

Interior of listening chamber, 200 foot (61m) mirror Denge, 1934

Listening chamber, Denge 200 foot (61m) mirror. In contrast to a previous view, the control desk is facing the window. The front wall and microphones are just visible, 1934.The listening chamber at the Denge 200 foot (61m) mirror survived until its collapse in the late years of the twentieth century. The remains could still be seen on the ground behind the mirror in the new century, and the former window survives as a hole in the centre of the mirror

Late 20th century view of the Denge 200 foot (61m) mirror showing ruins of the listening chamber. The window survives as a hole in the centre of the mirror.

CHAPTER ELEVEN

SIX MIRRORS

In the 1930s, there were ambitious plans to extend the mirror system, both in Great Britain and overseas. For example, in 1931, Major Inglis of the Air Defence Experimental Establishment sent a memorandum to the Royal Engineers Board about proposed mirror sites at Luccombe Chine near Dunnose, and Bembridge, on the Isle of Wight. He mentioned a familiar problem when he pointed out that "very careful consideration was given to the Luccombe site, and no latitude can be allowed in the direction of placing the site nearer the road. The noise of traffic would render the mirror useless."

In the event, the most comprehensive system of mirrors developed before radar made the whole idea obsolete was that completed by 1930, based at the Acoustic Research Station on the hills west of Hythe. These six mirrors have already been described in some detail, but as a reminder of the general layout, the mirrors were located at three places on the Kent coast. Hythe was the site of a 20 foot (6.1m) and a 30 foot (9.1m) mirror. A single 20 foot (6.1m) mirror stood on Abbots Cliff between Folkestone and Dover, and 20 foot, 30 foot, and 200 foot (61m) mirrors were sited on the shingle at Denge, between New Romney and Dungeness. The system was in operation during the Air Defence of Great Britain Exercises. (Maps 1 and 2)

An explanation of the title 'Air Defence of Great Britain' is relevant at this point. As far back as 1917, Lloyd George and General Smuts had put forward the idea of an independent air force with a primary role of protecting the country against aerial attack. Subsequently, the Air Ministry had pressed for a leading part in air defence, and in 1922, the Government put forward a scheme for the provision of a metropolitan air force of fourteen bomber and nine fighter squadrons. Those numbers suggest an emphasis on attack as the best means of defence. A Home Defence Committee was set up under Air Chief Marshal Trenchard, and responsibilities were split between the War Office and the Air Ministry, the former overseeing the guns and searchlights, and the latter in charge of Fighter and Bomber squadrons. The overall Commander was an Air Officer. The area to be defended was known as the "Fighting Zone", and the title for the whole defence organization was "Air Defence of Great Britain" or A.D.G.B. This organization lasted until 1935, when it was abolished, and replaced by Fighter, Bomber, and Training Commands of the Royal Air Force.

The newly completed mirrors were in action during the summer of 1930 in exercises involving the Royal Air Force. Details are given in a memorandum on 26 June 1930 from the RAF base at Calshot on Southampton Water, addressed to "Director, The Acoustical Station, The Roughs, Hythe". Included with the memorandum was a copy of "Training Order Number 23, 25 June 1930 - Co-operation with the Acoustical Station, Hythe."

The Order included the following instructions:- "Two flights per week to be made by flying boats in such a manner that they can be used in connection with tests of coastal listening stations now in progress near Hythe, Kent. The aircraft should cross the coast about 2 miles north of Dungeness Lighthouse, and after crossing the coast should circle once or twice above the coast line. Half an hour before the time the aircraft is expected to cross the coast, watch will be commenced at a temporary W/T (Wireless Telegraphy) station at the Acoustical Station. This watch will be maintained until after co-operation or until the flight is cancelled. Call sign of this temporary W/T station - 'N4T'. Wave frequency 258 K.C. (1163 metres). On the day after the flight, a log of the flight, including times, positions, tracks, ground speeds, and height is to be forwarded to the Chief Instructor for transmission to the Acoustical Station."

Further details of the participation of the RAF in exercises with the mirrors are contained in a memorandum to the "D. of A." (Director of

Acoustics) dated 9 July 1930. Unfortunately, the writer's signature is illegible, but he had visited RAF Calshot and recorded his impressions. The RAF was keen to co-operate with the Acoustic Research Station. A description of the aircraft involved is given:- "The boats are Supermarine Southampton Twin Engined Flying Boats. They carry two Napier Lion engines, and the normal engine speed at 8000 - 10,000 feet (2438 - 3048m) is 1950 to 2000 rpm. Some machines can fly at lower revs. down to 1850 rpm. The propellers are two bladed, diameter 12.35 feet. (3.8m) The exhausts for the Lion engine (arrow type with 3 banks of 4 cylinders) are as in the Virginia." Such details were important when tuning microphones at the 200 foot (61m) mirror to respond to sound waves produced by particular aircraft engines.

Reports by crews of aircraft participating in the mirror tests in 1930 give an indication of the flying duties involved. A typical example is headed: "Royal Air Force Base, Calshot, Fawley, Southampton, Hampshire to The Director, The Acoustical Station, The Roughs, Hythe, Kent. 24 June 1930. Co-operation by Flying Boats with the Acoustical Station, Hythe. A report on the flight of Southampton Flying Boat S.1038 on 23 inst. co-operating with the Acoustical Station is forwarded herewith. Signed: (illegible) Group Captain, Commanding Royal Air Force Base, Calshot."

From details in this report, the course of the aircraft was from Calshot, passing over Beachy Head and Dungeness to Cap Gris Nez. From Cap Gris Nez, the aircraft made two return trips over the Channel to Hythe before returning to base. Speeds ranged from 52 to 90 knots, at heights between 800 and 7,500 feet, (243m and 2286m) and the total flying time was about three and a half hours.

The brief high summer enjoyed by the Hythe mirror system in the years 1932 to 1935 was the culmination of experiments with sound mirrors at various sites, over a period dating back to the First World War. Much of the earlier experimental work was carried out by service and civilian personnel from Army establishments responsible to the War Office, but the Air Ministry and RAF also became involved in those few years in the 1930s.

On 25 November 1931, the Commander in Chief, Air Defence of Great Britain wrote to the Secretary of the Air Ministry: "I consider that these mirrors have now reached a state of development at which the value of the instruments in the hands of non-specialist personnel should be demonstrated. I should like a proportion of Regular Air Force personnel to take part in these exercises with the military personnel, and I propose with your approval to detail one officer and two other ranks for this duty."

There was further correspondence on this subject. On 28 April 1932, the Commander in Chief, Air Defence of Great Britain, was informed by the Air Ministry that "a letter had now been received from the War Office, concurring in your proposal to allow a proportion of Royal Air Force personnel to be trained in using the mirrors for a period of 6 weeks, commencing June 6, 1932." In reply, the Commander in Chief noted that arrangements had been made to man the 200 foot (61m) mirror during the period 6 June to 15 July by "Sappers of the Royal Engineers, supplemented by RAF personnel."

The Air Defence Experimental Establishment at Biggin Hill became involved in these arrangements, as detailed in letter to the Air Defence of Great Britain, Uxbridge on 28 April 1932. "Two junior officers are to report at the Acoustical Station, The Roughs, Hythe at 10.00 a.m. on Friday June 3rd. Two other ranks to report at the same station at 10.00 a.m. on Monday May 30th. It is intended that the Army detachment that is to work alongside this party shall be accommodated with one of the army units in the Hythe area. If you desire, I could ask this unit to accommodate your party as well. It would be of great assistance if a vehicle such as a Trojan Van could be provided to carry the party from its living quarters to the various places where it will work each night. "

These manning details were carried out, including the provision of the Trojan van. A letter of 23 May 1932 outlines the domestic arrangements: "The two officers will be accommodated by the Royal Army Service Corps, Home Counties East, and use their mess. The other ranks will be accommodated by the Queens Bays. Both the above units are in Shorncliffe." This letter goes on to give details of how the men should travel to and find their accommodation. Various other letters in 1932 give details of the officers and men employed, including one from RAF Uxbridge which mentions Flying Officer Burke, who was the "senior officer detailed for duty at Hythe. He will be responsible for the report which will have to be rendered to this

H.Q. on the conclusion of the tests."

The minutes of the Acoustic Committee of the Royal Engineers Board for 1932, in relation to the sound mirrors, contain a mention of "work done by troops and airmen under the supervision of Junior officers. These exercises had been carried out during June and July 1932, and very accurate performances had been achieved, and the installation had been thoroughly tested." Although there is a reference here to supervision by junior officers, it is apparent from documents of the period, that civilian experts from the Air Defence Experimental Establishment were also involved in training service personnel.

The intention behind the 1932 Exercises is outlined in an October report of the Air Defence Experimental Establishment: "To test the capacity of troops after a short training to reproduce the results already obtained by civilian personnel of the ADEE, and to devise methods for handling of personnel, so that on the outbreak of war, the installation could be immediately manned and operated."

This report gives a good idea of the state of the Hythe mirror system in 1932: "The installation of coastal mirrors on the Kent coast has been designed as one single unit operated from a coastal headquarters. Such a headquarters is provided at the Hythe Acoustical Station which is in telephonic communication with the whole system. At this station, the movements of raiding aircraft are reported and plotted and can be sent in direct to Air Defence of Great Britain headquarters."

"The system involves the employment of a 200 foot strip mirror (61m) equipped with microphones, amplifier and loudspeaker, capable of giving electrical indication with bearing of the first sounds produced by incoming raider or raiders. This instrument acts as a sentry and reports a zone of listening helpful to the other listening posts some time before such posts can get into operation. This mirror is sited at Denge, two miles from Dungeness. The system for which the 200 foot mirror serves as sentry consists of 3 smaller mirrors - Abbots Cliff 20 foot (6.1m), Hythe 30 foot (9.1m), Denge 30 foot (9.1m), the last alongside the 200 foot (61m) mirror. These mirrors employ aural methods of listening in which stethoscopes are connected to a collecting trumpet capable of being swung across the face of the mirror.

The first one is a segment of a sphere of 20 feet (6.1) aperture and 15 feet radius (4.5m) of curvature, and is of early pattern. The other two are hemispherical, but of the same radius of curvature. The 3 mirrors protect a coastline of about 16 miles (26km) and are spaced about 8 miles (13km) apart."

References to a control room at Hythe occur frequently in reports of the period. Early photographs and a site plan of the Acoustic Research Station on The Roughs at Hythe show a substantial wooden building near the 20 foot mirror. The foundations of the building remain in the 21st century. It is clear from documentary evidence that this building was the control room for the Hythe mirror system. A concrete bunker, situated some distance away along the hillside near the remains of the 30 foot mirror has been described as a control room but it does not appear on aerial photographs of the site taken in the early 1930s, and reminiscences by a scientist who worked on radar equipment sited here during the Second World War suggest that the bunker is a structure from that period.

The ADEE report of 1932 records the methods used at the Hythe control room when plotting aircraft movements over the mirror system: "The plotting board (at Headquarters) consisted of a reproduction in skeleton of a coastal map showing the position of the mirrors, and subdivided into numbered and lettered squares, so that co-ordinates of any point on it could be quoted. The board was surrounded by scales in degrees, one for each mirror position, and strings pivoted on these positions and laid against the scale could represent the bearing derived from the mirrors. The edge of the board also carried the boundaries of the sector appropriate to the 200 foot mirror, and the close proximity of the 30 foot and 200 foot mirrors at Denge made it possible to use the same string for either. The map on the plotting board was also covered by curves from which the appropriate lag of sound correction could be estimated. An essential feature of this operation is the drill necessary for the listeners, telephonists and controlling officers, in so far as messages may come in on demand from 4 mirrors continuously, although in general, only 2 are continuously active. This drill had to be perfected before effective work could be done."

These details of procedure have a familiar ring. One of the main reasons for the effectiveness of radar in the war which was soon to come, was that the coastal radar stations were integrated into a carefully planned and skilfully operated control and reporting system. Without such a system, the newly developed tool of radar would have been less successful.

The 1932 report also includes comments on the different types of mirror in the Hythe system, pointing out that the efficiency of the listener at the 20 foot (6.1m) Abbots Cliff mirror was affected by his open air position, and that the two 30 foot (9.1m) mirrors, at Hythe and Denge, had enclosed listening positions, although the Denge mirror was an improvement on that at Hythe. The report relates the design of the various mirrors to the results achieved: "That the output of these mirrors became so nearly equal does not represent an equality in efficiency, as the comfort and ease of manipulation of the later pattern place them in a different category to the earlier ones. Careful training on each of the mirrors, however, tended to overcome the disabilities of the less efficient types."

In addition, the report includes a summary of the problems of noise at the various mirror sites. Abbots Cliff was described as "well above sea level, and free from disturbance from the sea, with no traffic noise." The Hythe (30 foot) mirror was "better sheltered from the wind, but suffered from continuous noises from the town of Hythe to the east, and from the Hythe to New Romney road." These sounds were "nearly always in competition with the aircraft." The Denge mirrors were described as "half a mile from the sea" but "more exposed to wind and sea noise" which under east wind conditions could be "very troublesome." It was pointed out that all these variations made it difficult to compare the performance of the various mirrors.

The absence, in such reports, of any mention of the 20 foot (6.1m) mirrors at Hythe and Denge, suggests that they had been abandoned in favour of the 30 foot (9.1m) mirrors at those sites. It was necessary to retain use of the 20 foot (6.1m) mirror at Abbots Cliff, because there was no 30 foot (9.1m) mirror at that site which could be used in conjunction with the 30 foot (9.1m) mirrors at Hythe and Denge. Effectively at this time, the mirror system consisted of four mirrors: one 20 foot mirror (6.1m) at Abbots Cliff, one 30 foot mirror (9.1m) at Hythe, and one 30 foot mirror (9.1m) alongside the 200 foot mirror (61m) at Denge.

An important visitor came to Hythe in July 1932. Mr H. E. Wimperis, who from 1934 onwards was much involved in the development of radar, was Director of Scientific Research at the Air Ministry. He corresponded with Dr Tucker in connection with his visit.

"Air Ministry, Adastral House, Kingsway, WC2. 17 June 1932
Dear Tucker,
If I could manage to be in Hythe during the nights of both Tuesday and Wednesday, the 5th and 6th July, what would be the programme?
Yours sincerely,

H.E.Wimperis"

Plans for the visit were outlined in an unsigned reply, written for Dr Tucker in his absence, on 28 June 1932:
"If you can be at Hythe on the nights of July 5th and 6th, we could arrange for you to go to Dungeness on one night, and to be at the Acoustical Station, Hythe on the other night. Both the Dungeness mirrors are working, and the large one has new electrical equipment which has been giving very satisfactory results. I am sure that an evening in the control room at the Acoustical Station would be well spent. The observations are all reported there and the plotting and other operations are done by an RAF and an RE Officer. This is really the best place for forming an opinion on the performance of the mirrors."

Arrangements were made for H.E.Wimperis to stay at the Sutherland House Hotel, Hythe on 5 and 6 July 1932. His views on the acoustic defence system were not attached to the correspondence relating to his visit.

In December 1932, a memorandum from the Headquarters of the Air Defence of Great Britain gave details of the performance of the mirrors in the 1932 Exercises. The ranges obtained were related to the listening conditions. On 19 June, with aircraft at a height of 5,200 feet (1585m), in "quiet" conditions, the 200 foot (61m) mirror picked up aircraft at a range of 20 miles (32km), the unaided ear achieved only 6½ miles (10.46km); on 1 July, in listening conditions of "high wind", with aircraft at 3,500 feet (1067m), the 200 foot (61m) mirror achieved a range of 11 miles (18km), the 30 foot (9.1m) mirror 5½ miles (8.9km). It is also apparent from this report that Wireless Direction Finding equipment was used to check the performance of the mirrors.

Problems encountered during mirror operations in the 1932 Exercises are described in a report of the Air Defence Experimental Establishment dating from November of that year. "A feature of the trials was the jamming disability caused by the sound of the propellers of passing ships, which owing to somewhat unusual meteorological conditions were more prominent than in previous years." Unwanted noise was a continuing problem. The report outlines:

"... two sources of disturbance which affect the measurement of range:

1) Wind
2) Traffic sounds, and others of low pitch in the locality of the mirrors."

Steps were taken to tackle the noise problem at the 200 (61m) foot mirror:

"Wind disturbance has been greatly reduced by the process of screening the microphones and the construction of canvas screens carried on pulleys on rails, on either flank of the mirror. These curtains not only added greatly to the comfort of the listeners in the forecourt, but reduced the disturbing wind eddies. On June 1st and 9th, winds of 20 m.p.h. (32kmph) were recorded, and maximum ranges of 18 and 24 miles (29 and 39km) were observed respectively. Traffic sounds were chiefly those of shipping and were attributable to the beat of the propellers. The disturbance was greatest on some of the cargo boats, although a large passenger liner might be very troublesome. The sensitivity of the mirror installation is such that on June 6th, a cargo boat at over 16 miles (26km) range was being followed for a period of several minutes. It should be pointed out that there is a large amount of shipping passing Dungeness at this period of the year, and that it is improbable that any other likely mirror site would be subject to the same disability."

Bearing in mind that the microphones of the 200 foot (61m) mirror were tuned to pick up aircraft sounds, it seems from the preceding report of difficulties caused by the propeller beat of passing ships, that these sounds were of a similar low frequency to aircraft sounds.

The 1932 report included further operational details. "The whole mirror system of 3 small mirrors and the 200 foot mirror was employed for instruction of Army and RAF. personnel. An improved microphone system was installed on the 200 foot mirror." The 200 foot (61m) mirror was used as an "early warning in the system and served to correct the 30 foot (9.1m) mirror to yield an intersection when only one of the 3 mirrors could operate. A mean maximum range for all weather conditions on 14 occasions was 16 miles (26km), at a mean height of aircraft of 6,300 feet (1920m). The accuracy of bearings was checked and found to be within about 1½ degrees." There is an interesting detail about the manning of the 200 foot mirror: "The personnel employed by the mirror involved two listeners in the mirror forecourt for identification purposes, and one E.O. (Experimental Officer) in the mirror control room." It appears from this that the two listeners in the forecourt, picking up sounds acoustically as they were reflected from the mirror, worked as a team with the observer in the control room, who listened for sounds picked up by the microphones.

Further illumination on the manning of the 30 foot bowl type mirrors was given by Dr Tucker to the Sound Location and Acoustic Committee of the Royal Engineers Board on 2 November 1932. He explained that so far the detachment at a 30 foot (9.1m) mirror had consisted of one listener and a telephonist. "Future work would be with the object of having two listeners and a telephonist. The second listener would have 2 trumpets, one above and one below the existing trumpet and would permit of accurate listening in elevation, which was very important at the shorter ranges, and would enable the height of targets to be determined. Listening on the 2 trumpets would be carried out by bracketing the maximum intensity. It was not certain that this method would be more successful than the method of judging intensity alone as practised with the single trumpet. Experiments in this connection were proceeding."

Some thought was given in 1932 to the problem of the visibility of the sound mirror system from the air. A Royal Engineers Board Report of July gives some details. Referring to the Hythe mirrors, the report states that: "The 20 foot mirror is well concealed in a fold in the ground and is almost invisible from the air. The new 30 foot mirror is situated on open grassland, and its light colour is in striking contrast with its surroundings. Owing to the fact that its axis is slightly inclined upwards, the internal and external curvature is obvious, and the sound collecting apparatus can be seen clearly." Similar details were given about the visibility of the mirrors at Abbots Cliff and Denge. The observations were made at heights varying from 200 to 2000 feet (61 to 610m) in bright, sunny weather. Suggestions were made as to how to make the mirrors less visible from the air, including colour washing the surfaces to make them merge into the ground colour where possible.

One letter written in 1932 is prophetic. On 9 August, the Air Officer in Command, Fighting Area, RAF, wrote to the Air Defence Experimental Establishment on the subject of manning the mirrors. "I recommend that they be manned by women in wartime." Pointing out that this would result in a saving of manpower, he continued: "I am of the opinion that this type of work can be performed by women just as well, if not better, than by men." This is an interesting comment in the light of the vital contribution made by women, just a few years later, in the operation of equipment such as barrage balloons and searchlights, and in particular their contribution as plotters and radar operators in the air defence system during the Second World War.

On 22 October 1932, the Commander in Chief, Air Defence of Great Britain wrote from Uxbridge to the Air Ministry, referring to a report on the 1932 Exercises submitted by Flying Officer Burke. One conclusion reached was that efforts should be concentrated on perfecting the 200 foot mirror (61m), as that type was better suited to the needs of home defence than the smaller 20 to 30 foot (6.1 - 9.1m) mirrors.

Looking to the years ahead, the Commander in Chief proposed a more comprehensive system of 200 foot mirrors. "I envisage a continuous screen of them from St Catherine's Point, Isle of Wight, to say, Orford Ness or Lowestoft. The mirrors would be placed some 17 to 20 miles apart (27 to 32km). We should continue the principle of handling the mirrors by service personnel, and that they should be brought into the Air Exercises 1933."

The year 1933 is a suitable point for a temporary departure from the sound mirror story. In that year, another type of acoustic detection system dating back to the First World War was finally abandoned.

CHAPTER TWELVE

LISTENING WELLS

Sound mirrors were not the only devices used for acoustic aircraft detection. During the First World War experimental work with another system took place in special excavations known as 'Listening Wells.' In the spring of 1918, Lieutenant J. M. Moubray of the Royal Engineers was experimenting in such a shaft in the Somme area of the battlefield. On 4 April he wrote some notes on his work, describing "Listening Shafts or Wells for the Location of Aeroplanes in Space." The method made use of several listening stations in communication with a central station. Each listening station consisted of a shaft or 'well' sunk in the ground, at the bottom of which an observer was posted who listened for the sounds of aircraft passing overhead.

Moubray began his notes by saying that the method had first been tried in London "last October", that is in October 1917. He continued: "Acting under the instructions of the Anti- Aircraft Group Commander of the 5th Army, I commenced experiments in France at the beginning of this year. Shafts of different sizes were sunk and aeroplanes flown over them at known heights. A smaller shaft gave a longer detection of sound than a larger one. The ground speed of the 'plane was obtained by having two wires, one vertically above the other and about four feet from it, at right angles to the line of flight and at a distance of about a mile from the shaft. Thus when the bird (sic) was cut by the two wires at one time, it would be vertically above a line at right angles to the line of flight, from the point where the wires were situated. An observer at that moment pressed a button which rang a bell at the bottom of the shaft. By a somewhat similar method, the exact moment that the bird was vertically over the shaft was obtained, these observations thus giving a fairly accurate ground speed."

This description, which would be easier to follow if Lieutenant Moubray had provided a diagram, nevertheless demonstrates that in the early stages of the First World War, there was already a growing realization that aircraft posed a new threat, and that means had to be found for plotting the position, height and speed of hostile bombers.

Lieutenant Moubray provided further details and results of his experiments in France, continuing to describe aircraft as 'birds'.

"The shafts were situated close to a fixed anti aircraft battery, and as the bird passed over, the altitude was determined by two different height finders. The aneroid was read by the observer from above at the same time, so that it was possible to know with a fair degree of accuracy, the actual height of the machine. The observer at the bottom of the shaft listened with a stethoscope attachment from the bottom of a conical funnel, some 15 inches long by 9 inches wide (38cm by 23cm). Ordinary watches were used for timing. It was found that with a shaft 30 feet deep (9.1m) and 5 feet square (1.5m), the zone of maximum audibility extended approximately 25 degrees on all sides from the vertical, whereas with a shaft which was 6 ft square (c.2m) this cone extended only some 20 degrees on all sides."

"Using untrained men at the bottom of the shaft, and such appliances as were available, it was by no means uncommon to determine by sound the altitude to within 2 or 3 hundred feet (61 or 91m) of that given by the height finder, with the bird flying at an altitude of 5000 to 6000 feet (1524 to 1829m). The personal equation and imperfect methods of timing, both of which will be eliminated by the use of microphones, were each separately quite sufficient to account for the errors in the altitudes obtained."

This method was thought to be of use to anti-aircraft batteries in locating aircraft at night. Lieutenant Moubray continued: "I devised an instrument by which we were enabled to pick up different kinds of aeroplanes. A number of piano wires were stretched on a rigid frame. These were tuned to different notes. Each wire impinged on a pen connected to the centre of the disc of a small microphone. When a certain machine came over, it produced vibrations in one or more of the wires which thus altered the electrical impulse and enabled an observer to detect a very faint vibration."

Lieutenant Moubray ended on a plaintive note: "I am sorry to say that since I left France, all my material and shafts has fallen into enemy hands. I do not think however that enough data is available to enable any valuable information to be obtained therefrom."

In May 1918, Captain Tucker who has already figured in this account with his work on sound mirrors, commented on Moubray's listening wells. He pointed out that the principle of listening wells was that there was a "sharpness of sound shadows produced in shafts over which the aeroplanes were passing." He described how the listening shafts were used. The receiving stations were arranged to form the corners of an equilateral triangle with sides of 2,500 yards (2286m). The station was active when the aircraft was "in a cone of 60 degrees, and the courses intersect at a height of 6,500 feet (1981m). For 'planes flying higher than 6,500 feet two stations operate simultaneously since the cones overlap; at lower levels, one cone operates, and when one stops the next will begin. The speed of the aircraft is determined by the interval of "cut out" between the wells. This will work best if the bomber is on a straight course. Therefore the system must be positioned at sites in advance of where an aircraft will meet searchlights and gunfire which will make it veer from its course. Height can be calculated from ground speed and passing one cone to another. The angle of the cone is determined by the following limiting conditions:

1) Sharpness of cut in and cut out;

2) Area of country to be defended and width of trench employed;

3) Amount of cable connecting stations to the central station."

Despite the rather technical nature of some of the preceding descriptions, the whole idea was that the observer in a particular 'well' only heard the noise from an aeroplane while it was in a cone-shaped area of sky having its apex at the well. He was shielded from unwanted lateral noises at ground level, or the noise of other aeroplanes, by his position at the bottom of the shaft. One can imagine an observer, listening for an aircraft to fly through the invisible cone of sky projecting up from his well. Captain Tucker summed up the idea, stating that it was "essential to produce a cone of audibility while at the same time cutting off all lateral sounds."

Acoustic experiments in the Front Line were backed up by work carried out at government research establishments in England. Scientists with academic backgrounds were soon involved, as were serving officers, able to contribute from their experiences in France. Some, like the then Captain W.S.Tucker, a former University Lecturer with a Doctorate in Physics, had a foot in both camps.

In addition to experiments in France, acoustic work was also taking place in England during the First World War under the umbrella of the Munitions Inventions Department. This department was created in August 1915, with the idea of using the skills of scientists to aid the military. The M.I.D. was served by some of the best brains of the time.

Prime Minister Lloyd George announced to the House of Commons on 28 July 1915 that he had appointed Mr (later Sir) E.W.Moir, a Civil Engineer with experience as a Captain in the Royal Engineers, to head the Munitions Inventions Department. Moir selected the following panel of experts:

Sir J.J. Thompson FRS, Cavendish Professor of Physics, Cambridge University

Professor R.T.Glazebrook FRS, Director of the National Physical Laboratory

Professor J. Haldane, Reader in Physiology, New College Oxford

Mr S.Z. Ferranti, founder of Ferranti Ltd, Electrical Engineers

Mr F.W. Lanchester, consultant aeronautical and motor engineer

The War Office nominated other panel members, including Major-General G.K. Scott-Moncrieff, Director of Fortifications and Works.

One of the Munitions Inventions Department experimental stations was at Imber Court, Thames Ditton, in West London near Hampton Court. Captain Tucker was active at Imber Court, and many of the reports from the establishment are signed with his initials "W.S.T." One such report dated 18 February 1918, mentioned the facilities available, describing the laboratory, workshop and office accommodation as "all that could be desired for Acoustic Research. Equipment makes it possible to experiment with electrical instruments replacing the human ear and measurement of intensity of sound at all pitches." There is a reference in the report to Lieutenant Paris, later Dr Paris, another officer who became a key member of Tucker's acoustic research team in the years ahead.

"Working with Lieutenant Paris, an electrical syren (sic) was installed, controlled from the laboratory to reproduce pretty faithfully the sounds of an aeroplane, giving sounds comparable to a plane 5 or 6 miles away (8 or 9.6km). Acoustic experiments at Imber Court involved using a tuning fork of low pitch from the Victoria and Albert Museum. It is hoped to work on the roof at Imber Court to analyse the notes of a Gotha or others of a more recent type in order to adapt my instrument to them. Details of the results obtained underline the superiority of the hot-wire microphone." The 'Gotha' mentioned was a German bomber aircraft of the First World War, and the hot-wire microphone was the 'Tucker' microphone, first used in gun sound ranging. A valuable property of this microphone, already mentioned in relation to the 200 foot sound mirror, was that it could be tuned to detect sounds of different frequencies.

Lieutenant Moubray's work was also evaluated at Imber Court. "There is a possible use for the hot-wire microphone in association with Lieutenant Moubray's Listening Wells. There is a suggestion that the listening wells would be useful when visible sighting of an aircraft was not possible, and that microphones are sufficiently sensitive to distinguish between enemy and friendly aircraft. Experiments in Professor H.L. Callendar's laboratory at Imperial College indicate the possibility of an automatic method of indicating when a 'plane, friendly or enemy, is overhead, when used in conjunction with the 'listening well' method". Before enlisting in the Royal Engineers in 1915, Captain Tucker had been engaged in research at Imperial

College with Professor Callendar, and such contacts with scientists from his former academic world were to prove useful on more than one occasion.

Captain Tucker discussed Lieutenant Moubray's work on listening wells with him, and related comments appeared in a Munitions Inventions Department Report for the week ending 30 March 1918, signed 'W.S.T.' "Two modified shafts are now being made to serve as wells, and tests will be made of these as soon as the workshop can turn them out. The theory of the 'Listening Well' is not all that simple, and it is evident from the evidence that Lieutenant Moubray has given, that resonance plays an important part. The sharpness of coming-in and cutting-off can best be found by experiment, and at present, this seems to provide the only satisfactory way of arriving at the useful dimensions of the well." The terms 'coming-in' and 'cutting-off' were used to describe the points when the first and last sounds were heard from an aircraft, as it passed through the area of sky covered by the cone of audibility above the shaft.

Further details of listening wells constructed at Imber Court for experimental purposes are to be found in a Munitions Inventions Department Report of April 1918, which mentions "three listening wells built to a depth of 7 feet (2.1m). Tests carried out determined that they were effective at picking up sounds. Machine gun firing produced a deeper note in the well than on the surface, and all sounds were much louder than on the surface. Reports later in the same month give an account of some of the difficulties encountered in testing the wells. Poor weather prevented flights, and problems arose because the noise of a gas engine used for powering some of the facilities of the station "clashed with the receding plane's note." The report stated that this could be avoided by making arrangements, "with considerable inconvenience to the station, for the stopping of this engine."

A week later, things were even more difficult. "Poor weather allowed only one test. The wells had a foot of water in them through abnormally heavy rain." However, there was some success. A galvanometer was placed in the bottom of the well to measure sounds received, and the instrument was not disturbed by heavy traffic noises nearby, or the sound of the gas engine. When a plane appeared the galvanometer "was driven hard over," a reference to the movement of the needle over a scale on the dial of the instrument.

Meanwhile, Captain Tucker was in correspondence with his former research colleague at Imperial College of Science, South Kensington, on the subject of listening wells. Professor Callendar wrote to him on 24 April 1918, heading his letter "Indicating results from listening wells by the use of a galvanometer." The letter ends: "I don't think the wells need be closer than 2 miles (3.2km) apart , so that 16 will cover an area of 64 square miles. (166sq.km) If 8 miles (12.9km) square, the furthest well from the centre will be 4.3 miles (6.9km)."

With the benefit of hindsight, an aircraft detection system relying on listeners confined to the bottom of deep shafts seems rather absurd and primitive. Although a slightly more sophisticated approach involved the use of hot-wire microphones in the shafts instead of human observers, experiments to find a better system were carried out both on the Western Front and at research stations in England during the latter part of the First World War. Eventually, the shafts were replaced by horizontal discs and microphones at ground level.

CHAPTER THIRTEEN

DISCS

It became apparent to scientists conducting listening well experiments that for effective collection of sound waves, listeners or microphones at the bottom of a well needed the assistance of a larger sound collector, with a greater surface area. Trials were carried out using various forms of tubes, horn-like collectors, and discs, using the spelling of the latter word common in all documents of the period. Descriptions of the adoption of discs occur in reports by Captain Tucker in 1918. He used the word 'azimuth' to describe a horizontal plane of listening. "The employment of 2 or 3 tubes is necessary for azimuth and a similar number for altitude. All these require microphones which must be connected up, and then the whole system must be mounted. The tubes may be replaced by a disc of air, separated by 2 wooden discs, and the microphone system can be mounted at the centre between these discs. The annular opening between the wooden discs replaces the openings at the ends of the tubes, and communicates a large supply of energy to the centre. If the double disc be mounted so that its surface lies in the wave front, a strong sound maximum occurs which can be read in terms of deflections in a micro ammeter."

A Munitions Inventions Department report of 20 April 1918 included references to the next development. "If experiment agrees with theory, the two discs should be capable, when resting on the ground, of behaving acoustically in the same manner as the listening well". The 'theory' mentioned here is quoted by Captain Tucker elsewhere: "when a sound-proof disc is placed so that it faces on to a source of sound, an image of the source is formed at the centre of the disc on the side away from the source." The Munitions Inventions Department report continued with an explanation that "if the lower disc be replaced by a bed of cement or other flat surface, the single disc should perform the function of the well when supported a few inches above this bed and parallel to it. It is anticipated that, in this manner, the listening well may be replaced and yet give the requisite sharpness of 'coming in and cutting out' without trouble from noises on the ground or in the vicinity. This listening device is much more easy to construct than the well, and much cheaper, besides being capable of use in low lying country." As in the case of listening wells, the terms 'coming in' and 'cutting out' refer to the effect produced by an aircraft entering and leaving the cone of sky covered by the disc.

On 11 May 1918, a report from Imber Court experimental establishment mentioned a disc " at present lying on the ground with its axis vertical; it is equipped with microphones with a view to picking up the sounds of aeroplanes flying overhead."

By the 25 May, Captain Tucker reported that "a new 20 foot disc (6m) is being made consisting of eight sectors with a central disc 3 feet in diameter. (91cm) The surface is to be lined inside and out with 3 ply wood, and the intervening space will be filled with felt. Tests are to be devised to test the "relative sound-proofness" of these materials." He went on to say that experiments were not helped by the fact that very few aeroplanes passed over Imber Court.

In another report of 27 May 1918, Captain Tucker explained the practical details of installing a horizontal disc. It would be mounted about 18 inches (46cm) from the ground, which was levelled and covered with a thin layer of cement, soil, or other suitable material in order to give a hard, smooth surface. "The microphone must be on the axis of the disc and below it. A trap door in the centre of the disc could be arranged for setting the microphone in place. The circular disc so mounted could be surrounded with a wall of turf or sand bags, giving protection from wind and ensuring cutting off of such lateral sounds as might affect the system, although this effect is known to be small. One advantage of the disc over the well is that it gives magnification from 5 to 10 times that of sound outside."

Turf covered horizontal disc, Hendon July 1918.
Note the annular opening for the entry of sound

Captain Tucker's papers include a concise description of the properties of a horizontal disc. "The theory of the disc receiver is that the acoustical effect at the centre is the sum of the contributions from each element of the annular opening through which the sound enters."

The essential point about the transition from listening wells to discs was that the disc replaced the well, and the microphone at the centre of the disc replaced the observer.

As at Joss Gap, Captain Tucker proposed to use his adjustable, hot-wire microphone in the centre of the disc. He also explained how a group of discs could form an early warning system. Several discs would be sited in the area to be defended, and as an aircraft flew overhead, its progress as it flew in and out of the cones of audibility extending upwards from the discs would be detected by a microphone under each disc. The disc sites would be connected by land lines to a central control room, where sensitive instruments would convert the signals from the microphones into responses which could be seen on an illuminated map.

Captain Tucker gave further technical details of the proposed system in one of his reports, where he used the term 'station' to mean the site of a particular disc.

"The effects received at the various stations are recorded by motions of galvanometer spots on a translucent screen at the central station. This screen roughly represents a map of the system, and when the galvanometers are unaffected, the light is obscured by a black spot which represents the corresponding station. When the galvanometer spot emerges and is deflected it indicates the passage of the 'plane over that particular station, and the deflections will be greatest for the stations over which the' plane passes most centrally."

Captain Tucker also thought about the practical problems of manning the system. "The experimental station would require 2 officers, 1 NCO (non-commissioned officer) and 4 linesmen, 1 telephonist, 1 carpenter, an electrician who could make up simple instruments or modify them, as well as a men's cook, an Army Service Corps driver, and an officer's batman, in all, 2 officers and 12 men. They would also need a Ford box car for transport, and 2 bicycles."

A report of 1 June 1918 not only mentions an officer already featured in this account, but demonstrates that experimental work in acoustics was continuing in France in the later stages of the Great War. According to this report, in addition to his experiments with listening wells in France, Lieutenant Moubray was also involved with 'concrete resonators'. These resonators are not described, but it is likely that they were either discs, or some sort of tuned cavity in which a microphone could be mounted, such as those placed in the centre of wooden or concrete sound discs. Further reports from later in June 1918 confirm that moulds for making the concrete resonators were sent out to France. Although the discs used in early days were constructed in wood, those used in later experiments, and in the more extensive systems laid out in the field were made of concrete.

Experiments with horizontal discs were also carried out in 1918 at

Rochford in Essex (Map 1 - p.23), which is described in a report of 8 June as a 'Sub-Station', probably meaning an outstation working in association with a main centre such as Imber Court or Woolwich. The report is signed by 'Lieutenant A. Ward RAF.' and after mentioning Captain Tucker's work at Imber Court with discs and microphones, he explains his own experiments. "I have had a similar pair of discs prepared and tested for use in aiding audition." The tests involved use of an aircraft fitted with a horn as a sound source.

"Tests of Audibility of Klaxon Horn carried out by Sopwith Camel Machine, Rochford Sub Station, Anti-Aircraft Experimental Station, 2 June 1918". The idea was that the klaxon horn might act as an identifying sound for friendly aircraft at heights where engine sound was not very audible. Details of some of the results are included:- "Ground wind estimated at 10 mph(16kmph). The machine climbed to 15,000 feet (4572m). From 3000 feet (914m) to what was estimated as 10,000 feet (3048m), the note of the horn was predominant. At greater height both the machine and the horn were only audible intermittently."

Apparently, Lieutenant Ward was also experimenting with trumpet type receivers, as his report continues with the statement that "discs as a means of finding the direction of a sound, have a quarter of the accuracy of the 42 inch trumpet at best." This conclusion may be explained by a later report in August, in which he describes the listening gear attached to his discs, which unlike the microphones used at Imber Court by Captain Tucker involved "stethoscopes attached to a small set of collecting trumpets at the focal point."

In July 1918, the Controller of the Munitions Inventions Department gave instructions for the installation of a small experimental station at Hendon Aerodrome, consisting of a headquarters hut at the aerodrome and three discs. The centre disc, known as the 'home' disc was adjacent to the headquarters hut, and there was a disc to the east at Burnt Oak and one to the west at Mill Hill. The two outer discs were 5000 yards (4572m) apart. In the light of his experience with listening wells and discs, Lieutenant Moubray was put in charge of the system. Later, a fourth disc, with a listening chamber for an observer underneath, was installed at Hendon

Aerodrome. The problem of unwanted noise which afflicted all acoustic experiments was a factor at Hendon. Details are to be found in a contemporary report.

Disc at Hendon Aerodrome in 1918 showing access to the observer's underground chamber

"Owing to the proximity of the three discs at Hendon Aerodrome it was found impossible to obtain reliable information as to the behaviour of the system from observations made on casual aeroplanes. At that time, the testing of machines in flight was carried on continuously at low altitudes over the aerodrome, and the noise from these, combined with that from engines in the sheds, rendered the home disc quite useless during the greater part of the day. It was therefore necessary to ask for an aeroplane to be detailed specially for the purpose of carrying out trials with the disc system. Unfortunately, no machine could be obtained until the beginning of

November.

A trial flight was made with this machine (an Avro) during the first week in November. The test was carried out at dusk and the weather conditions were very good. The primary object of the flight was to get the apparatus "tuned up" and in good working order.........As regards extraneous noises, it may be noted that trains passing along the Midland main line within 100 yards (91.4m) of the home disc produced only a very small irregular deflection, about 1/100th of that produced by the Avro at 5000 feet (1524m). No further trials were carried out before November 11th, since when it has been impossible to obtain an aeroplane and pilot to continue the experiments."

Researchers from the Signals Experimental Establishment were more successful in experiments with the Hendon discs in the summer of 1919. A report written in June of that year mentions that "during the past fortnight an Avro aeroplane has been available for carrying on the experiments with the Disc System at Hendon Aerodrome. The method of taking the observations was as follows. The pilot had instructions to fly at a given height, 5000 feet (1524m), and at a given speed, 70 mph, (113kmph) in a straight course above one of the discs. The deflection of the galvanometer indicates the approach of the aeroplane, and the readings are taken every ten seconds until the instrument again indicates zero. On June 19th two discs were in operation and an attempt was made to determine ground-speed and height. Ground speed is obtained by timing with a stop-watch from 'cut-in' (at the first minimum) on the first disc, to 'cut-in' on the second disc. Height is obtained by timing from 'cut-in' to 'cut-out' on one disc (i.e. from minimum to minimum)." A mathematical formula for working out the height was quoted in the report at this point.

Results were "very satisfactory." With suitable weather conditions, practice bore out what had been projected theoretically. In relation to weather conditions, the best results were obtained "at night or just before sunset. The middle of the day is most unsuitable." Irregular deflections of the galvanometer were noted on "several days during fine weather." Very hot conditions with "a very still atmosphere" produced "exceedingly irregular deflections, continually rising and falling as the aeroplane flew over the disc, so that no symmetrical curve could be plotted." This was probably due to "irregular distribution of temperature in the atmosphere, and to the presence of pockets of air either above or below the average temperature, which form obstacles in the path of the sound." The result was that the aeroplane sound was "not heard evenly" but was "continually changing in intensity." Periods just before, or after sunset "show the atmosphere in a very suitable condition for the transmission of sound."

Reading through these reports, many years after they were written, prompts the thought that successful detection in time of war would have required suitable weather conditions and a co-operative enemy.

On June 16 and 17 one disc was used in the Hendon experiments. "The aeroplane flew at 5000 feet (1524m) at 70 mph (113 kmph) on a straight course." The use of the term 'deflection' in this report refers to the needle of the galvanometer connected to the disk microphones. "Readings were taken every 10 seconds from first deflection to last. The deflection in inches is plotted against time in seconds. As the ground speed was not determined independently, and only one disc was used, the results are qualitative rather than quantitative." On June 19 two discs were used in "attempt to determine ground speed and height." The weather was "unfavourable, with a ground wind of 15 - 20 mph (24 - 32kmph) and low cloud, so that the machine was obliged to fly at a low altitude. Ground speed was determined by using a stop watch. Height was determined by timing 'cut-in' to 'cut-out' on one disc i.e. from minimum to maximum."

These various disc experiments must have inspired some confidence in the idea, as on 15 December 1919, the Signals Experimental Establishment produced a document outlining a system for the defence of London. This paper proposed that the area should be "encircled by disc stations forming a belt of about 20 miles radius (32km). Within the belt, 13 sections of 16 stations per section would be laid down, making a total of 480 stations. Each station would consist of discs of iron or concrete mounted horizontally 1 foot above the ground on a concrete bed and equipped with microphones coupled to the Headquarters of the section for registration purposes." Estimates for the cost, hire or purchase of land, together with a map of part of the system covering south-east London are included with the document.

In 1920, further sophistication was introduced when efforts were made to record the effects of aircraft flying over the discs by photographic means. Some of this work was done at the home base of the Signals Experimental Establishment at Woolwich. Relevant reports in January, February and March 1920 are headed "Experiments with The Concrete Disc Locator on Woolwich Common." The object of the experiments was "to test the working of a photographic recording apparatus" and "to determine the efficiency of the concrete disc as compared with the wooden disc previously used at Hendon. In the present experiments the light from the reflecting galvanometer was focused on to the moving strip of sensitive paper in a sound-ranging photographic recorder." When this paper was fed into a developing medium, a permanent record was produced which could be used for comparison in subsequent experiments.

Some trouble was experienced with the photographic equipment, and one report stated that "throughout the experiments with aeroplanes, the photographic apparatus has behaved in a very erratic manner, frequently breaking down at the critical times during flight. If the photographic method were adopted for general use, the apparatus would have to be redesigned." Despite the problems, it is worth noting that these were pioneering attempts to automate the plotting of aircraft, a process which has continued with increasing sophistication throughout the period of aviation history.

Various charts and lists of results were included with the reports. For example on 19 February the height of an aircraft flying over the disc was calculated at 4810 feet (1466m). "This was considered satisfactory - the pilot was actually flying at 5000 feet (1524m). This shows the satisfactory character of the disc collector in its present surroundings- although there are huts in the area which at first sight might be expected to interfere with the sound.

For future work at Woolwich, it is proposed to establish two auxiliary stations, from which visual observations will be made during the flight of an aeroplane, and an accurate record obtained of the ground speed and course. With such additional information it should be possible to obtain very valuable data as to the cone angle of the concrete disc, the extent to which this angle may vary with different types of machine, and the correction to be applied to the estimate of height when the aeroplane does not pass exactly over the disc."

Even in 1920, Woolwich Common seems to have suffered from unwelcome background noise. "Considerable difficulty has been experienced in obtaining good aeroplane records with the Woolwich disc owing to the disturbing noises caused by passing traffic. Some results were ruined. The disc is situated only 40 yards (37m) from a road along which cars, lorries and motor bicycles are frequently passing, and at this short distance, the effect produced on the microphone by a petrol driven vehicle is often comparable with that produced by an aeroplane."

These experiments with discs at Imber Court, Hendon and Woolwich were the prelude to the setting up of a more extensive system at Biggin Hill, leading eventually to the final system on Romney Marsh.

CHAPTER FOURTEEN

BIGGIN HILL DISCS

For a few anxious months in 1940, Biggin Hill airfield in Kent became well known as a base for fighter aircraft in the Battle of Britain. What is not so well known is that long before that time, in the years immediately after the First World War, it became a centre of research into methods of air defence. The activities of such bodies as the Munitions Inventions Department and the Signals Experimental Establishment at Woolwich have already been touched upon in this account, and a logical development was the eventual concentration of acoustic research in a main centre. (Map 1 - p.23)

Before 1914, the only facility available to the Army for designing signal equipment was a small experimental wireless organization, mainly concerned with testing existing equipment produced by Marconi and the General Post Office. Following the outbreak of war, there was a rapid growth of signalling activities, and experience in the field led to the setting up of the Signals Experimental Establishment, under Lieutenant-Colonel A. G. Cousins in a "hutted camp on Woolwich Common." The brief of the Establishment was "to design signal equipment which could not be obtained more appropriately from elsewhere, and to test and if necessary adapt equipment available from other sources."

The fact that many reports relating to disc experiments were produced by the Signals Experimental Establishment is a reminder that the use of sound detecting equipment was initially regarded as a branch of signalling.

W.S.Tucker, who has already appeared frequently in this story, was in charge of the acoustics section of the SEE. In the light of his war time work in gun sound ranging, both at Kemmel on the Western Front and Lavington on Salisbury Plain, his rapid rise through the ranks from Sapper to Major in the Royal Engineers, and his Doctorate in Physics, which he had held since 1915, it is not surprising that after the war, Major Tucker was encouraged to stay in the Service. He was engaged by the Royal Engineers Board, on behalf of the War Office, to direct experiments and research into the detection of aircraft by acoustic methods. He was demobilized in August 1922, and in that year, the activities of the various research establishments in the acoustic field were brought together and concentrated at Biggin Hill in the new Air Defence Experimental Establishment, under his leadership.

The Minutes of the Royal Engineers Board include reports on the subject of discs systems, submitted by the Chief Experimental Officer, Signals Experimental Establishment, in October, November and December 1919. Proposals were put forward in these reports for the laying down of a disc system and field trials. These were approved by the Board and "the necessary work was put in hand." According to the reports, "the laying down of the disc system is progressing, and from the few actually constructed, promising results have been obtained."

The first record found relating to discs at Biggin Hill dates from 28 April 1920, and it contains references to the construction of a prototype 20 foot (6.1m) concrete disc, formed from 19 segments. Reports in June and July 1920 mention a hut to be used as a base at Biggin Hill, and it is apparent that work was going ahead to set up a more comprehensive disc system than those previously tried out at such places at Hendon and Woolwich.

"Information is still awaited relating to the sale of land on which we desire to place one of our most important disc positions. When this information is to hand, the whole of the remaining positions can be fixed. Stores are now being collected for the wiring operations. The process of making the discs ready for installation in the field is going on continuously, and as they are entirely of concrete, some time must elapse before all the discs are ready. At Biggin Hill, the site needed to be altered because of the resonance caused by the large hangars nearby, but further records must be taken before deciding. Another week's work has been done on the hut which is being adapted for Acoustical work." The reference above to 'wiring operations' relates to the connection of each disc position by land lines to the central control point at Biggin Hill.

A Royal Engineer officer, Lieutenant J.B. Browning, wrote a report in October 1920 which provides further details of activities at Biggin Hill. "The disc at the reservoir near Addington Lodge is now in position. There are now 4 discs in working order and 3 in a straight line. The disc at Hesiers Lane is partly constructed. The remaining sections are ready but is has not been possible to take them to the position owing to transport difficulties."

There were also difficulties in persuading land owners to allow the construction of discs on their properties. This is understandable, as for technical reasons, the disc sites had to be spaced precisely, and it was sometimes necessary to place a disc in a field position which was not convenient to the farmer. One farmer agreed to provide a disc site when the annual fee was raised from £1 to £5. The relevant department of the Royal Engineers was asked about fencing the discs, but the report states that "no fence has been erected yet."

Another detail in Lieutenant Browning's report concerns the central control point at Biggin Hill, where "a new screen has been made which will allow of readings from 7 discs being taken instead of 6 as before." The 'screen' mentioned here was a visual display in the headquarters hut, showing the course of an aeroplane over the discs.

A Report of 2 November refers to a delay, because the wood ordered in August for moulds for the 'disc elements' had not arrived. Also, the land agent of Eastern Command had not negotiated to secure the remaining disc sites. A further difficulty in obtaining results was due to there being no electricity supply.

On 26 October 1920, three discs in a straight line were tested by a Bristol Fighter flying at 3000 feet (914m). The pilot found difficulty in getting into line and "got off course towards the end of the flight. No visual observation of the course of the aeroplane was possible as the men were fully occupied on the ground. A new hut is now being furnished and equipped with apparatus required for experiments accessory to the disc location experiments."

Moving into 1921, a report in March from the Signals Experimental Establishment gave details of progress and difficulties in setting up the Biggin Hill disc system. "The section is still without transport. Two hand carts have been lent, and these are very useful for moving line stores. If the motor cycle and two push cycles applied for could be supplied, much time would be saved." There is a reference to a meeting for the showing of "photographic records of a Handley Page in flight on 24 February between 5 and 9 p.m." A photograph taken under a 4 foot (1.2m) disc and another under a 20 foot (6m) disc show the 'beats' of the 'double engine'. It was proposed that Tuesday and Thursday should be 'required field days' in order that flights could be organized at sunset. There was also a plea that the timetables of the London to Paris commercial flights be obtained so that they could be used for regular tests.

Further particulars of the work at Biggin Hill, including references to the activities of the men involved, are supplied by a report from the Acoustical Section of the Signals Experimental Establishment on 16 April 1921. "Disc Sound Locators, Biggin Hill. The strength of the Section is now one NCO (non-commissioned officer) and ten men, employed as follows:- Constructing discs 2; Woodwork 1; Lines 4; Laboratory 1; Cook House and Fatigue 2; Fetching rations (mornings only) 1. During special flights, four men are required for theodolite work, and every day, one man is required as a look-out for 'planes crossing on the Continental air route.

All discs in position have now been fenced. The disc at Biggin Hill village will be erected as soon as the line reaches the position. There are now four extra complete discs constructed. These will be erected as soon as possible. Construction has now been commenced of lines to Biggin Hill, Tatsfield Church, and Bedlestead sites."

Descriptions are included of flights over "the Luxstead, Home and Reservoir discs." The disc site described as 'Reservoir' was near Addington Lodge, and both names are used in documents of the time. A later report states: "lines OK except Downe, the resistance of which varied as much as 2 ohms." Downe is perhaps more famous for Down House, home of Charles Darwin.

A sad note appears in another report, which explains that the flight arrangements for 1 April 1921 were abandoned. This was because of an "accident which occurred earlier in the afternoon in which Lieutenant Helmsley and passenger were killed." Flights on 5 April and 8 April 1921 were cancelled, due to petrol economy in the light of "coal stoppage."

On 8 April 1921 "a new double resonator was installed at the Hesiers disc." In terms of experimental work "flights were made at Biggin Hill in April. Research on sources of sound will not proceed until the appointment of a Research Officer has been approved by the D.S.I.R. (Director of Scientific and Industrial Research.) Mr Morris Hart, BSc. (Eng.) is put forward as a candidate with the status of a 'D' class Experimental Officer." In the event, Mr Hart, became a member of the team engaged over the years in acoustic research under Dr Tucker.

Homely details are provided by a report of 20 May 1921. Due to the demobilization of a particular individual "a bricklayer to replace him is very much needed." There had evidently been some progress in both the erecting of the discs and in the transport arrangements. "The Biggin Hill discs are now in position, and two Triumph motor cycles have now been supplied."

The extended Biggin Hill disc system was still under construction in the summer of 1921. A report from Lieutenant Browning on 24 June, outlines some of the details. Difficulties with local farmers and landowners were not the only problem. Animals also had to be taken into account.

"Three discs are awaiting erection. It has not been possible to erect more discs as no fences are available. Also horses are grazing around the Biggin Hill disc - can we have a fence to protect it? It has been impossible to erect the Bedlested disc as a fence is needed to keep cattle off. Fencing is needed, at £15 a disc. Cross Channel aeroplanes have been recorded daily but they tend to pass to the west of the disc positions."

By 1 July, under the heading "Disc Sound Locators at Biggin Hill" it was reported that "eight discs are connected up, though one central disc is not working because of difficulty with the landowner."

Following earlier complaints about protection of the discs, a report by Lieutenant Browning on 29 August confirmed that "fencing has now been erected" and "three new discs now mean that the London - Paris flights go over the disc system properly." One report mentions that on 30 June, a plane flying to France was estimated to be at 1,060 feet (323m) "by acoustic methods only". The speed was calculated at 121.4 ft. (37m) per second. On 7 July a "Handley Page machine" was detected, on 7 July 1921, and a Bristol Fighter was followed on 12 July. This latter test was spoiled by a "Farman Goliath flying over one of the discs." Visual observations were made to check the information coming from the disc system, and the report claimed that visual and acoustic results were very similar.

Construction of the Biggin Hill disc system continued in 1922. On 2 January, there was a report from the Signals Experimental Establishment that two discs were nearing completion at "Camp and Farley positions; lines 3½ miles (5.6km) long are in place from the former." This report also contained details of tests involving aircraft during the latter part of 1921, including a remark that "poor weather conditions provided few opportunities."

"On 10th and 14th of November night flying took place using a Bristol Fighter over the Disc Systems. On the 10th, six crossings were made over Luxsted, Home and Reservoir discs at an altitude of 3000 feet (914m). Some discrepancies between positions observed by discs and pilot reports were put down to possible 'wind refraction' - a similar discrepancy had been experienced in a night flight on 16th September. The Map Indicator was in operation." The reference to a "Map Indicator" is a reminder of the system of land lines from the discs which were connected to lamps on a map in the central control room.

Further developments of the disc system are described in a report of 28 February 1922. Under the heading "Disc Sound Locators, Biggin Hill" there is the information that "lines were installed to discs between 29.12.21 and 24.2.22" and that the "Camp disc is now erected. There has been no permission yet for use of land for the Farley disc. A suitable site has been found for the Titsey disc near Woldingham." Some of the early discs were in need of repair. Much work had been done in installing the land line connections, and this wiring amounted to "50 miles in all" (80km). The report included a summary of work with the discs. All the test flights were carried out in daylight at heights up to 6000 feet (1829m), and some progress was made in the ability to distinguish " exhaust sounds from propeller sounds."

The experimental character of the Biggin Hill disc system is shown by the constant changes reported in various documents, for example on 4 December 1922: "Since the last report, the laboratory and all instruments have been moved to the southern end of the aerodrome." The report continues with a reference to the land lines connecting the discs to the central station: "the routes from the home disc and the mirror to the old laboratory and from the old laboratory to the valley have been dismantled. A new route will be laid from the new laboratory to the valley to connect with the lines running to the discs which are west of the aerodrome." This report also mentions disc sites at Warlingham, Downe and Luxstead.

In 1922, at the time of the experimental work at Biggin Hill, the War Office produced a textbook on the subject of acoustical defence systems, probably secret at the time, and intended only for use by military people. The book includes a description of a typical disc system, and it gives an idea of the philosophy behind the work at Biggin Hill.

"The system would consist of a central station and a number of disc stations. All the electrical recording or indicating apparatus is placed in the central station, and the leads are run out to the microphones. Probably the best way of arranging the disc stations is to place them so that any three adjacent stations form the corners of an equilateral triangle." At this point, there is a diagram of a system of 10 stations arranged as a group of overlapping circles. The circles represent the intersection of cones of audibility in the sky above the discs. Each invisible cone has its apex at a disc, and the circles in the diagram represent a horizontal plane in the sky at a height of 10,000 feet, supposing the stations to be 2000 yards apart.

The description continues: "by drawing straight lines at random on such a diagram, it can easily be seen that in all but a few cases, the course of an aeroplane flying over the system is such that the ground-speed and height can be accurately determined. Time intervals are recorded by observers with stop-watches. Ground speed and height can be deduced from these very easily and quickly. Height is the more difficult of the two, but once the information as to time is given it can be obtained in a few seconds by the use of a slide rule. As mentioned above, errors may arise from the course of the aeroplane not passing directly above the disc. In addition to this there are other causes, notably the Doppler effect, and variation in the note emitted by the engine, which may give rise to errors in practice. As far as can be seen, however, there are no errors which cannot be eliminated by suitable alterations in the apparatus, or by the taking of auxiliary observations, if necessary. The magnitude of the errors involved and the effectiveness of the steps taken to counteract them could only be determined by actual work in the field."

Although there are many contemporary reports of experiments with multiple sound discs at Biggin Hill, no map of the system has come to light, but it seems that the layout was based on ideas expressed above in the War Office textbook.

What is certain is that it was a system of some size, and an idea of the overall layout can be inferred from the names of the sites.

References to twelve disc sites occur in documents of the period. These are at Biggin Hill Aerodrome, Biggin Hill Village, Addington Lodge, Hesiers Lane, Tatsfield Church, Bedlestead, Luxstead, Downe, Farley (Farleigh on current maps), Titsey, Woldingham and Warlingham. Plotting the sites on a map of the area reveals that the discs were arranged in a roughly circular pattern in the vicinity of Biggin Hill Aerodrome. A hint of this type of layout occurs in a report from the early days of the system in November 1920. "It is specially desired to complete the first ring of disc positions before winter sets in."

Four sites were within about one and a half miles of the aerodrome, and six within about four miles. Two site names which occur are 'Home' and 'Camp'. It has not been possible to place these on a map, but there is a reference to a land line three and a half miles in length from the 'Camp' position, which places that disc within the pattern formed by the known positions. The 'Home' site is a mystery, but it is likely to have been within the pattern, and the term possibly refers to a disc near the home base at Biggin Hill.

The disc sites were connected by land lines to a control centre or laboratory at Biggin Hill, and the signals from microphones under each disc could be interpreted on an illuminated screen in the control room, thus giving an indication of the position of the aircraft over the system.

By 1923, there had been further thinking as to the best way of laying out a disc system, and a report on 'The Development of Acoustical Methods for Anti-Aircraft Defence' by the Acoustical Section of the Signals Experimental Establishment in October 1923 points the way to the final development of the system at a new site on the Kent coast.

"The primary object of the defence is to engage the enemy aircraft with guns or aeroplanes and thereby to destroy or repel them before they reach their objective. A second objective may be to intercept them on their homeward journey and so prevent them from returning to their base. Both guns and aeroplanes may be dependent to a greater or less extent on the co-operation of searchlights, and all three will require the assistance of acoustical methods whenever darkness or cloud interfere with visual observation."

One requirement is spelt out as "sufficiently early warning of the approach of hostile aircraft to enable the defending machines to get off the ground and gain the necessary height before the enemy reaches the Aeroplane Fighting Zone." This statement is exactly in line with the philosophy behind the early warning system developed about 15 years later, based on radar. That system gave Fighter Command the ability to dispense with standing patrols, and to use outnumbered forces effectively, by keeping fighter aircraft on their airfields until directed to climb towards known enemy positions for interception.

In the 1923 report, discs are regarded as a first line of defence, supplemented by sound mirrors. "The ideal warning system would consist of a double line of discs at the proper distance from the outer boundary of the aeroplane fighting zone. This distance should be not less than 50 miles (80km). If for any reason, it proves impracticable to locate the discs so far away as this, they should be placed at the greatest possible distance from the threatened area and supplemented at the limiting boundary concerned by mirrors. At the present time, the technique of the use of mirrors had not yet been sufficiently developed to enable definite conclusions to be formed as to whether or not they can be made automatic or substantially infallible."

There is no indication in reports of the Biggin Hill disc experiments as to why the work was eventually moved to the coast, but one factor may have been the existence of a newly established acoustic research station on the hills at West Hythe, overlooking the marshes and the sea. A site was needed featuring a flat landscape with room to lay out two long lines of discs, at a location where the system could be tested against military and civilian aircraft. All these conditions were to be found on the coast of south-east Kent.

CHAPTER FIFTEEN

THE ROMNEY MARSH SYSTEM

The low lying country of the Romney Marsh in Kent was well suited to the construction of a disc system for aircraft detection. With the co-operation of local farmers, it was possible to arrange the discs in long lines, and civilian aircraft of the time setting course for France over the area, using the nearby Lympne airfield as a turning point, provided free test flights. Lympne airfield was also a base used by RAF machines in experimental flights over the disc system.

Mr Percy Rothwell, one of Doctor Tucker's team of scientists who has appeared already in this story, was closely involved in the establishment of the Romney Marsh disc system. In a report to Dr Tucker on 13 March 1924 he relates that he had been hard at work pegging out positions for discs on the Marsh. Apparently, he was not at first provided with any transport for what was tiring work, and he pointed out that he had "only my own legs and cycle to carry me." In a further report of 17 June 1924, Percy Rothwell describes activities by the Post Office in erecting poles for lines connecting the discs to the headquarters hut at Newchurch. Rothwell also refers to a telephone line connecting the hut at Newchurch with Hythe, indicating that the disc experiments were under the overall control of the Hythe acoustic research station.

The Romney Marsh disc system was in operation by the summer of 1924, as detailed in a report from the Signals Experimental Establishment on 31

October. "The system is located on Romney Marsh and consists of 20 discs arranged in two lines of 10 discs each, spaced at half mile (0.8km) intervals. The landward line is 3 miles (4.8km) behind the seaward line. The system has now been under test for six weeks."

A sketch map of the system, included with contemporary papers, shows the positions of the discs. The first disc in the seaward line was situated about a mile (1.6km) inland from the coast, just behind Dymchurch. The remaining nine discs were spaced at half mile (0.8km) intervals in a straight line heading in a south-westerly direction, the line ending with disc number ten at a point midway between New Romney and Ivychurch. The landward line began a mile from Bilsington, to the south of the Royal Military Canal. It also extended in a south-westerly direction, ending with the tenth disc a mile south west of Snave. The two lines were three miles (4.8km) apart, and the headquarters hut at Newchurch, roughly in the centre of the system, is marked on the map. This wooden hut appears in old photographs, and it was positioned near the church at Newchurch. The land lines connecting the disc sites to the headquarters hut are marked with dotted lines. Many of these routes were along existing marsh roads, making it possible to string the wires on poles at the roadside (Map1 - p.23 and Map 2 - p.64).

Although there were some similarities with the Biggin Hill arrangements, various reports from the Signals Experimental Establishment indicate progress towards a better system on Romney Marsh. "Each receiver consists of a collector and a microphone. The former is a concrete disc 20 feet (6.1m) in diameter and 2 inches (5.1cm) thick, built up in sections and supported on wooden pillars a foot (30cm) high, the bases of which rest on concrete footings. Surrounding the disc is a parapet of concrete 18 inches (46cm) high, which provides an annular space between the disc and the parapet 2 feet (61cm) wide. This device is a directional receiver, defending the cone of the sky about 30 degrees semi-vertical angle, the apex of the cone being at the centre of the disc and the axis a perpendicular through that centre. The sound, which enters the receiver through the annular ring, is received at the point under the centre of the disc, and its intensity depends on the elevation of the plane. Thus, at an elevation of 6000 feet (1829m) the sound begins to be effective and attains a maximum at the zenith position. The microphone is of the hot-wire type, and is tuned so that it responds especially to the low notes of the propeller."

A view of the hut at Newchurch, Kent in 1924, Headquarters of the Romney Marsh disc system. A military truck of the period can be seen in the background.

Further reports include details of night flying exercises over the discs in 1924. For example, test flights took place "at around 22 hrs on 8th, 9th, 10th, 11th, 12th, 13th, 14th and 15th August, and on 1st, 4th, 9th September." According to this report "the purpose of the Disc System is to provide an outpost observation installation capable of detecting without failure the passage of aircraft over the area occupied by the system. The information it provides is instantaneously and automatically communicated to a central station."

Operational methods are described in other reports dating from 1924. "In order to visualize the movements of an aeroplane over the system, a translucent map showing the position of the discs and the more important map details was mounted on a table. Under each disc position as shown on the map was arranged a small lamp operated by the appropriate relay, so that when an aeroplane passed over the corresponding disc, the lamp was lighted." Special arrangements were made with the Post Office and Air Ministry so that information collected at Newchurch could be transmitted direct to Biggin Hill.

Horizontal concrete disc as used on Romney Marsh in 1924

Additional details of the 'Summer Programme' are reported. "The aeroplanes were to leave Lympne and fly out to sea, and then return via the disc system which lies between Dymchurch and New Romney, with the Headquarters at Newchurch, and thence to Biggin Hill. The data as to times of crossing the Disc System, together with height, speed, and course deduced there-from, were despatched by telephone to Biggin Hill where the Prediction system Computing Centre was situated." On August 8th, "two Vickers Vimy Machines flew from Lympne." The pilots were "Flying Officers Higgs and Humphreys. The following warning message was received at 22.45 hrs:- 'Early warning 10.22.00; crossed first line 10.37.30; crossed second line 10.40.30; ground speed 57 mph (92kmph); course 320degrees."

Flying Officer Higgs, pilot of one of the Vimy's, reported on this flight: "As arranged at the conference with Major Tucker, I left Lympne at 21.20 hrs, proceeding via Canterbury, Deal and the Downs to Gris Nez. I left Gris Nez at 22.15 hrs. I extinguished my lights when ten miles (16km) inland. At Biggin Hill, when I was over and in line with Tatsfield and the Aerodrome, five searchlights were opened out about one mile behind me. I immediately put on my navigation lights. I continued on the same bearing for another mile, but the beams did not touch me. I then fired a white Very light and returned to Lympne." It appears from this description that the flight involved the Biggin Hill disc system in addition to the coastal system.

A further reference to activities on Romney Marsh in 1924 is to be found in the Proceedings of the Royal Engineers Board. "The results of two months operation of a disc system at Romney Marsh were rendered in an interim report by the Signals Experimental Establishment. Satisfactory accuracy was obtained in the location of aeroplanes at a height of 10,000 feet (3048m)."

By 1925, the disc system on the Marsh had been extended. Details are included in a report from the Signals Experimental Establishment relating to experiments in the summer of that year. "Since last year, the system on Romney Marsh has been extended by the addition of 12 discs:- 4 new ones at the NE end of the seaward line, 2 at the SW end of this line, 1 at the NW end of the landward line, and 5 at the SW end of this line."

As a result of these additions, the final system consisted of 32 discs, arranged in two parallel lines of 16 discs, 3 miles (c.4.8km) apart and 8 miles (12.9km) in length (Map 2 - p.64).

The report outlined further developments. "A new and improved switch-board has been built on the same line as last year's to accommodate the extra number of discs. The crossing of a disc by an aeroplane is now shown by the lighting of a small lamp on the switchboard itself, in addition to the dropping of an indicator and the lighting of the lamp on the map board. These additional lamps facilitate the work of the observer." The lamps and indicators can be seen in a contemporary photograph of the control panel. At the top of the panel are two rows of indicators, and someone has added the letters 'S' and 'L' to point out that the 16 indicators in each row represent 'Seaward' and 'Landward' lines of discs.

Aircraft used in testing the marsh system were from the Night Flying Flight, Biggin Hill. This Flight was stationed at Lympne, and it consisted of 3 Vickers Vimy machines, with Flight Lieutenant Humphreys in charge. The normal procedure involved aircraft flying out to sea and returning over the disc system. The time taken by an aircraft to fly from one line of discs to the other could be used to calculate its ground speed. Reports of aircraft crossing the discs, with courses, ground speeds and heights were telephoned to a control centre at Uxbridge.

Various flights in the summer of 1925 were recorded. For example:

June 12th, 5.30 - 6.30 p.m. 4 crossings of the disc system
June 15th, 10.00 p.m. 2 crossings
June 16th, 6.00 p.m. 2 crossings
June 18th, 10.00 p.m. 2 crossings
June 19th, 10.00 p.m. 1 crossing
June 22nd, 6.00 p.m. 2 crossings.

These flights were usually at an altitude of 6000 feet (1828m).

"In the period 29 June to 28 August, weather permitting, 24 flights were made at heights between 8000 and 11000 feet (2438 and 3353m). All flights were in the evening or at night, the earliest just after 7.00 p.m. (twice) but mostly between 10.00 and 11.30 p.m. The number of crossings varied between 3 and 8. Sometimes, alternate discs only were used. In addition to Vimy aircraft, a Bristol Fighter was used, operating up to 14,000 feet (4267m). Poor weather conditions prevented tests between July 31st and August 6th, and again between August 17th and 28th".

Some flights involved two aircraft flying on parallel courses 3 miles apart, and also on courses at "various angles of obliquity", but "on no occasion was any great difficulty experienced in following the movement of each aeroplane individually." 140 crossings of the disc system were recorded, compared with 60 in 1924.

One 1925 report explained that "tests of the Disc System were carried out using an aeroplane flying at heights up to 26,900 feet (8199m). The previous ceiling for tests was generally 11,000 feet (3352m). For the first time, tests were carried out at heights over 20,000 feet (6096m). The aircraft involved was a DH9A with a supercharged Liberty engine and 2 bladed metal propeller, the pilot was Flying Officer H. J. Saint D.S.C. Flights were made on August 13th, 14th and 17th; the greatest height reached was 26,900 feet (8199m) on August 17th, 1925. Before the tests, information about the engine and propeller note was received, but it was then discovered that the tuning of the Disc System was such as to be completely insensitive to this aeroplane sound even at small heights."

The control panel as used in the Romney Marsh disc system in the 1920s

Judging by the next sentence in this report, someone must have realized that this inconvenient aeroplane, with its uncooperative sounds, posed a problem likely to be encountered if the discs were ever to be used in anger. "Nevertheless it was decided to perform the experiment, in view of the fact that foreign aeroplanes of unknown type might be encountered in war conditions. The experiment here described therefore imposes on the system a double handicap of being completely out of tune, and of working at heights 2 or 3 times as great as those previously employed. The present microphones fitted to the discs respond to 58 - 72 frequencies a second; the fundamental propeller note of the DH9A was 51-53 c.p.s (cycles per second), the first partial was 102-106 c.p.s. The results obtained show that there is little doubt that with properly tuned microphones, the usual disc observations of aircraft at 10,000 feet (3048m) could equally well be made with aeroplanes at

20,000 or 30,000 feet (6096 or 9144m)."

In the circumstances described, the responses from the microphones were too small to activate the indicators in the control room properly. More delicate instruments were brought into use. "Attention was therefore transferred to the deflections shown by a reflecting galvanometer." This was an instrument designed for detecting small electric currents which were displayed on a dial. There was also visual tracking of the aircraft. "Six flights were made over the system with aircraft's propeller revolutions set at 1560-1590. On 13 August, visual observation was not possible on four of the flights as the observer was looking into the sun. Flights 3 and 6 were plotted complete. Heights of flights varied from 18,200 to 26,500 feet (5547 to 8077m). "Jamming" was "caused by traffic noises which gave wrong recordings on Flights 1 and 4".

Conclusions were drawn from the experiments on Romney Marsh in 1925. "The results show that the disc system in its present condition is effective for use as a sentry system for detecting automatically aeroplanes of all types at present extant. With the employment of proper tuning, it can be claimed that it is capable of giving course, ground speed and height for all aeroplanes at any practicable height within the limits of accuracy already reported in the Vickers Vimy experiments."

There was an admission that "the conditions affecting the determination of height need a fuller analysis before the value of the results can be estimated. The experiments however have been very successful, and a considerable amount of additional knowledge and experience in the working of the system has been gained. Numerous demonstrations have been given during the summer of the Disc System in effective operation."

One advantage claimed for the disc system was that it was economical in staffing. A contemporary document stated that "a front of ten miles (16km) could be kept under observation by two observers who could report rapidly and accurately the position, course, and ground speed of raiding aircraft crossing the system."

Although the tests carried out in the 1920s were experimental in nature, the lines of un-manned discs across Romney Marsh, linked to a central control room, represented an automatic detection system in embryo.

CHAPTER SIXTEEN

MARSH DISCS ABANDONED

The acoustic research station on the hills west of Hythe commanded a fine view over the Romney Marshes, the scene of continuing experiments with discs. A memorandum from Major Inglis, Superintendent of the Air Defence Experimental Establishment to the Secretary of the Royal Engineers Board on 29 July 1927, asked for approval that "the Disc System should be in complete operation for a further period of a fortnight from September 19th to October 1st inclusive, and that the staff should concentrate on determination of height from the Disc System alone, and should make exhaustive tests of the accuracy of the methods already advocated; but no Trumpet Sound Locators should be employed. The personnel required would be that normally at Hythe, together with two experimental officers from Biggin Hill, and Messrs Handford and Allen." One Vimy aircraft was to be used "stationed at Lympne."(Map 2 - p.64)

By 1928, doubts about the effectiveness of the disc system begin to appear in contemporary papers. An Air Council Minute of 6 July includes a comment that results similar to those obtained from the disc system could be arrived at "by employing Observer Posts with simple sound locators." This minute suggested that the Air Ministry should "withdraw all support from the 'Disc' measure." There was also a concern about the possible costs of extending such a system. At £250 each, the total cost of providing a line "from Felixstowe to Portsmouth" was estimated at £400,000, a very large sum in 1928.

These doubts appear again in April 1929 when reports contain hints that the end of the disc system was in sight. For example: "Disc System Romney Marsh. This experiment is in abeyance except for certain tests of microphones which are being conducted at Hythe with the object of detecting any deterioration with age."

Experiments of a different kind were carried out on the Marsh in June 1929. Studies of the effects of atmospheric conditions on the passage of sound waves were of basic importance in the development of any listening devices. The 1929 experiments were concerned with "Attenuation of Sound in the Atmosphere", and use was made of a piece of equipment designed by Major Inglis. "In June, a special BSA rifle producing a loud explosive sound was used as the source in an aeroplane which flew to and fro in the neighbourhood of the 104 ft (32m) Inglis tower on the ranges of the Small Arms School at Hythe. Two hot wire microphones of a special form were installed near the top and near the bottom of the tower and the times of arrival of the sound at the microphones were measured by a short base gun sound-ranging apparatus." Percy Rothwell's papers include photographs of this tower, with the hills to the west of Hythe in the background. Similar towers nearby were used in experiments which involved firing an anti-aircraft gun at Lydd. The sounds were recorded "by microphones in a high mast or tower at Newchurch, Romney Marsh, and by microphones in the front line of the Disc System, Romney Marsh." (Map 2 - p.64)

In October 1930, a gun was fired "SSW of Lydd out to sea, provision being made for a lookout to ensure safety for shipping." The seaward line of discs were used to observe the sounds. Observations were made over a range of 11 miles (18km). Two towers were used. A "50 ft (15m) Inglis Tower" carried 2 microphones, 1 at the top, and 1 at the bottom, and a 158 ft (48m) lattice-work tower at Newchurch, 100 yards (30m) from the headquarters hut, provided a mounting for 3 microphones at heights of 10 ft, 100 ft and 158 ft (3m, 30m and 48m)." Newchurch was a logical place to erect the towers, as it was the headquarters of the Romney Marsh Disc System. During the experiments, meteorological data was collected, as well as acoustical information from the discs. "Photographic records were taken every 2 minutes. At Newchurch, wind velocity was measured at the top of the tower. Wireless direction finding equipment was also used to plot tracks. The Direction Finding sets were installed in two huts on the ridge north of Romney Marsh, about 7 miles apart, at Hythe and Colliers Hill."

Bearing in mind the relatively low altitudes flown by civilian aircraft in those days, and the proximity of Lympne airfield, it is not surprising that the Air Ministry, in a 1930 memorandum to Major Inglis at the Air Defence Experimental Establishment, expressed concern about the towers at Newchurch, pointing out the danger to "civil aircraft flying to and from the Continent." In reply, Major Inglis explained the use of the towers, and said that warning lights were to be fitted as an aid to aircraft in the vicinity. Major Inglis was later to play a part in the Air Defence of Great Britain organization, and like some of the other participants in acoustic experiments, he eventually achieved high rank, ending his career as Sir Drummond Inglis.

Robert Ferguson, one of Dr Tucker's team at the Air Defence Experimental Establishment, wrote from Hythe to the Superintendent at Biggin Hill on 17 October 1932. He had been busy dismantling the wiring of the disc system. Under the heading "Disc Circuits, Romney Marsh" he reported that "all circuits are being recovered on the Marsh, the Post Office having being informed that the War Office has no further use for them. The landward line will be completely taken up and also most of the seaward."

In a reply to Mr Ferguson a few days later, Major B.B. Edwards, the Superintendent of the Air Defence Experimental Establishment mentioned "removing the telephone lines from the discs," and possibly keeping a few discs which happened to be "within a reasonable distance of a General Post Office poled route. The other discs are of no use to us, and might as well be abandoned. The discs will then have to be removed and the sites made good and handed back to the owners."

On 9 November 1932, Major Edwards reported to the President of the Royal Engineers Board that "the actual experimental layout on the Romney Marshes has had to be dismantled as the experiments on it have been completed."

The following day, he sent another memorandum to the RE Board relating to problems arising from the abandonment of the Marsh disc system.

"The Commander Royal Engineers has reported that the fencing of some of the sites has fallen into disrepair, and asks whether he should repair this or whether he should take up the actual discs and surrender the sites. He cannot just leave the sites to go back to the jungle as there would be a risk of sheep and cattle damaging themselves in the disc pits, and of claims against the War Department. I therefore suggest that the CRE be asked to conclude the agreements, remove the discs and hand the sites back to the owners. The Headquarters hut at Newchurch should remain for the present until a decision is given about the 150 ft tower (46m)."

On the 14 November, the President of the Royal Engineers Board advised Major Edwards that "it is probable that the tower will be removed this financial year."

As on so many occasions in this story, Dr Tucker was involved. He made a request to Major Edwards on 17 November 1932. "I would like one of the discs re-erected at the Hythe Station, otherwise they can be broken up, as they will certainly not stand much knocking about in taking down. The resonators are already in." In this last sentence, the word 'in' must mean that the microphones and resonators had been removed from the discs and were safely in store.

It appears that members of the Royal Engineers based at Shorncliffe were responsible for the demolition of the disc sites, as Major Edwards wrote on the subject to the Deputy Commander Royal Engineers at that barracks on 18 and 23 November 1932. His first memorandum related to Dr Tucker's request, and asked for "one of the discs to be salved and re-erected at the Hythe Acoustical Station." No reference has been found in contemporary documents to confirm that one of the discs was in fact taken to Hythe, although there is shallow circular depression hidden in the undergrowth near the site of the 20 foot (6.1m) mirror which could be the remains of a disc pit.

The second memorandum from Major Edwards suggested that the discs be broken up and "local farmers be allowed to take and use them for paving or hard filling on condition they release you from any obligation to make good the disc sites."

The end of the Romney Marsh experiments is recorded in the Proceedings of the Sound Location and Acoustic Committee of the Royal Engineers Board, dated 22 November 1932, under the heading 'Disc System.' "The President stated that a draft memorandum for the consideration of the Air Ministry had been sent to the War Office in order that this experiment, which had been in abeyance for some time, might be finally closed. All the data required had been obtained, and it was not intended to carry out further experimental work in this connection."

Confirmation of the abandonment of the system appears in a War Office File of the period which records that "the disc system generally is being dismantled." A final note is sounded in a memorandum from the Commander, Royal Engineers, Home Counties East at Dover, to the Command Signal Officer, Headquarters, Eastern Command on 1 December 1932. "It is proposed to give notice to terminate the agreements for hire of the sites on which these discs have been erected on 31 March 1933."

A letter in October 1996 from a resident on Romney Marsh brings a personal touch to this account. The late Mr Richard Body was involved at both the beginning and the end of the story. "In 1923 I accompanied a Royal Engineer Colonel round Romney Marsh to help identify the occupiers of the land on which he had some 24 sites marked on an Ordnance map. I am afraid that I was not a great help, but he did divert enough to take me to lunch at the George Hotel, Rye. About 1932, my father bought a block of land here at Snargate on which were still the remains of two Acoustical Discs. Apparently the farmer who occupied this land had been given the material for clearing up the sites."

Mr Body was given the task of clearing the sites. "I got that job. The deal wood timber posts had all rotted, and the three or four strands of multi-strand fencing wire were well entangled with thistles and nettles. I enclose a photograph of one of the slabs which I took about a fortnight ago. Man killers they were! As you will see they have lasted 68 years pretty well, especially as the reinforcing iron has not apparently cracked the concrete after all this time. At the bottom of the photograph stand the centre iron ring and one of the outside wall blocks."

At the time of Mr Body's letter, the wedge shaped concrete segment of a disc was still in existence, stored in a farm building on the Marsh. It was probably the only surviving relic of attempts to develop an early warning system based on the reception of aircraft sounds by horizontal discs. Although experiments were carried out over a considerable period, extending from 1918 up to 1932, this obscure field of research remains largely unknown and forgotten, but it has its place in the overall story of acoustic defence.

This segment of a concrete disc in a farm building near Ruckinge is a rare survival of the Romney Marsh disc system

CHAPTER SEVENTEEN

A UNIQUE DISC

In addition to experimental aircraft detection systems using flat discs at ground level as on Romney Marsh, a similar but unique device was erected on the Kent coast at the end of the First World War. Reference has already been made to the use of sound mirrors at the Joss Gap acoustic station near the North Foreland, in particular, a mirror cut in the face of the chalk cliffs. Experiments in aircraft detection were also carried out at the station using a vertically mounted movable disc sound locator erected in front of the cliffs.

As a prelude to the installation of the vertical disc at Joss Gap, experimental work was carried out at both the Signals Experimental Establishment, Woolwich, and the research station at Imber Court, Thames Ditton.

Captain Tucker wrote various reports on the experiments in the Spring and Summer of 1918, and again in 1919. These provide a detailed picture of the development, installation and operation of the vertical disc at Joss Gap, and it is worth quoting from them at some length. He explained that tests were carried out "in order to find in what way the sounds of aeroplanes could be detected electrically, and if possible, to devise some system by which enemy aircraft could be located without the use of the ear."

Although Captain Tucker assumed a certain amount of scientific knowledge on the part of his readers, it is possible, by taking the reports as a whole, to gain a fair idea of the principles governing disc location of aircraft.

The reports include a reminder of disc theory. "When a sound proof disc is placed so that it faces on to a source of sound, an image of the source is formed at the centre of the disc on the side away from the source. This is the acoustic analogue of a well known optical experiment which demonstrates the existence of a 'Bright Spot' at the centre of the shadow thrown by an opaque circular disc. In constructing a double disc for the purpose of detecting and locating aircraft, it is necessary to choose dimensions which will be suitably proportioned to the wavelength that will be met with. The fundamental notes emitted by aeroplanes have generally a wave-length of 10 to 15 feet (3 to 4.6m), and in order to get a well defined central maximum, the disc must be at least 20 feet (6.1m) in diameter."

Initial experiments began at Imber Court experimental station with a smaller disc. "A single disc 10 feet (3m) in diameter has been suspended on a frame so that it can rotate about a vertical diameter. A very interesting effect was observed if the disc were kept fixed in position and the source of sound moved. Corresponding to every position of the source of sound in front of the disc, we have a sharp maximum at the rear of the disc. This arrangement of a fixed disc in either a horizontal or vertical position may form the basis of a locating device quite simple to construct, and experiments will be continued both with this arrangement and with the moving disc." During the experiments at Imber Court, it was discovered that a double disc consisting of two discs mounted on a common axis gave better results than a single disc, having "the advantage of greater intensity at the centre and less interference from disturbing noises situated in the plane of the disc or near the plane."

Captain Tucker's reports include a description of the experimental double disc tested at Imber Court. "The discs are 10 feet (3m) in diameter, 8 inches (20cm) apart, vertically suspended, and the wavelength of the sound is 43 feet. The magnification of the sound produced at the centre of the double disc when broadside to the source is 5 times its intensity as observed when the discs are absent." By the summer of 1918, the 10 foot disc locator on test at Imber Court had been provided with a mounting, making it possible to search for sounds in both horizontal and vertical planes. A balloon, tethered at 100 feet (30.5m), with a "siren source of sound" attached was used in testing the capabilities of the disc."

A description of the method of operation is also included in these reports. "The double disc was suspended so that it could rotate about the vertical axis. It is tested for resonance by insertion in the rear disc of an untuned microphone. The human voice humming a sequence of notes uniformly, constituted the variable source. Some notes appeared to come out more strongly than others. The results could not be said to be conclusive. Casual noises such as the passing of trains and traffic on the road were examined. The microphone was replaced by a stethoscope and the sound appeared to be magnified - this magnification being especially evident for the lower notes. At the same time no "humming" occurred, or sounds like the "sea shell" effect, although there was a good breeze. While the stethoscope was employed the disc was tested by a number of observers for getting a bearing by intensity effect alone. The best arrangement of microphone installation is being worked out so that the disc may be used as a long distance detector recording its effect in terms of galvanometer deflections." It is clear from this last reference that sounds picked up by a microphone in the centre of the disc were transferred as electrical signals to a galvanometer, an instrument for measuring electrical currents. The operator was able to aim the disc at the loudest sound by watching the movements of the needle over the dial of the galvanometer.

As a result of these experiments, a decision was made to employ a large double disc consisting of two 20 foot (6.1m) discs mounted one foot apart, designed to respond to notes of low frequency such as those emitted by aero engines. According to the reports "the disc was nearing completion in June 1918, and during the week ending 29th, a visit was made to Joss Gap and "a site selected for setting up a 20 foot (6.1m) disc." Hopes for a good performance from the disc were expressed in one report, which claimed that "such a disc will detect the approach of an aeroplane from a direction facing the disc up to a distance of 50 miles (80km)."

The 20 foot (6.1m) double disc was eventually installed "at Joss Gap near Broadstairs". (Map 1 - p.23) Its function was "to give long distance detection of raiding aeroplanes and at the same time to provide a bearing by working on a maximum effect produced during the rotation of the disc."

Vertical 20 foot (6.1m) disc at Joss Bay, summer 1918

As in the case of the earlier listening wells, the disc had "a definite cone angle of audibility within which the aeroplane produces an effect on the microphone."

Reports from the Signals Experimental Establishment include particulars

The Joss Bay disc from the opposite angle

of the installation of the disc, and further details of the site, described as a "sandy cove half-a-mile across, (805m) enclosed by cliffs whose heights vary from 20 to 80 feet (6.1 to 24m). Its aspect is nearly due east, hence a disc mounted below the cliff's edge is protected from westerly and south-westerly gales. It was decided to select a point at which the cliff was 40 feet high (12m) and to run out a strong staging at a level of 15 feet (4.6m) above the beach. The disc was supplied with two ball pivots and the lower one was supported on a carriage capable of motion along a horizontal bed, one end of which was embedded deeply into the face of the cliff. The upper pivot was received by a socket fixed beneath a gantry erected on level ground at the edge of the cliff. This gantry was capable of being elevated on strong iron pins and when the disc was vertical some of the weight of the gantry was carried by the upper pivot of the disc. For the purposes of erection, a differential pulley and winch were also supplied with the gantry."

The components of the disc were assembled on the sand, and then the whole disc was hauled into place by means of the gantry and winch. The reports also give details of the construction of the disc. In order to make it easy to handle and transport, the disc was made in sectors. "The sectors were made of two panels of 3 ply wood separated by crosspieces. The panels were an inch (2.5cm) thick, and each surface of 3 ply wood was separated by sheet felt. To prevent the felt from slipping out of place, bolts were passed from front to back of each disc element, and great care was taken to ensure uniform packing in order to give the necessary sound-proofness to the disc surface. The selection of these materials was made after careful experiments on sound-proofness conducted at Imber Court." The disc had to be light in weight so that it could be easily manipulated either by hand or by some simple mechanism, and it had to be "capable of swinging about an axis whose inclination could be varied between the vertical and 15 degrees to the vertical." But the disc also had to be "sufficiently strong to support the stress due to its own weight and to a possible large wind pressure." The compass bearing of the disc was indicated by a protractor attached to the disc, which moved relative to a pointer fixed to the carriage.

An important feature of the vertical disc at Joss Gap was the type of microphone employed. Captain Tucker's detailed description of his hot-wire microphone has already appeared in this account in relation to the 200 foot sound mirror at Denge. He invented the microphone in 1916 for detecting enemy guns, and his experience on the Western Front proved valuable when choosing a microphone for installation in the centre of the Joss Gap disc.

Further details are supplied by Captain Tucker in reports to the Signals Experimental Establishment. "As regards the microphone, it became obvious from early experiments that those in common use were unsatisfactory, both as regards sensitivity and consistency of behaviour. In designing the new type, advantage was made of the knowledge obtained in the use of gun microphones in the field, and it was thought that such microphones in a modified form might be usefully employed. The type adopted combined, with the microphone grid of specially fine wire, a resonator of the Helmholtz type, capable of being tuned for a certain range of frequency. The principle of resonance must be employed since in this way only can faint sounds be detected."

The device known as a Helmholtz resonator was named after a 19th century German scientist. When air in a cavity is set in vibration it will produce a note. A large cavity will produce low notes or sounds of low frequency, and similarly, a small cavity will produce high notes or high frequency sound waves. These effects can be understood in relation to organ pipes of differing lengths. Also, the shape and size of a cavity or resonator relate to its responsiveness to certain sounds. Captain Tucker installed his microphone in a resonator tuned to the pitch of sounds he wished to detect, such as those emitted by aircraft engines.

Following experiments at Imber Court experimental station, an arrangement using a microphone mounted in the disc, coupled to a galvanometer to allow visual observation of the sounds detected was also adopted at Joss Gap. In Captain Tucker's words: "The intensity of the sound at the centre of the disc was recorded electrically, the receiver being a hot-wire microphone fitted to a resonator of the Helmholtz pattern, which is tuned to the source of the sound. The microphone is used in conjunction with a wireless amplifier, the telephone terminals of which are connected through a crystal rectifier to a reflecting galvanometer. It has been shown by experiment that when a hot-wire microphone is used in this way, the deflection of the galvanometer is nearly proportional to the intensity of the sound received by the microphone, so that to find the relation between intensity and bearing, it is only necessary to observe the deflections on the galvanometer with the disc set at various angles. Observations are made by searching with the disc until the sound of an aeroplane is heard. A more accurate bearing can then be obtained by manipulating the disc until the sound is heard as a maximum."

Some success was achieved with this method of operation, as shown in a comment by Captain Tucker. "The trials carried out up to the present have been mainly with Sopwiths, Avros, and Short seaplanes at distances of 7 or 8 miles (11 or 13km). At this range, the sound heard in the receiver is very loud, even when, under the conditions on the shore, it is quite inaudible to the unaided ear."

Further practical details are recorded in the reports. "The surface of the disc towards the sea was covered with a screen of canvas upon which an excellent camouflage of the face of the cliff was painted. Lieutenant Cooper of the School of Camouflage carried this out so well, that at a distance of half a mile, the disc was indistinguishable from the face of the cliff. A hut, situated about 25 yards (23m) from the disc, is divided into three compartments, two of which are used as sleeping bunks for the men of the detachment, and the third contains the electrical apparatus used with the disc. The apparatus consists of a 'Field Amplifier Set' i.e. a Mark II amplifier with its potentiometer, rheostat, accumulators and cells, arranged in compact form for transportation. The hut is connected telephonically through the listening post of the 45th Anti-Aircraft Co., R.G.A. (Royal Garrison Artillery) at Joss Gap, to the control headquarters and so through to any trunk line."

The operating crew of the Joss Gap disc consisted of "an NCO (non-commissioned officer) and two men, and the Officer in Charge was Lieutenant Sibree, Royal Engineers." The disc did not function in isolation. "A liaison was established with the Dover Anti-Aircraft Command under Colonel Dittman, and with the Officer Commanding 45th Anti-Aircraft Company, Royal Garrison Artillery, Major Boreham; also with the Commanding Officers of the flying grounds at Bekesbourne and Manston, and with the Commandant of the Seaplane Station at Westcliffe. There was a Naval Listening Post on the North Foreland Lighthouse from which we obtained assistance."

"The Controller also obtained authority for us to perform experiments with Lieutenant Commander Saunders RN, the Officer in Command of the armed drifters at Ramsgate. Our relations with the surrounding aerodromes however, enabled us to employ experimental flights which were of two types:- 1) over the disc and 2) directly out to sea along a track parallel to the shore. The flights out to sea were undertaken at a certain amount of risk on the part of the pilot owing to the existence of a large mine field covering that portion of the coast and the possibility of attack from enemy aeroplanes. Throughout the whole of the time the winds were adverse to the return of the pilot."

Important people visited the Joss Gap station to observe the operation of the disc, as described in a Munitions Inventions Department report. "An official inspection of the station was made on October 12th 1918 by Major-General Ashmore (London Defence Area), Major Forster of GHQ, (General Headquarters) GB, and other officers. The conditions were very unfavourable on the day of the inspection and there was a ground wind of 15 miles per hour (24kmph) producing a very rough sea from the North West. The Bekesbourne and Manston Aerodromes supplied Sopwith Camel and Avro machines, but conditions were too rough for seaplanes. The aeroplanes would not undertake to fly under a height of 9000 ft (2743m), and were quite inaudible at the station when overhead. They were followed up for a distance of 3 or 4 miles (4.8 or 6.4km) by the telephones connected with the apparatus, and General Ashmore was able to observe a maximum effect as the disc was swung round. It should be noted that aeroplanes at a height of 9000 ft (2743m) would not pass into a favourable position for the disc until they were at least 7 miles (11km) out to sea."

The report lists observations made with the disc, giving details of the aircraft and people involved, and the distances at which the sounds were detected.

"September 17th 1918, by Lieutenant Paris, a Short Seaplane, height 3000 feet (914m), distance 2 miles (3.2km); September 18th 1918 by Lieutenant Paris, a Sopwith Camel was heard for 7 or 8 miles (11 or 13km) with an adverse wind."

Observations were made by Captain Tucker and Lieutenant Paris on September 21st 1918, and on October 31st 1918, an "Avro at 4000 feet (1219m) and 4 miles (6.4km) out" was "heard by Captain Tucker and Lieutenant J.O. Sibree. The sounds "went in and out of the cone quite plainly." The term 'cone' referred to the cone of audibility of the disc.

Evidently the mechanical design of the disc was successful despite the rigours of a cliff face site on the Channel coast. "Dealing with these conditions it will be seen that one must take into account not merely the strength and character of the materials but also the local conditions obtaining at Joss Gap. Both were very carefully considered by Captain Smith and his staff at Imber Court, and the success of his design is proved by the fact that the disc has withstood some months of winter weather in a most exposed position without showing any sign of deterioration."

The reference in one of the reports above to the possibility of 'attack from enemy aeroplanes' is evidence that the Joss Gap disc was in operation during the latter stages of the First World War. A type of German bomber is mentioned by Captain Tucker in a Munitions Inventions Department Report about the mounting of listening microphones in tuneable resonators: "This principle is made use of in aeroplane detection, where a German Gotha gives a characteristic note of a higher pitch than the British Scouting aeroplane". Although an exact date for the installation of the Joss Gap disc has not been found, it is possible to infer from the various reports and dates previously quoted that the disc was erected in the late Summer of 1918.

A definite date for the end of experiments with the Joss Gap disc has not been found in contemporary documents, but it seems likely that it was dismantled when the station was closed prior to the move to Hythe in 1922.

CHAPTER EIGHTEEN

SOUND LOCATORS

The story of acoustic aircraft detection would not be complete without some focus on devices known as 'sound locators'. A distinctive feature of this type of apparatus was that incoming sound waves were detected by trumpet-shaped collectors which could be directed towards the sound source. Sound locators remained in action with searchlight units into the early years of the Second World War.

Reports and photographs relating to the use of sound locators in the First World War are to be found in the archives of the Royal Engineers. A collection of sepia-coloured photographs includes several with pencilled captions such as 'Home Front 1914 - 18', 'Richmond Park' and 'Nooks Hill, Essex'. These particular pictures show the activities of a searchlight detachment, and one view depicts a group of soldiers carrying equipment. The photograph is labelled 'Sound Locator'. The men are holding a framework supporting two trumpet-like devices which appear to be several feet in length. In another set of photographs, there is a view of a fully assembled sound locator ready for operation. The instrument has four trumpets, arranged in two pairs mounted at right angles, allowing listening in both vertical and horizontal planes. In this simple type of sound locator, which was in essence a set of large ear trumpets, flexible tubes conveyed the sounds detected by the trumpets to ear pieces worn by the listeners. Because of their shape, trumpet type sound detectors tended to be most effective when the central axis of the trumpet was directed towards the incoming sounds. As a consequence, in locators of this type, the cones were always attached to a flexible mounting, designed to allow scanning of the sky for aircraft sounds.

First World War photograph of soldiers carrying the components of a sound locator

The theory behind the design and use of trumpet type sound locators is explained in War Office publications of the 1920s and 30s. Although no author's name is attached, based on reading many of his reports, and on anecdotal evidence, it is likely that the hand of W.S.Tucker was at work here. A fundamental problem for human listeners is that although they are binaural, the distance between the two receiving devices, the ears, is only about 6 inches. "The angle through which a listener must turn his head in order to get a right or left sensation is 9½ degrees, and it is clear from this that, with the short base-length between the ears provided by nature, a listener is not well equipped for determining accurately the source of a sound. The most obvious way to improve accuracy is by an artificial increase of the natural base-length between the ears, for when this length is increased, a correspondingly smaller angular movement will be required to

First World War sound locator assembled for action

produce a sensation of right or left and thus location will be effected with greater precision."

Assuming an improvement in the distance apart of the receivers, the next design problem was the shape of the receiving device, which tended to be conical. "The cones must be of great length in order to receive successfully the low-pitched constituents of aeroplane sound. Narrow cones were tried up to a length of 100 inches (254cm)." Wind disturbance proved to be as great a problem with sound locators as it was with mirrors. Wide angle cones were found to be more successful in this respect. "Wide angle cones of 18 to 24 inches (46 to 61cm) in length were decided on as being sufficiently good and not too cumbrous." The trumpets on the sound locators which appear in various pictures of searchlight units in the First World War appear to be about the size described.

Two methods of listening were used. The first, already mentioned, was similar to that employed with early sound mirrors. Flexible tubes running from the necks of the trumpets led the sound to stethoscopes worn by the listener. But microphones were also used "placed in the throat of the trumpets."

The problem of relating the size of a collecting device to the low frequency sounds emitted by aircraft engines was familiar to the designers of sound mirrors, and reports of the period expressed similar concerns in relation to trumpet type sound locators. "The directional properties of a cone depend mainly on the ratio of the diameter of the mouth to the wave length of the sound. If this ratio is large, the directional properties will be well marked, so that the collector will be effective in concentrating the listener's attention in one direction. If the diameter of the mouth is only a fraction of a wave-length, the directional properties will be poor. It follows that the same conical receiver may be highly directional when used to collect sounds of high pitch, and only poorly directional when used for sounds of low pitch."

It is no surprise to find that Captain Tucker, who seems to have taken a close interest in all areas of acoustic research, was involved not only with discs and mirrors, but also with trumpet sound locators. In a report dating from March 1918, he described experiments at Imber Court experimental establishment, Thames Ditton, with "service locating trumpets". He hoped that the equipment would be "in the field if possible during the coming raid period." In the Imber Court experiments, two trumpets, mounted on a frame and connected by tubing to the listener, were used to give a binaural effect. Evidently, the Tucker hot-wire microphone was not used in these tests.

Microphones, of a type used in telephone receivers, connected to amplifiers, were mounted at the base of the trumpets, giving "powerful magnification" and making the "estimate of direction of the plane very easy." Captain Tucker claimed that "one should be able to get the direction of a plane at considerable distances, and wind, traffic noises, conversation and gun fire should be eliminated." Apparently, the device did not always eliminate conversation, and during a demonstration arranged for a visit by the Minister of Munitions, it was noted that "a human hum of conversational loudness was heard at 150 yards (137m)." That at least demonstrated the sensitivity of the apparatus.

At the time of this visit to Imber Court, the Minister of Munitions was Winston Churchill, a visionary in his view of air power, as in so many other areas. In 1914, Lord Kitchener asked him to take on the responsibility for the air defence of Britain, and he was also a keen advocate of the use of aircraft for reconnaissance on the Western Front. By 1917, he was Minister of Munitions, urging that aircraft production be given priority for the use of steel and other scarce raw materials. In 1918, he impressed upon the Prime Minister, Lloyd George, the importance of securing air supremacy before attempting any further offensives on the Western Front. In 1919, Churchill became Secretary of State for Air, and as a former pilot, he understood the importance of preserving the Royal Air Force during a time of financial stringency in the immediate post war years.

Trumpet sound locators were tested against both friendly and enemy aircraft during the First World War. Some of the work was based at Orfordness. In documents of the period, this place name was usually written as one word, but it also appears on present day maps as 'Orford Ness.' The site, on the Suffolk coast, was the home of research in many fields over a long period, beginning in 1915 and ending in 1971 when research by the Atomic Energy Commission was finally closed down. Early radar experiments which have become part of history were carried out at Orfordness in 1935. (Map 1 - p.23).

A report headed "Munitions Inventions Department, Anti-Aircraft Experimental Section, Orfordness, Royal Flying Corps" on the subject of "Work with Sound Locating Trumpets at Orfordness" describes acoustic experiments during the First World War. The term 'projector' is often used in such reports to describe a searchlight. "It was arranged in December 1917 that the Munitions Inventions Department should co-operate with the Royal Flying Corps at Orfordness in the development of sound locating trumpets. Work has been carried on at Orfordness since 23 December 1917." In relation to night experiments, the main idea was "to develop the directing of searchlight beams by means of sound locators, for facilitating the attack of aircraft. A set of trumpets was placed 10-15 yards (9.1-14m) from the projector. Two men operated the trumpets for bearing and elevation, and an observer, usually an officer, stood beside the trumpets looking along the sights. When both listeners reported 'on', the beam was exposed, and the observer gave directions to the operator at the projector so as to bring the apparent end of the beam on to the leading edge of the ring-sight."

The reference to the 'leading edge' of the ring-sight relates to a problem inherent in all forms of sound location of aircraft. As the speed of sound is much lower than the speed of light, it follows that the position of an aircraft plotted by sound is always behind its true position in space, usually referred to as the 'line of sight'. The two listeners were able to aim the locator along the 'line of sound,' but to illuminate the target, it was necessary to make a correction in order to aim along the 'line of sight'. The duty of the third member of the team, the observer, was to estimate the speed of the target and adjust the sight accordingly. By using the leading edge of the ring-sight, he was able to aim the searchlight beam along the line of sight to the target aircraft. In the early stages of the 1917 Orfordness experiments, the observer gave verbal orders to the searchlight operator, but later, a signalling device was used because "when the sound of the target is faint, the noise of the observer giving orders is very disturbing to the listeners."

These particular trumpets were mounted on portable stands, and must have been similar to those in the early photographs mentioned previously. The equipment described above, and the method of operation, formed the basis in later years for the design of the Mark III portable sound locator, which was widely used by searchlight detachments.

Although much of the experimental work with sound equipment was carried out by the Army and the Royal Flying Corps, the Navy was also involved at Orfordness. Captain A. Hill, Director of the Anti-Aircraft Experimental Section, Munitions Inventions Department, HMS Excellent Portsmouth, wrote a letter on the subject to "The Comptroller MID" on 13 January 1918.

"I have received the following account of trials with sound locating trumpets from Lieutenant E.A.Milne at Orfordness." Lieutenant Milne's report, signed "E.A.Milne, Lieut. RNVR Anti-Aircraft Experimental Section, Munitions Inventions Department, Armament Experimental Station, Royal Flying Corps, Orfordness, 9 February 1918" included conclusions arising from his experiments with acoustic trumpets. For example, he stressed that the trumpets should be "as large as possible consistent with low inertia, say 2 feet 3 inches in diameter", and in the matter of length "this should be at least 5 feet, even 6 feet would not be too large, provided inertia is kept down." The term 'inertia' refers to the need to design trumpets and mountings to allow easy movement of the locators by listeners when searching for sounds. The report includes a suggestion that a gun type mounting would be helpful.

Another paper, of 18 February 1918 contains further details of Lieutenant Milne's work. "Experiment of February 17th, Evening. Two 60 cm, searchlights and two sets of trumpets were installed at the ends of a three mile base line. (4.8km) It was intended that one machine, a 'raider,' should patrol at 8000 to 12000ft (2438 to 3658m), and that a chasing machine should attempt to find it by the direct searchlight beams. The 'raider' however, had to descend owing to engine trouble; the 'chaser' a Bristol Fighter was then sent up above as a target machine, and both stations were in action against it for 84 minutes. During this period one of the beams was exposed and directed by the sound for about 32 minutes, the other for about 22 minutes. The beams were not exposed unless the trumpets were in action. The machine's height varied from 3000 to 13000 feet (914m to 3962m), for 25 minutes of the time it was above 9000 feet (2743m).

General Summary of Results:- The observer in the Bristol Fighter reported that his machine was caught in beams on 23 to 24 separate occasions. The pilot, who had had considerable experience overseas, and some slight experience of random searching by enemy lights, considered that the searching was extraordinarily good, and that a chasing machine could not possibly have failed to find him had the lights been directed equally well when other machines were in the sky. To sum up - small 60 cm searchlights, directed by small sets of trumpets have been accurately directed onto an aeroplane at heights up to 13000 feet (3962m), the aeroplane being invisible from the ground practically the whole of the time."

Another 1918 report was signed by "F.W.Mussen, Captain, B.M.Jones, Major, and A.C. Boddam-Whetham, Lieut. Colonel, Officer in Command, Armament Experimental Station, Royal Flying Corps." The subject of the report is 'sound locating and aircraft'.

"During the past month, January, a number of experiments on this subject have been carried out at Orfordness in conjunction with the Munitions Inventions Department. To get satisfactory results from the trumpets it is important to have intelligent observers, as the power of concentration required cannot as a rule be expected from men of indifferent mental capacity any more than from those of defective hearing." As in the case of the early sound mirrors, the sound locators were used against German bombers. "The question of actually picking up a Gotha in the trumpets has, however, been found perfectly possible at Rochford and elsewhere in recent raids." (Map 1 - p.23)

The reference to Rochford is a reminder that Orfordness was not the only coastal site associated with acoustic work. Rochford, in Essex, was a sub-station of the Anti-Aircraft Experimental Section, (AAES) itself a branch of the Munitions Inventions Department. The AAES was established in 1916 in a corner of the small airfield at Northolt, Middlesex, but was obliged to move to the National Physical Laboratory at Teddington because of "lack of interest" (sic!) and facilities at Northolt. In 1916, the section moved to HMS Excellent on Whale Island in Portsmouth Harbour. In 1918, the section collaborated with the RAF in experiments on the sound location of aircraft. Both Rochford and another sub-station at Stokes Bay on the Solent were involved in sound location experiments.

Sound locator tests at Rochford were in progress as early as 1917.

"The sound locators which have been used to the present are of the binaural type, with four simple wooden conical trumpets, one pair being used to determine the azimuth direction, and the other pair the elevation." 'Azimuth direction' refers to the use of a pair of trumpets to search in a horizontal plane. "The first apparatus was set up east of Rochford in December 1917. Several attempts to plot British planes were made, and moderately good results were obtained."

Sound locator 1918

Sound locator from the rear, 1918. Note stethoscopes

The tests continued in 1918, as detailed in a report of 29 January. "Two sets of MID sound locating trumpets were placed at Barling and Ashingden, at the ends of a base 8,600 yards long (7864m). Both stations were in direct telephonic communication with the office at Rochford which served as a plotting station. Several enemy aircraft passed within range during the night, but owing chiefly to the presence of British machines searching for the enemy, on all save one occasion it was impossible either to get both stations with certainty on to one target, or to get more than two or three readings before the sound was confused with that of another aeroplane."

At the end of February 1918, "it was arranged for three 13 pounder gun sections between the Crouch and the Thames, commanded by Captain Langham, to co-operate with the Rochford Station, and this arrangement continued until the beginning of June. On three occasions only, enemy aircraft came within range of the sound locators. One occurred in a dark period, and the apparatus was out of action. No results were obtained in the second, as owing to an S.O.S. call being made by a gun section north of the Crouch, the guns commenced to send up a pre-arranged barrage in the neighbourhood of that section. On the third occasion, the enemy aircraft kept a little outside the range of the guns and fire was not opened."

Another paper marked "Private and Secret" gave further details of the plotting of enemy aircraft by means of sound locators:

"Results obtained by the MID at Rochford in recent raids have shown that it is possible to follow a Gotha aeroplane at 14,000 feet, when other defending aeroplanes are within hearing, but that the difficulty of doing this depends largely upon the number of defending machines in the neighbour-hood, the difficulty increasing rapidly with the number of machines present. There is thus good evidence to suppose that an attacking Gotha can be located by defending machines directed by 'Ears' and searchlights, provided the defending machines are not too numerous, and that their position in relation to the 'Ears' are carefully controlled."

In addition to his activities at Orfordness, Lieutenant Milne RNVR collaborated with Captain Tucker and one of his colleagues Lieutenant Paris in experiments carried out during the summer of 1918. These experiments made use of the microphone invented by Captain Tucker. "Hot-wire micro-phones were used in determining the resonance properties of sound-location trumpets and their connections using electrical methods. A microphone placed at any particular point in a trumpet or its connections, may therefore be used to give a measure of the intensity of sound passing this point." The conclusion reached was that "the hot-wire microphone can be used to explore the resonance properties of trumpets."

There are references in National Archive reports to the use of sound locators in the defence of London, including details of Anti-Aircraft Gunnery during the night of 28 - 29 January 1918. "Hyde Park Guns... the sound locator was not much assistance. Only one target was located by it, any chance they had on others being spoilt by Machine gun Fire." "Wanstead Gun..the sound locators were only able to feel certain about one Target, that which passed South travelling East at 21.28...This locator was as usual handicapped by the noise of the Gas Engine, the sound of the Targets was also very faint in most cases." "The sound locator at Sub-Command Headquarters was of great assistance in checking reports as in all cases where sounds were heard, a valuable cross bearing was instantly (sic) available to check the plotting reports received from stations. The Sound Locator is now installed on the observation platform with voice pipe direct to the operations table.." A further report from West Sub-Command London A.A. Defences refers to raids on 18-19 February 1918. "The Locator at Headquarters proved of considerable value, and during the lulls between firing, succeeded in following targets accurately and well....I recommend in spite of the comparatively bad location of Dulwich Light that in order to attempt to obtain cross bearings with Putney, Croydon and Bromley, a locator be placed here (Dulwich?) when available."

It is clear from all the reports quoted that trumpet type sound locators were tested both at research stations and against enemy aircraft on bombing raids over England. Similar activities were also taking place on the other side of the Channel.

CHAPTER NINETEEN

TRUMPETS, GUNS AND LIGHTS

It is apparent from reports of the period that sound locators were deployed in France during the First World War of 1914 - 18. A Board of Inventions document dating from December 1916 includes references to "work undertaken in 1915-16 by Lieutenant Richmond and the Western Electric Company, using trumpet shaped collectors. Their adoption for aircraft detection and location probably resulted from their use on the Western Front."

Further illumination is provided in "Sound Location Reports from France" written in June July and August 1918 by Lieutenant A. Ward R.A.F. of the 24th Anti-Aircraft Searchlight Section, British Expeditionary Force. For example, in June 1918, he reported that "a set of apparatus was installed in the British Army Area in France about 10 miles behind the line. From the experience gained it seems certain that if the enemy aircraft follows a straight course, and the plot obtained be good, it is possible to predict a barrage square with sufficient rapidity for the Gun Commander to make use of it." Lieutenant Ward described experiments at Saint Cyr, where he arrived "in time for the usual evening flight of an experimental aeroplane." His reports give various details of the use of sound locator trumpets with anti-aircraft guns, and on a visit to Pont-sur-Seine, Paris on 10 August 1918 he noted that "the difficulty of locating Gothas appears to be almost, if not quite, entirely due to the low pitch of the note emitted." It is evident from this last point that larger sound locator trumpets were needed. Similar concerns occupied the designers of sound mirrors, highlighting the physical fact that for low pitched, long wavelength sounds, such as those produced by the engines of German Gotha bombers, a large collecting surface was necessary.

Naval officers continued to be involved in experiments with sound locators. Lieutenant E.A.Milne, RNVR has already been mentioned in relation to his experimental work with sound locators at Orfordness, and he was also active on the Western Front. He was attached to the Anti-Aircraft School, First Army AA Defence, from where he sent a report to the Munitions Inventions Department on 23 September 1918. "Lt. Pollard and myself arrived in France on 24 August and proceeded to the First Army A.A. School. The three 27 inch (69cm) sound locators arrived in the course of the next few days. Two of these were installed at the ends of a base line ready for height-track finding. The third was kept at one end of the base for training purposes." The report continues with a description of training methods for personnel operating the trumpets. Bad weather was given as a possible reason for the fact that "during the period in which the sound locators have been manned and ready, no enemy aircraft have come within range."

In July 1918, Lieutenant Roy W. Chesnut an American officer, wrote an account of comparative tests of three types of sound locator. These were English, French and American devices. "Tests were made using the naked ear, an English 18 inch (46cm) cone, an English 36 inch (91cm) cone, a Baillaud paraboloid, and a Perrin Telesitemeter." The weights of the three locators were "English 18 and 36 inch cones: 100 kg, Baillaud Paraboloid: 850 kg, Perrin Telesitemeter 1500-2000 kg." No price was available for the French locator, but estimated costs were given for " English Cones: 500-1000 francs, and Perrin Telesitemeter: 15,000 francs."

In his report, Lieutenant Chestnut points out that the English locator was a simple portable device, whereas the other two were rather complicated pieces of equipment. Writing after the war, Dr Tucker described the Baillaud Paraboloid, and it is clear from his description that it was a type of sound mirror incorporating trumpet type sound locators. "A movable sound-mirror, the Baillaud Paraboloid was adopted by the French Army for aircraft location in 1918." The device was named after Captain R. Baillaud and it comprised "a light paraboloidal mirror mounted on an altazimuth stand, and having two pairs of binaural sound-collectors fixed at the focus. These collectors are used by two listeners in much the same way as the pairs of sound collectors in a binaural sound locator." The mirror was "3 metres in diameter" and it "swung in a U-frame which turned about a central vertical pivot." An illustration of the Perrin Telesitemetre shows it to be a complex device, employing multiple trumpets mounted in four large clusters on a metal framework, mounted on a steel base, with seats for the operators and control wheels for moving the collectors in elevation and azimuth. It is plainly not very portable.

Lieutenant Chestnut's report also dealt with such practical matters as the problems of transporting sound locators. The Baillaud locator was "heavy to handle," and it was "transported on a trailer behind a motor truck. Most of the time consumed is in moving it on and off the transport by skids or other means." This locator was described as "solid- not breakable." The American 'Perrin Telesitemeter' was "light to handle and demountable." It was "packed in special crates to protect it during transport. Each piece in its crate can be lifted onto a motor truck by two men. It takes 6 men 1½ hours to set up; 4 men can do it in 2½ hours." The English locator was "light to handle, and transportable without demounting. It is not easily broken."

Lieutenant Chestnut's conclusions were that "the Perrin is not favoured for use near the front, owing to setting up time and its cost." It is superior to "ordinary horn devices, or to the Baillaud for the purpose of directing anti-aircraft fire. An instrument of less precision than the Perrin which could be easily portable would be better for directing searchlights." In relation to the Telesitemeter, the American report also mentioned that "it is sensitive to neighbouring parasitic sounds of great intensity e.g. clattering noises of carts on a road, railroad trains, or violent rustling of leaves in nearby trees." However, a report was sent to the Scientific Attaché at the American Embassy listing the advantages of the Perrin Telesitemeter.

In a letter of 15 August 1918 to Major A.V. Hill at the Munitions Inventions Department, the American conclusions were questioned by Lieutenant-Colonel W. M. Pritchard, who commented "our instrument was better than the Perrin." As the French had ordered 600 Baillaud Paraboloids, they were also reluctant to admit that the Perrin Telesitemeter was a superior device.

Following trials of various types of sound locator, some of them fairly complicated in design, it is apparent that eventually, a simple locator, equipped with four trumpets and mounted on a portable stand, became standard equipment for searchlight units in the British Army.

Detachments of Royal Engineers from a base at Stokes Bay, Gosport, Hampshire, operated sound locators in France in the summer of 1918. The sound locators were sited about six miles behind the front line, and were used to guide searchlights. "Gotha type aircraft" were plotted at altitudes of 6000 to 8000 feet (1829 to 2438m) and "machine gun fire, either from the ground or from the target itself did not put the locators out of action.

Bombs dropped at approximately one and a quarter miles in front of the trumpets did not affect the listening. The noise from an FE (Farman Experimental) friendly machine passing overhead prevented effective listening for a Gotha type target at long range. On one occasion, four hostile machines were present at different points of the compass; it was found possible to get bearing and elevation of any of the machines as required. None of these machines were in range, and no attempt to illuminate them was made."

A report on these activities ends with details of an exercise back in England, involving sound locators, searchlights, four BE12B aircraft as 'friendly' and six 'Handley Page machines from Stonehenge' as the attackers. The exercise took place around Portsmouth, the objectives of the raiders being Southampton Docks and Portsmouth Dockyard. The experiment was not entirely successful; bright moonlight resulted in less effective use of searchlights to illuminate 'enemy' aircraft, but one BE12 pilot reported that he could see that an 'enemy' was "a Handley Page", and in fact he was able to approach 3 separate 'enemy' aircraft and could have attacked them.

Civilian experts also played a part in acoustic developments during the First World War. Mr C. Jakeman, from the National Physical Laboratory wrote a "Secret Report" on 31 July 1918 for the Munitions Inventions Department, concerning a visit he had made to France. His report included records of plots made by sound locators working with gun batteries and searchlights.

Mr Jakeman remarked on the reactions of people on the spot to visits by scientists. "The attitude with regard to sound plotting was not encouraging. There seemed to be an impression that our party consisted of inventors who were going to end the war by shooting down every aeroplane by gunfire as soon as it was within sound range."

During his visit to France, Mr Jakeman was invited to give a lecture on the principles of sound location. Seventy five people arrived, and as they were crowded into a room big enough for only thirty, some of them had to sit on ammunition boxes. Mr Jakeman felt he had succeeded in putting over his ideas. "I should judge that more interest will be taken in the matter in future."

Shortly after the First World War, the Signals Experimental Establishment at Woolwich produced a summary of the state of development of trumpet sound locators at that time. Three of the people mentioned, Lieutenant Milne, Lieutenant Ward, at this time promoted to Captain, and Mr Jakeman have already appeared in this account in relation to their work with sound locators during the war.

"As a result of a very large amount of work initiated at the National Physical Laboratory, chiefly done by Mr C. Jakeman and later by Captain Ward, in co-operation with Lieutenant Milne RNAS (Royal Naval Air Service), the service trumpet-locators have taken their present form. These service patterns have three standard sizes of trumpets:- 18 inches (46cm) (diameter of mouth); 27 inches (69cm); and 39 inches (99cm). The lengths of the trumpets are about 4/3 (sic) the diameter of the mouth." The strange expression "4/3" makes quite good sense if used to calculate the lengths of the three types of trumpet, giving lengths of 24 inches (61cm) for the 18 inch (46cm) diameter trumpet, 36 inches (91cm) for the 27 inch (69cm) trumpet, and 52 inches (132cm) for the 39 inch (99cm) trumpet. The report continues with a discussion of the relative effectiveness of various trumpets related to the pitch of the sounds from aeroplanes. "So complex is the sound that no microphone can be employed to measure it electrically."

Another person who was to play a significant part in acoustic work is mentioned in a report from the Signals Experimental Establishment on 29 August 1921. "The Handford Trumpet was used on 7 July 1921. It was found to be good at magnifying the sounds." Mr Handford was part of Dr Tucker's acoustic team, and he eventually played a considerable part in the sound mirror experiments on the Kent coast and elsewhere. Further details of the trumpet locator designed by him appear in another S.E.E. report of 2 January 1922. "A sample Handford Trumpet has been received from Messrs. Dobson. It appears to be of good quality and is now awaiting an aural test at Biggin Hill. If tests are satisfactory the manufacture of the remaining 15 trumpets can be put in hand forthwith" There was also comment on tubes for the stethoscopes worn by listeners. " A sample of branded stethoscopic tube has been received from Messrs. Maw. This was not of sufficiently good quality, and another sample is being submitted within a few days." On the subject of "screening of Handford Trumpets from wind and lateral sounds" it was reported that "after trials the 'lagging' with felt or rubber was found to be unsatisfactory, as in addition to stopping extraneous noises it adversely affected the performance of the trumpet." The trumpet was found to lose its 'ring' or 'sonorous quality.' To overcome this, a sheath type screen which only made contact 'at the ends' was proposed. "The trumpet will thus be protected by a kind of air jacket." Wooden and metal sheaths were tried.

Experiments with trumpet locators took place at Biggin Hill and Croydon Aerodrome in 1922. At Biggin Hill, experiments were carried out with "trumpet Sound Locators of both metal and wooden construction, mounted on stands." A Mark II locator was installed at Croydon, and it was reported in December that "a trumpet set erected at Croydon Aerodrome was inspected by Colonel Blandy last month. Weekly reports are received from the operator at Croydon. (Mr . C. G. Gent) The following is the report for the week ending 24 November. On 19th, a Breguet was picked up 3 minutes before being sighted. On 20th a Handley was located at 15.49 and was seen over the Aerodrome at 15. 54. On 21st a Goliath was picked up at 14.10 and seen at 14.14."

In the years after the First World War, continuing efforts to produce a satisfactory portable sound locator culminated in the design of the Mark III. Dr Tucker described the process. "In 1923, the Acoustical Section of the Air Defence Experimental Establishment had the problem of producing a portable sound locator which could be packed in a case after dismantling.

The base length of 4 feet 6 inches (137cm) was used. The horns are conical. They are made of thin tin and are mounted within a wooden casing from which they are sound insulated by rubber. In this way the sound of wind and falling rain on the horns is eliminated. The magnification of the horns is about 10 times for high pitched aircraft sounds."

Sound locator with Handford trumpets

Further details are to be found in a Handbook for the Mark III Locator. "The instrument consists of a framework carrying four wooden trumpets. The framework is itself mounted on a tripod in such a way that it can be rotated into any position. The tripod is made collapsible, and the framework may be removed from it and dismantled so as to enable the whole to be packed into a wooden travelling case. The weight of the case with the instrument packed into it is 2 cwts 3 qrs 6lb, (c.142kg) and handles provided enable it to be carried by four men." A built-in spirit level allowed for levelling of the locator.

Operating methods are also explained in the Handbook. "The locator requires three operators, namely the azimuth (or bearing) listener, the elevation listener, and the parallelogram sight operator." Movements of the trumpets in a horizontal plane were shown on a scale of bearings located on the top of the tripod, and the elevation scale showing movements of the trumpets in a vertical plane was is the form of a drum, mounted on the end of the horizontal arm of the locator. "The azimuth listener stands on the pointer side of the elevating shaft with the shaft running to right and left of him. He moves the trumpets in azimuth by placing his left hand on the shaft between the left hand clamp and the parallelogram sight." The elevation listener could stand either opposite the azimuth listener, or at one end of the apparatus. A little thought will show that it was necessary to have some sort of procedure to avoid conflicting movements by the two listeners, and one solution was to give precedence to the listener responsible for searching in the horizontal plane, often described as the 'azimuth' listener. When he had found the bearing of an aircraft sound, the elevation or altitude listener could then move his trumpets to locate that target in the vertical plane. In Dr Tucker's words "the azimuth listener must be correct before the altitude listener can function satisfactorily; the azimuth listener is, so to speak, the senior partner."

The duties of the sight operator, or 'sighting number' in Army jargon, and the adjustments required to cope with the time lag of sound have already been mentioned briefly in connection with the early types of sound locator used at Orfordness in 1917. Further clarification of the procedure is to be found in the Handbook. The sight operator had to adjust the ring fore-sight

Sound Locator Mark III Note two listeners wearing stethoscopes.
The third crew member is using the ring-sight

for the estimated speed of the target, by moving it nearer to or further from him, along a slot marked in miles per hour. He looked at the ring-sight via a bead back-sight. "The line of sight from the back-sight to the centre of the ring-sight is the direction in which the trumpets are pointing. The true line of sight, by which the searchlight beam must be directed, always passes through the back-sight bead and some point on the periphery of the ring-sight. This point is known as the 'leading edge' and it is the correct estimation of the leading edge that is the first duty of the sighting number." The object of the exercise was to aim the searchlight beam by means of the leading edge of the ring- sight on the sound locator.

Some insight into the state of sound locator research by 1929 appears in a paper on "Tests for Listeners" by Dr Tucker. This contains a description of the optical equipment attached to a Mark III Locator used for training listeners. A telescope was used to check the bearings obtained aurally.

"If listening is good and the correct air speed has been set, the target will appear in the middle of the field of the telescope. In this way, the target can be continuously observed, and the errors in listening cause the target to move away from the centre of the field of the telescope." A link to the next phase of development occurs in a sentence about transporting this equipment. The Mark III Locator could be carried on a "Medium Six Wheeler, but any increase in size will necessitate a trailer or a second vehicle."

A memorandum to the Royal Engineers Board on 16 May 1931 contains a reference to the "obsolescence of Marks I and II Sound Locators" which were tripod types. Nevertheless, tripod mounted locators continued in use for many years, in particular the Mark III, later modified as the Mark IIIx.

The ring- sight was the subject of a letter from Major-General Salt, Commander Air Defence Formation, Territorial Army, to the President of the Royal Engineers Board on 8 September 1933. "In view of the increased speeds of modern bombers, it would appear that a re-design of the ring-sight of the Sound Locator Mark IIIx now requires consideration." He suggested that the sight should be modified to cope with "at least 150 mph (241kmph) to cater for the speed of modern bombers." His estimate of likely bomber speeds was soon overtaken by events.

Details of the Mark IIIx were sent to the Royal Engineers Board on 13 December 1935 with a covering note: "We enclose the latest specification and drawings for the Sound Locator Mark IIIx. The modifications to the trumpets and tripod introduced at the tender stage of the current contracts for the Mark IIIx Sound Locator are also included in these drawings."

Photographs from the 1930s reveal tripod-type locators in use by the 1st Anti-Aircraft Searchlight Group at Watchet, Somerset.

Sound locator in action in the 1930s at Watchet, Somerset,
1st Anti-Aircraft Searchlight Group. Note Lewis gun to
the left on anti-aircraft mount

In 1936, Dr Tucker gave a lecture at the Royal Institution on "Direction Finding By Sound." He referred to the Mark III Sound Locator. "Its performance after training was adequate for the slow moving and heavy bombing aircraft of ten years ago, but, owing to the high speed of modern aircraft, it is gradually losing its usefulness."

A photograph from the Folkestone Herald of 20 February 1937 shows a sound locator in use in Kent, manned by the "Romney Marsh Detachment, Cinque Ports (Fortress) Royal Engineers." An adjacent photograph shows a searchlight at St Mary's Bay, operated by the same RE personnel. The sound locator has four collectors, square at the open ends, and tapering in cross section, and the instrument is mounted on a tripod.

It is apparent from documents of the time that simple portable sound locators were still in use at the outset of the Second World War. According to a War Office memorandum of 26 July 1939 on the subject of the Mark III Locator, "these Sound Locators are not likely to become obsolescent for some time." On 11 April 1941, the Director of Ordnance Services wrote to the Air Defence Experimental Establishment, under the heading "Locator Sound Mark IIIx". He continued: "I am directed to refer to the above sound locator and say that it will be modified by replacing the existing bead back-sight by an aperture sight."

Although more sophisticated electrical sound locators were in action with searchlight units in the Second World War, it is evident from documents of the period that use was still made of portable acoustic locators. Various notes from January to June 1942 concern problems with the tubing connecting the sound collecting trumpets to the listener's earpieces, and a letter from Anti-Aircraft Command of 25 August 1942 ruled that "until the liability of jamming of Sound Locators is removed, Locators Sound Mark III are our second line of defence." This implies that when the more sophisticated electrical sound locators were subject to jamming, searchlight units re-activated simple acoustic locators, very similar to those used in the First World War.

CHAPTER TWENTY

LISTENING AT SEA

In the chronology of the acoustic story, the year 1926 is a good point at which to digress briefly from the story of sound locators. In November of that year, a report from the Air Defence Experimental Establishment described acoustic experiments carried out for the Admiralty.

An ideal early warning system defending an island should be capable of detecting hostile aircraft as far offshore as possible. This was the basis for experiments carried out at sea in 1926. As a mirror could give an extra five miles range over the ear, it was suggested that "if listening could be conducted from a ship, the outpost line could be extended away from our shores, and it was thought desirable to investigate the possibilities of listening at sea. Trials were made using a 16 foot conical horn, an exponential trumpet, and a paraboloidal mirror with a small collector at its geometrical focus. Each was supplied with stethoscopes and served not only as a powerful magnifier but also as a direction finder."

These devices were mounted for a period of three months on *HMD Lunar Bow*, a former drifter-type fishing vessel in naval service, commanded by Lieutenant G. S. Tuck, RN.

The ship was moored at Woolwich Arsenal Pier at the beginning of August 1926. For communications, a wireless set was installed in a cabin in the forecastle by the RAF. After fitting the apparatus, the ship was moved to a base at Dover Harbour on 5 September. The aircraft involved were from "a detachment of the Night Flying Flight of 56th Squadron under Flight Lieutenant Harcourt-Smith".

The Flight was detached to Hawkinge aerodrome just inland of Folkestone in Kent, and it consisted of two "Vickers Vimy bombing aeroplanes. Each was fitted with Wireless apparatus. When night flying operations took place it was found essential to use Lympne aerodrome to facilitate landing." Lympne aerodrome was sited on top of the escarpment adjacent to the Acoustic Research Station on The Roughs at West Hythe. Visual observers were placed at the South Foreland Lighthouse and North East of Folkestone "at a point about half a mile (805m) from the pier." The observation party was made up of six ratings and two petty officers. Theodolites were used to observe bearings of ships and aeroplanes. Very lights, flags and lamps were used in communications. (Map 1 - p.23)

HMD (His Majesty's Drifter) Lunar Bow 1926. The 16 foot horn is ready for action, the sound mirror under protective cover can be seen on the searchlight mounting in front of the bridge

The report described the mirror used. It was "made of cast iron, half an inch (13mm) thick, and was a pure paraboloid of which the aperture and depth were both four feet (1.2m). The focal length was three inches (76mm) . The collector was a copper trumpet 12 inches (30.5cm) long, tapering to a quarter inch (6.3mm) at its narrow end. The mirror was supplied with a counterpoise and was carried in the mounting of a 120 cm searchlight projector. When listening was taking place, the ship's engines were stopped and all possible precautions were taken to ensure silence."

Sound Mirror on HMD Lunar Bow with Dr Talbot Paris, 1926

In addition to illuminating photographs of the construction of the 30 and 200 foot (9.1 and 61m) sound mirrors, th papers of Percy Rothwell, Air Defence Experimental Establishment also include pictures of *HMD Lunar Bow* and its equipment, taken in Dover Harbour, with the White Cliffs in the background. Various photographs show the three listening devices ready for action. The paraboloidal mirror can be seen on a searchlight mounting in front of the bridge, and erected on the forward deck is either the exponential trumpet or the 16 foot (4.9m) conical horn. Members of the acoustic team dressed in suits, caps and trilby hats lend a period flavour to the pictures. One of the people has been identified as Dr Paris, a close colleague of Dr Tucker.

Exponential trumpet collector mounted on HMD
Lunar Bow Dover Harbour, 1926

Charts were included with the ADEE report, showing the performance of the listening apparatus on *HMD Lunar Bow*. One conclusion reached was that there was "a definite advantage to be gained by the use of listening apparatus on a ship under all conditions." This appears to mean that placing the listening apparatus at sea gave a longer period of warning. Another conclusion was that "the advantage is more definite under adverse conditions" and that "information obtained by ear is not only anticipated but a good bearing can be given."

*Rowing out equipment to HMD Lunar Bow. Dover Castle
and the White Cliffs in the background*

The report ends with a statement of the relative merits of the various listening devices on the ship. The 16 foot conical horn headed the list, followed by the exponential trumpet and the paraboloidal mirror. Worst of all was "the unaided ear." "It appears definite that with listening instruments, the approach of an aeroplane can be observed for at least 5 minutes before it arrives under present flying conditions."

There was much correspondence between the Admiralty and the Air Defence Experimental Establishment about the alterations needed to *HMD Lunar Bow* to enable the acoustic equipment to be fitted, and as to who would be responsible for restoring the ship exactly to its former condition after the experiments. Percy Rothwell's photographs of the ship fitted with sound collecting devices illustrate the concerns of the Admiralty. In partic-ular, the 16 foot horn was an ungainly device, sticking up in the air almost as high as the funnel. There is no mention in the reports of possible operating problems when the ship was at sea. It seems likely that the gaping mouths of the trumpet and 16 foot horn on the open deck would be greatly affected by wind noise, and the movements of this small vessel in a rolling sea would have created difficult conditions for listeners operating the equipment.

Despite such problems in an experimental system, the idea of placing acoustic devices at sea to detect aircraft approaching the coast was an attempt to achieve a degree of early warning not realised until the radar age.

CHAPTER TWENTY-ONE

MOBILE SOUND LOCATORS

Based on a lack of further documentary evidence, it appears that the previously described experiments at sea on *HMD Lunar Bow* proved to be a brief departure from the main stream of acoustic research. Resuming the story of sound locators, from about 1925 onwards scientists in the Air Defence Experimental Establishment at Biggin Hill were engaged in the development of a more advanced type of sound locator. By the early 1930s, experiments were in progress with a substantial device on a solid mounting resembling that used for guns. This work eventually led to the design of a mobile sound locator, subsequently used in action in the Second World War.

Four sound collecting cones were positioned on a mounting which enabled operation by two listeners, one searching in a horizontal plane, and the other in a vertical plane. Seats were provided on the locator for the listeners and a sight operator. A more detailed description of this locator, together with a photograph of the apparatus is contained in another document of the period.

The device is described as "an experimental sound-locator designed for the direction of searchlights in fixed positions." This instrument was designed "with the object of securing the greatest possible accuracy of sound location without regard to the restrictions of weight and portability which must necessarily be imposed on a sound-locator intended for use with a mobile unit. The principal new features of the locator and the advantages

Fixed sound locator Biggin Hill 1932. The operator seated at the top of the locator is aligning the bow with a pointer on the sight which is indicating the line of sound produced by the two listeners, thus deriving a line of sight to the target.

which they possess are enumerated below."

"The sound-collectors are paraboloids cast in aluminium, the diameter of the mouth of each paraboloid being 3 feet (91cm)". The acoustical properties of paraboloid collectors are favourable in that "they possess a high degree of directivity which is of advantage in several ways. Firstly, it assists the listener to locate the target, since when the collectors are moved round not only does the 'image' of the sound move right or left, as the case may be, but the loudness of the sound is diminished. Moreover, since the directiveness of the paraboloid is a function of the wave-length of the sound, there is a change in quality of the sound heard when the collectors are moved round. The highest pitched constituents are only heard when the axis of the paraboloid is pointing towards the source."

The superiority of this sound collector over previous types was stressed. "The directional properties of the paraboloids screen off most of the unwanted sounds which often distract the attention of listeners on the Mark III Sound-Locator and similar patterns. These disturbing sounds generally arise from speech or motor traffic."

Further points relating to the new locator were made in a report of 23 January 1930. The fact that the listeners controlled movements of the paraboloids by use of hand wheels made for greater precision in following the sounds, compared with the problem of "rotation of the locator by hand" with the older type of equipment. There was also a reference to the need for protection of crew members in a war situation, mentioning in particular the exposed position of the sight operator, high up on the locator. "Anyone who has occupied the sight operator's seat on the locator will have no difficulty in appreciating what his feelings would be if the station were attacked from the air with light bombs or machine guns." The report stressed the need to 'dig-in' the equipment in such circumstances.

An unsigned copy of a 'secret' memorandum of December 1932 to the Secretary, the Air Ministry, probably from the Air Defence Experimental Establishment, implies that the new non-mobile locator at Biggin Hill was seen as a prototype for the development of mobile sound locators using similar paraboloids and control mechanism.

Major Inglis, Superintendent of the Air Defence Experimental Establishment wrote on the subject to the Secretary of the Royal Engineers Board on 20 February 1930. His memorandum discussed the merits of various sound locators, and he indicated that "the Non-Mobile Locator can be accepted as having reached sufficient finality for the purpose of static defences, and that the next step should be the design of the urgently needed Mobile Locator."

Desirable features were listed including improved sound collectors and "seating accommodation for listeners and sight operator, with hand wheel operation for listeners."

The memorandum suggested lines of development under the headings: "Investigation of Collectors", concerned with the shape and size of trumpet or paraboloid; "Base Length", the distance between the sound collectors, and "Searchlight Control", a system enabling a searchlight to follow the movements of a sound locator by automatic remote control, sometimes abbreviated to 'ARC'. The memorandum ended with the suggestion that future efforts should be devoted to "the design of a Mobile Locator, assuming ARC, 3 ft (91cm) paraboloids, and 7 ft (2.1m) base length. The locator should be mounted on a trailer." Two final points were included in the proposed specification. There should be "no mutual interference between operators" and there should be "quick get away", meaning that the crew should be able to escape quickly if the locator was attacked from the air. This was a real possibility, as by necessity, the locator had to be in an exposed position near the searchlight.

Dr Tucker commented that the design of a mobile locator should not be compromised by the need to fit it on to an existing searchlight trailer. He was obviously in favour of designing a special trailer to carry the sound locator.

By May 1931, the Superintendent of the Air Defence Experimental Establishment was able to write to the Royal Engineers Board with a detailed description of progress in the development of a mobile sound locator.

"A new design of Mobile Sound Locator is now under trial at ADEE Biggin Hill. The purpose of the Sound Locator is to direct the movement of a searchlight beam so that night-flying aircraft can be illuminated with as little delay as possible. In the present series of trials the sound locator is being used in conjunction with a 90 cm projector, the movements of which are directly controlled by one of the personnel, the 'sighting number', on the sound locator. The sound locator consists of two nearly independent parts, namely the listening unit, and the sighting unit. The listening unit

*Mark VIII mobile sound locator equipped for electrical listening via
earphones connected to microphones in the centre of each paraboloidal
sound collector. Note steering wheels for directing the sound collectors
in vertical and horizontal planes.*

works on the binaural principle, and is employed to find the 'line of sound',
that is, the direction in space from which the sound waves generated by the
aircraft arrive at the sound locator. The essential parts are four paraboloidal
sound collectors, 36 inches (91cm) in diameter, two of which are used for
finding the azimuthal bearing of the line of sound, and the other two for
finding its elevation." The term 'azimuth' refers to movements of the sound
locator in a horizontal plane.

"Two listeners are employed, one for finding in azimuth, and the other
for finding in elevation. The sound is led from the sound collectors to the
listener's ears by flexible tubing, ending in stethoscopes. The listeners are

Mark VIII mobile sound locator equipped for acoustic listening. Note sight operator in his central position, and tubing connecting sound collectors to stethoscopes worn by the two listeners.In the background left is the Night Flying hangar at Biggin Hill.

seated, and control the movement of the locators by means of hand wheels. Owing to the relatively slow velocity with which sound travels in air, the line of sound as determined by the listeners is always a line of sight to some past position of the aircraft. The present line of sight can however be found if the course and speed of the aircraft are known. The operation of finding the present line of sight from the observed line of sound is performed by the sighting unit, which is situated near the middle of the sound locator between the U-arm." The 'U-arm' mentioned is the mounting for the trumpets. "The speed of the aircraft must be estimated, but the course is found automatically by the sighting unit. The sighting unit is operated by a sighting number. It is the duty of the sighting number to set the estimated

*Details of sighting mechanism on Mark VIII sound locator. The binocular telescope,
the 'sighting rod' projecting from the centre, and the projection on the 'bow'
known as the 'follower pin' for use in the dark can all be seen in this view.*

speed of the aircraft on a scale on the sight, and thereafter the sight will
itself automatically indicate the line of sight to the target. This is done by
means of a short rod, which projects up from the middle of the sighting
mechanism and always points along the line of sight to the target.

The sighting unit is so constructed that the indicated line of sight is

225

communicated to a telescope, through which the sighting number can look, and also to electrical transmitters, and thence to power control units on the searchlight." Dr Tucker commented on the sighting equipment of the new sound locator.

"A great feature of this new locator is the device whereby if the aeroplane is not immediately located, power of search is aided. Remember that for searchlight operators, listening takes place after dark, and the observer has to define in space the location of his visual pointer. This is done by sense of touch. The pointer, whose position is actuated by the listener, is first corrected for lag of sound. The next process is to convey that position and its motions to the searchlight nearby. This is done by means of a co-ordinator, employing the principle of a rotating magnetic field which, as it rotates, drives round a step by step motor on the searchlight. This rotating field is operated by the observer through the motion of a bow in space, the inside of this bow carrying a stud, which by sense of touch, the operator brings in juxtaposition with the pointer (See p. 220). In this way the searchlight is made to follow the pointer."

There are numerous descriptions of this new type of course finding sight, but although the mechanism was more complicated, the problem to be solved was similar to that facing the operators of a simple Mark III locator, namely, to aim the searchlight at the target aircraft along the 'line of sight', rather than the 'line of sound'

Some of the explanations of the workings of the new course finding sight tend to be confusing, but it is possible to summarize the essential points (See p.225).

The estimated speed of the target was set on the course finding sight by the 'sighting number', army jargon for the member of the crew operating the sight. The 'line of sound' to the target was communicated to the course finding sight through the movements of the trumpets, operated by the hand wheels of two listeners, searching in horizontal and vertical planes.

The course finding sight compensated for time lag, and converted the 'line of sound' to a 'line of sight', indicated by a 'sighting rod' which projected from the sight and pointed at the target.

The binocular telescope was mounted on the' bow' of the locator - a metal arm which could be aligned with the sighting rod. In the dark, a projection on the bow, known as the 'follower pin' was aligned on the sighting rod by sense of touch.

The binocular telescope was a prismatic, right angle device. When it was aligned on the sighting rod, the observer could see along the line of sight to the target. The telescope was connected with the electrical mechanism which caused the searchlight to follow the line of sight, and it also enabled the observer to follow the target once it was illuminated, and to direct the beam in a 'search' around the target area.

The Air Defence Experimental Establishment memorandum of May 1931 ended: "The sound collector is mounted on a four wheeled trailer. The aircraft used as a target was a Hawker Horsley single engined bomber flying on straight courses in the vicinity of Biggin Hill Aerodrome."

A table of results was attached to the memorandum.

"December 12: aircraft at 10,000 ft (3048m), speed 100 mph (161kmph) aircraft illuminated on 8 runs out of 14, visibility 'poor'. December 19: aircraft at 6000 ft (1829m), speed 100 mph, illuminated 9 out of 9, good visibility. December 20: aircraft at 9,500 ft (2896m), speed 100 mph, illuminated 3 out of 3, good visibility."

By February 1932, Major Edwards, Superintendent of the Air Defence Experimental Establishment was occupied with practical details, as shown in a letter he wrote to the Ordnance Officer at Farnborough. "I am building an experimental Sound Locator which is trailed on its own wheels behind the Searchlight Lorry. For this, I will require five covers and tubes size 34 by 7½ (86 by 19cm) low pressure, as fitted to the latest Morris six-wheelers. Can you supply or shall I buy from the trade?"

The Ordnance Officer replied that he had the tyres, but asked under what authority he was to supply them. "Has a money grant been specially allocated for this service?" Major Edwards sent a reply quoting many references and authorities in support of his request for the tyres. There is no reference as to whether or not he got his tyres, but he probably did, as pictures of the Mark VIII sound locator show Morris type wheels and tyres on the trailer. This incident is another illustration of the economic limitations imposed on military research in the 1930s.

The need for a new type of sound locator is highlighted by a remark by Dr Paris, a close colleague of Dr Tucker at the Air Defence Experimental Establishment. In a memorandum of 1 September 1932, he commented that "sound locators of the Mark III and IIIx type require very skilled handling if good results are to be obtained. One of the aims of the new design now being developed is to make things easier for the listeners."

The mobile locator built by Major Edwards was evidently the first of its type, as the Minutes of the Royal Engineers Board for November 1932 contain a reference to "the experimental sound locator" and state that "it was very necessary to construct a second mobile type of sound locator."

Experiments in the summer of 1932, involving sound locators manned by Sappers of the Royal Engineers, and aircraft from Biggin Hill and Kenley, highlighted the problems of predicting the positions of aircraft to enable searchlights and guns to find targets. It is apparent that at that time, automatic searchlight control equipment of the type described by Dr Tucker, had not been fitted to all mobile sound locators. A Royal Engineers Board Minute from 1933 drew attention to the fact that with the increasing speed of high flying aircraft, co-ordination of searchlight and sound locator by telephone was no longer effective, and that "some form of automatic co-ordination is needed, with power control of the searchlight."

The 1st Anti-Aircraft Searchlight Battalion had also carried out experiments at this time, using a Mark VII mobile locator. A report on this work refers to various problems, such as the misting up of the optical parts of the equipment in cold weather, but also states that there was no problem with the trailer.

Late in 1933, the Superintendent of the Air Defence Experimental Establishment was in touch with the Commanding Officer of the 1st Anti-Aircraft Searchlight Battalion on the matter of transport for the mobile sound locator. "I would suggest that you select the lorry that is to tow the new Mark VIII Locator to be issued to you in February" an implication that locators were developed at ADEE, and then tried in the field by the Army. Following this correspondence, two Guy Medium Six-Wheeled Searchlight Lorries were sent to the Air Defence Experimental Establishment to be adapted to haul the locator.

A mobile locator mounted on its trailer was a fairly heavy piece of equipment. Weights and dimensions are given in a memorandum from ADEE to the Royal Engineers Board dated 2 February 1934. "Mark VII, Load on front axle 2500 lbs(1134kg); load on rear axle 2850 lbs (1293kg) ; wheelbase 120 inches (3m); track 68 inches (1.7m); overall width 81 inches (2.1m); Mark VIII front axle loading 2550 lbs (1157kg); rear axle loading 3000 lbs (1361kg). Wheelbase, track and width as for Mark VII."

There are references to various Mark numbers in contemporary documents, but it seems that Marks VII, VIII and IX were the main types of mobile sound locator, and that they were basically similar, with differences in details of ancillary equipment. The later Marks were equipped with a better course finding sight, and the construction was generally more robust, to meet service conditions. Despite the development of mobile locators, Dr Tucker commented in March 1935 that "the Mark IIIx Sound Locator is now in general use. It will gradually be replaced by Marks VII or VIII." He anticipated that "Marks VIII and IX will be incorporated into the Service; Mark VIII, which is fully mobile, for the regular forces, and Mark IX, semi-mobile, for the territorial forces." Good photographs exist of a Mark VIII mobile locator on its trailer. Other photographs, taken in the field, but with no captions, show another variant, fitted with electrical equipment, and with four paraboloids arranged in a diamond pattern, mounted on a flat base with no apparent travelling wheels. Sketches of this type of equipment in a Handbook of 1940 are captioned "Locator, Fixed, Mark I."

The transport of the newer type of sound locators was a continuing concern. Many documents of the time refer to 'fully mobile' and 'semi-mobile' locators. Various trailers for carrying 'semi-mobile' locators were tested in this period. An Air Defence Experimental Establishment blueprint of 10 January 1936 shows a three wheeled trailer. In the plan view, an outline of the sound locator is superimposed. It has a round base, and four 'feet' mounted on outriggers. The elevation view shows that the method of operation was to jack up the sound locator, thus transferring the weight to the 'feet', and then wheel out the trailer.

Another type of trailer was tested which had four wheels. The sound locator base formed the trailer body, and by jacking up the locator on to its 'feet', it was possible to remove the road wheels from the axles. This must have been a typical method of transporting the 'Locator, Fixed, Mark I', which appears without wheels in photographs of the period.

Sound locator hitched-up and ready to move.
Note legend by driver's door:
"Air Def. Exp. Est
MAX SPEED 20 M.P.H."

A letter from Colonel C.E.Colbeck, President of the Royal Engineers Board to the Superintendent, Air Defence Experimental Establishment on 22 September 1936, helps to clarify the difference between fully mobile and semi-mobile sound locators. It was largely a matter of cost in that semi-mobile equipment involved a cheaper and less sophisticated trailer. Colonel Colbeck confirmed that the fully mobile sound locator, for example the Mark VIII, was intended for use by Regular Army units, and that Territorial units would be equipped with semi-mobile equipment. He wrote that the "so called semi-mobile trailer was not intended for such fast work on roads or as much use across country as the more mobile types."

One of the problems which gave rise to considerable correspondence was the noise made by the engines of the lorries and generating sets used to power searchlights. This interfered with the work of listeners at the sound locators. Dr Paris reported on 18 April 1935 that "the noise produced by the existing Guy lorry interfered seriously with the working of the Sound Locator even at a distance of 300 yards (274m)."

The Royal Engineer's Board minutes of 24 March 1935 mention the silencing of the engines of searchlight lorries. According to one statement, generator engine noise was a new problem, because aircraft were getting quieter! A report of 11 June 1935 stated that there was an improvement of 3 - 4 decibels when the chain drive to a generator was changed to belt drive using grooved pulleys. On 15 July 1935 a report on the testing of a new lorry, concluded that there was "very little to choose between the old and the new lorry." On 29 July, it was reported that further modifications would result in an improvement of 8 decibels; the ultimate aim was an improvement of 15 decibels.

In August 1935, Dr Paris concluded that a Lister generator was better than any modified Guy lorry. A Tilling-Stevens chassis gave 10 - 15 decibels less noise than the Guy tested at Brasted on 25 March 1935, which was the starting point for these tests. A report of 24 September 1935 mentioned that 6 and 8 cylinder engines were quieter than 4 cylinder types, and also that in civilian lorries, noise was not important!

After various other tests with Tilling-Stevens, Guy, and Lister engines, a report of 13 May 1937 confirmed that the Dennis lorry was the quietest searchlight vehicle tested up to that point, but on 21 May, another type of Guy lorry was tested which proved to be even quieter. A summary of the various tests of engines used in generating for searchlights concluded that a level of 40 - 45 decibels was "good, but there was room for further improvement". A level of 50-55 decibels would be a nuisance on a quiet night, and 55 decibels and over was "noisy", and every effort should be made to reduce such levels.

These comments about the problem of generator noise at searchlight sites are related to a more general point. Interference by unwanted sound was one of the greatest problems in all acoustic detection systems. Despite such successful devices as Dr Tucker's microphones, tuned to respond to particular aircraft engine notes, the work of listeners became more difficult, due to the inevitable and ever increasing noise in the environment.

CHAPTER TWENTY-TWO

SOUND LOCATOR DEVELOPMENTS

On 16 September 1935, Dr Tucker wrote to the Superintendent of the Air Defence Experimental Establishment about the training of sound locator personnel. "With reference to the trials of the Mark IX Sound Locator at Biggin Hill, the date of delivery appears to be October 12th. Subsequent to this, staff will be available at Biggin Hill for instruction immediately delivery of the Locator has been assured."

The Commanding Officer of the School of Electric Lights, Gosport, advised the ADEE at Biggin Hill on 19 September of personnel detailed for training. "A detachment consisting of 1 officer and 8 men will arrive at ADEE on 29 September 1935 for training on the Mk IX Sound Locator for a period up to October 8th as considered necessary by you."

During the inter-war years, particularly in the 1930s, acoustic activities involved a mixture of service and civilian personnel. Some, like Dr Tucker, who became Major Tucker from time to time, were occasionally addressed by their former military ranks. Documentary evidence shows that much of the research work and operation of acoustic equipment was in the hands of civilian scientists and technicians.

The training of service personnel in the use of sound locators, undertaken at Biggin Hill in 1935 by civilian experts from Dr Tucker's team such as Dr Paris and Messrs Rothwell and Ferguson, was in line with similar activities at the sound mirror sites, reflecting the increasing contribution of science to warfare. A few years later, university academics, including some from the acoustic field, were to play a vital role in the development of radar.

By the end of 1935, successes in the development of radar, or RDF as it was known at that time, began to have an effect on experimental work with existing forms of early warning, including sound locators. A. P. Rowe, a Civil Servant at the Air Ministry, wrote to Dr Tucker on the subject on 26 November 1935, mentioning in his letter 'Mr Tizard'. H. T. Tizard, (later Sir Henry) a scientist and ultimately Rector of Imperial College, was Chairman of the Committee for the Scientific Survey of Air Defence, largely responsible for the development of British radar.

"Air Ministry, Adastral House, Kingsway, WC2 26 November 1935

SECRET AND PERSONAL

Dear Tucker,
You will remember that when we saw Mr Tizard at the Imperial College on 21 November, it was agreed that I should write a note on Sound Locator Experiments for your approval. I enclose the note herewith. It is intended only to define what has been done; this is really an operational question. If the Committee agrees, the next step will be to approach you officially. Would you kindly telephone me tomorrow and let me know whether you have any objection to the enclosed document being circulated to members of the Tizard Committee.

Yours sincerely,
A.P.Rowe."

Rowe's note reveals that the Committee was concerned at that time with the need to protect a gap in the coverage offered by the early radar stations. A characteristic feature of these stations was that before the development of rotating aerials offering 360 degree coverage, the fixed aerials, mounted on towers, could only radiate beams of radio energy outwards towards the sea. These stations could thus detect aircraft approaching the coast, but the problem was to find some means of tracking aircraft flying inland behind the coastal radar chain.

"Committee for the Scientific Survey of Air Defence, Means for Determining the movements of Enemy Aircraft.

It is conceivable that RDF will enable interception to be effected before or when the coast is reached. Means must be developed for recording the movements of enemy aircraft over the land and for transmitting the data to Headquarters."

The note explained that during daylight, aircraft movements could be plotted by the Observer Corps, using visual methods. But at night "the only means for tracking obscured aircraft over the land, likely to be available within two years, is sound location. Mr Tizard has suggested that tests should be made to determine with what accuracy aircraft can be tracked with Sound Locators and with what rapidity the data can be transmitted to Headquarters."

Various tests for Sound Locators were outlined, and the Air Defence Experimental Establishment was asked to co-operate in trials. The ending of the note expressed some doubt on the part of the Committee as to the outcome of these suggestions. "It is possible that the proposed experiments will show that it is impracticable, under war conditions, to effect interception by transmitting to Headquarters data obtained only by sound location."

Dr Tucker suggested equipping Observer Corps posts with simple sound locators, and a memorandum of 21 February 1936 includes a sketch of the proposed locator, showing a device with four paraboloids, arranged in a similar manner to those on a Mark VIII mobile locator. From the lack of any other documentary evidence, it seems unlikely that this proposal was carried out.

Mark VIII and IX type sound locators were generally used to assist the direction of searchlights, using automatic remote control of the light from the locator. However, a report from the Air Defence Experimental Establishment Biggin Hill on 27 July 1936 headed "Sound Control of Anti-Aircraft Fire" demonstrates that experiments were also carried out to test the use of a sound locator electrically connected to "a 3 inch (76mm) 20 cwt (1016kg), semi-mobile Anti-Aircraft gun."

For these experiments, sound locators were sighted at Westerham and Brasted in Kent, and a device known as a 'Kiné Theodolite' was used during the tests. From contemporary documents, it appears that the 'Kiné Theodolite' was a type of cine-camera, used for filming targets, with the purpose of evaluating the efficiency of sound locator operators.

The report stated that "all the equipment for fire control was mounted on the sound locator trailer. As this included high speed remote control motors and a large amount of mechanism, great trouble had to be taken over silencing to avoid disturbing the listeners." A conclusion from this was that if such equipment was approved for general service use, a separate trailer would be needed for the fire control gear. A series of charts showing the aircraft tracks plotted during these experiments was included with the report.

One section of this report includes a remarkable statement. "Air co-operation was provided by 23 Squadron, RAF. Biggin Hill, who performed well in difficult circumstances, as the Squadron comprised one officer, one Hawker Demon aeroplane, and no wireless equipment. Communication between ground and Aircraft had to be carried out with ground strips." It seems extraordinary that, even given the financial constraints of the period, an RAF Squadron in 1936 could be reduced to single figures in terms of men and machines.

Experiments with another type of sound locator were carried out in the 1930's. Dr Paris of the Air Defence Experimental Establishment described what seems to have been a portable sound mirror in a report dating from 22 April 1936. "Enough information has been obtained to indicate that the proposed portable bowl should be of paraboloidal form and 10 feet (3m) in diameter. A paraboloid of this size should have approximately the same range of detection as a 30 foot (9.1m) sound mirror when the aircraft is on the axis in both cases. The focal length of the proposed paraboloid is to be 1 foot (30cm)".

Dr Paris suggested that "the mobile sound mirror should have electrical listening from the outset." He also pointed out that experiments with this type of portable mirror could have implications for the development of mobile locators such as the Marks VIII and IX. "The experimental work on the acoustical properties of paraboloids which has been proceeding in connection with the design of the mobile mirror, should continue, so as to clear up the whole question of the acoustical magnification of paraboloids, and the optimum values for focal lengths and aperture, so that in the future, data will be available for specifying the alterations in shape or size necessary to meet any changed requirement. The results of these investigations would be applicable to the mobile mirror and to improvements in the paraboloidal sound collectors used in the Mark VIII and IX Sound Locators."

Tenders for this type of equipment were placed by 27 May 1936. Messrs J. Stone quoted £193. Another firm quoted £200, and £80 for the associated trailer. On 13 August 1936, Major R G Lamb of the Air Defence Experimental Establishment complained that the trailer promised for 1 April had not been delivered. On 21 April 1937, Major Lamb reported that as the trials at ADEE had not started, he could not recommend sending the equipment "to the Battalion." Tests were planned at Hythe, starting "next week, and being concluded by the end of June." It was proposed to take the equipment back to Biggin Hill on the night of 23/24 June. The police in Ashford, Kent, were to be consulted. It appears that the locator was to be taken on from Biggin Hill to another site, possibly to the 1st Anti-Aircraft Battalion at Blackdown, Dorset, as the correspondence states that it would travel at 4.0 a.m. on 25 June and be "through Dorking before traffic becomes heavy."

A slightly embarrassing question was put to the Superintendent, Air Defence Experimental Establishment by Colonel Colbeck, President of the Royal Engineers Board on 4 September 1937. "As a matter of interest, if in theory the 10 foot (3m) portable paraboloid should be only slightly inferior in range to the 30 foot bowl, why are we bothering with the fixed 30 foot mirror?" Dr Tucker replied on 13 September 1937. He pointed out that the 10 ft mirror suffered a loss of efficiency because of its metal construction which was not as good as concrete; also, the listener at a 10 ft (3m) mirror was not as protected as the listener in the underground chamber of a 30 ft (9m) mirror. The work of a listener at the 10 ft (3m) mirror was heavier, involving moving the whole bowl when searching.

A report on tests of the 10 ft locator by Lieutenant Colonel M. Luby, RE,

Commanding Officer of the 1st Anti-Aircraft Battalion, RE, Blackdown, on 25 January 1938 suggests that it was not a particularly successful piece of equipment. He described the device as "only semi-mobile", and in perform-ance, although it gave "early warning of an approaching raid," it was "unreliable in direction." In the event, the 10 foot (3m) locator proved to be a mere distraction from the main line of mobile sound locator development. More important work was soon in progress on the Essex coast.

CHAPTER TWENTY-THREE

TESTING THE MARK VIII

A seaside pier, familiar to many London holidaymakers, was the unusual setting for further mobile sound locator tests. In the summer of 1936, Colonel Colbeck, President of the Royal Engineers Board wrote to the Superintendent of the Air Defence Experimental Establishment, suggesting arrangements for the 28th Anti-Aircraft Battalion to try out a Mark VIII or IX Locator. The proposed venue for the tests was Southend Pier (Map 1 - p.23).

Dr Paris wrote to the ADEE on 30 June outlining a few practical problems. "We can be ready for these trials by August 1st, but think that August Bank Holiday weekend should be avoided because of the crowds likely to collect at Southend. We suggest therefore, that 28th Battalion be notified that we shall be ready to carry out trials any time after August 7th. Captain Young will be in charge."

Major D. Tritton, on behalf of the Commanding Officer of the 28th AA Battalion reported back to the Superintendent ADEE in July:

"The Borough of Southend-on-Sea will only allow a 90 cm projector and a Mk III sound locator to be used on Southend Pier Head between 22.00 hrs and 08.00 hrs 19 to 30 July 1936. The equipment must then be removed to allow for preparations for the town illuminations. The siting of the light will not be ideal in that the sound locator will be within 20 yds (18m) of it. By day, the light and sound locator have to be removed to one side of the upper deck. Until suitable positions have been constructed on the pier, it will not be possible during the summer season to erect a Mark VIII locator and light. The proposed positions to be provided are above the Upper Lounge Deck, and above the Sun Lounge Tea Room. It may be possible to obtain permission of the Borough of Southend-on-Sea to erect a Mark VIII locator and light on the main deck of the pier in the off season i.e. October to May, but this is doubtful as the Corporation requires all available space for steamer passengers and visitors."

Aircraft for the experiments were to be provided by RAF Hornchurch, Essex.

On 7 July 1936, the Superintendent of the Air Defence Experimental Establishment reported the unsatisfactory state of negotiations with the Corporation of Southend. As the 28th Anti-Aircraft Battalion was not able to operate with a Mark VIII sound locator on Southend Pier until October at the earliest, he proposed testing that particular piece of equipment at Hythe.

The unhelpful attitude of the Corporation was not unique. For example, the General Post Office had also from time to time given fairly low priority to the acoustic researchers, particularly in the matter of allocating telephone lines during holiday periods. Looking back with the benefit of hindsight, it seems that people trying to develop an acoustic defence system to protect the country against hostile aircraft were constantly in difficulties, working to a very tight budget, and enjoying little co-operation from others. They certainly had the quality of perseverance.

The Mark VIII and Mark IX Locators could be operated not only as purely acoustic detectors, with tubes connecting the sound collectors to the ears of the listeners, but could also be fitted with microphones which were mounted in the base of the paraboloids. A reference to the two systems occurs in correspondence by Colonel Colbeck, President of the Royal Engineers Board, dating from 1936 (See photos on pages 223 & 224).

"We hope that the electrical sound locator, Army pattern with microphones in Mark VIII or IX paraboloid sound locators, may be in the extended troop trial stage before long. The electrics can be fitted to a Mark

VIII or Mark IX Sound Locator after removing the ordinary stethoscopes and tubes. The particular advantage of this electrical pattern is in cases where listeners on stethoscopes would require protection from the effect of gunfire in their proximity."

Sound Locators were again the subject of a letter from the President of the Royal Engineers Board to the Superintendent of the Air Defence Experimental Establishment on 15 July 1936. "In a discussion at the War Office today, I was asked whether with our paraboloidal sound locators we could pick up the latest fast aircraft, and if so, with what degree of accuracy we could determine their position in space. I said that I considered it was quite possible to use our sound locators on lines similar to those employed for sound control of Anti-Aircraft fire, and if required give a prediction as to when an aircraft target would cross a given line." He suggested using "the two Mark IX locators" from a Sound Control, Anti-Aircraft Fire unit, and proposed basing the trials at Sheringham, Norfolk; Biggin Hill, Kent; and Culver, Devon.

A memorandum from No. 48 Squadron on 14 August 1936 made reference to night flying by an Anson aircraft from Biggin Hill. This demonstrates that a more modern type of aircraft was coming into use at that time for testing the sound locators. The Anson was a twin engined monoplane which, although by later standards was not an advanced aircraft, it was at least not as obsolete as biplanes or machines such as the Heyford bomber used in previous tests.

Major Lamb, Superintendent of the Air Defence Experimental Establishment reported to the Royal Engineers Board on 4 September 1936 that "the first trials with the Anson and the Electrical Locator were promising, but owing to defects in the course finding sight, the results were not definite, in that the target was not located by searchlight with the consistency which we expect when using a modern locator." Some of these experiments made use of an earlier type of locator, but Major Lamb assured the Board that a Mark VIII locator, fully equipped for electrical listening, would be used in further trials.

A reversion to the use of biplanes occurred in tests carried out in the Biggin Hill area in September 1936. Two locators were used, sited at Titsey and Brasted, and three Gloster Gauntlet Aircraft from Number 32 Squadron co-operated in the tests. These and other experiments with sound locators were discussed in a meeting at the Air Defence Experimental Establishment in September of 1936. Some very important people were present at that meeting. The list included "Mr Wimperis" and "Mr Tizard."

As mentioned previously, H. T. Tizard (later Sir Henry) was Chairman of the Committee for the Scientific Survey of Air Defence, of which H. E. Wimperis was a member. Indeed, Wimperis, Director of Scientific Research at the Air Ministry, with his concerns about impending war and deficiencies in the air defence system, pressed for the setting up of the committee in 1934.

Reference has already been made to the crucial role played by Tizard's Committee in the development of radar in the late 1930s. Chairman Henry Tizard's experience dated back to the First World War, when in 1915, as a pilot in the Royal Flying Corps and scientist, he was a member of the Armament Experimental Squadron at Upavon, Wiltshire, later moving to Orfordness and Martlesham Heath in Suffolk.

Dr Tucker wrote to Tizard in October 1936 to inform him that "we have located an Anson bomber flying at 20,000 feet (6096m) and the test of the accuracy is that it has been illuminated by a searchlight every time in a series of eight or more raids."

There were irritating problems with mobile sound locators in field use. Some of these were brought to the attention of the Air Defence Experimental Establishment in a report from the 1st Anti-Aircraft Battalion Royal Engineers, dated 11 September 1936, describing tests of Mark VII and Mark IX sound locators. "Both types were used throughout the Sussex Exercise. The Mark VII was only used once as an Automatic Remote Control set, being subsequently out of action." There were also transport difficulties. The so-called 'semi-mobile' trailer had limited stowage space, and as a result, two of the paraboloids and some of the ancillary equipment had to be carried on the towing lorry. This point was mentioned in the report under the heading "Trailers." "The Mark VII is too heavy for the Crossley Lorry to tow. The Mark IX is too short, two trumpets have to be carried on the lorry which is a serious inconvenience. The mudguards have to be removed for action, and even then, the sound locator has to be elevated to 30 degrees to clear the wheels."

Another report from 1st Anti-Aircraft Battalion, included various complaints, such as "noise from gearing," and the fact that the pipes which conveyed sounds from the trumpets to the ears of the listener, and which were fastened to the sound locator at various points, had "worked loose."

One can sense the annoyance of a scientist dealing with careless troops in Dr Tucker's rather terse reply to these points. In relation to the sound pipes he wrote: "this is entirely due to rough use and lack of intelligence. The sound tubes are held on by metal clips with felt linings. They are quite firm in position and never work loose. Apparently the felt linings are pulled out, and no other attempt is made to hold the tube in position. It is left to rub about in the clip, and of course, noise results. We have had no trouble with these felt packings in cases where they have been in position for seven years." In relation to noises from the gearing, he remarked: "it is perfectly all right when used normally. Any train of gears must make a noise if the locator is moved in a wild and erratic manner."

The Acoustic Research Station on the hills to the west of Hythe overlooks a stretch of the Kent coast which became the scene of experiments with a mobile sound locator for a brief period in 1936. The Air Defence Experimental Establishment produced a report on this work, headed "Siting of Sound Locators at the Coast."

"The object of the trials was to determine the effect of sea noise on the range and efficiency of the service sound locator, and to deduce the minimum distance from the coast at which it can be sited without loss of efficiency. The trials were carried out at Hythe from October 15 to 17, 1936. The sound locator used was the Artillery Locator No 2, Mk IX type. It was sited at the Dymchurch Redoubt, where it could be operated on the sea wall in full view of the breaking waves, or in the shelter of the sea wall, about 15 ft high. (4.6m) The locator was manned by Air Defence Experimental Establishment personnel." (Map 1 - p.23)

The aircraft used in the tests were from No. 25 Squadron, based at Hawkinge airfield near Folkestone. Charts showing details of such matters as the levels of background noise measured in phons[1] were included in the report. For example: "15 October: on sea wall 56 phons, behind sea wall 36 phons."

These tests gave rise to several conclusions. The effect of noises from the sea was to reduce the range of the locator, but not its accuracy, and the resolving power of the paraboloidal trumpets did not assist in eliminating sea noise. With an off shore wind, the noise was found to have a high-pitched character, and therefore any reasonably sized obstacle such as a sea wall gave almost complete shielding. With a prevailing offshore wind, the locator could be sited about 70 yds (64m) away from the water's edge without loss of efficiency if a direct view of the breaking waves was avoided. With a wind off the sea causing the waves to pound on the beach, the character of the sea noise was very different, and the locator would "require more careful siting."

Shortly after these trials at Dymchurch, the Army Director of Mechanization, Lieutenant-Colonel Loch, and Colonel Colbeck, Royal Engineer and Signals Board, visited Orfordness and Bawdsey on 14 December 1936. After seeing something of the radar work in progress at those establishments, they included a query in their report. "Is it worthwhile putting the utmost possible effort into producing apparatus for the control of Anti-Aircraft gun fire, in view of the importance of being able to bring effective fire to bear on targets not visible from the ground? If so, additional research and technical development staff must be provided by the Army for the purpose as soon as possible. It is possible that complete success might eventually eliminate the necessity for anti-aircraft searchlights."

Following discussions on 18 December, the Director of Mechanization, the Director of Staff Duties, and the Director of Military Operations and Intelligence, urged the development of means "to engage the unseen target by anti-aircraft fire", and proposed a review of "the need for two large sound mirrors, already approved for Singapore defences which had not yet been built." The mirrors were in fact cancelled as a result of radar progress.

In March 1937, Mr H.S.Young, one of the War Department Scientific Officers in the Army Cell at Bawdsey, submitted a paper on the application of 'Cuckoo', a code word for radar, to anti-aircraft gunnery. He also put forward a proposal for combining radar with the Mark IX Sound Locator for anti-aircraft fire control, employing "radar range and acoustic angular measurements of bearing and elevation, all to be read continuously."

Despite these advanced ideas, stethoscopes were still used in 1937 by the operators of sound locators, although considerable efforts were made to move towards electrical methods of listening. The acoustic method had one advantage in that it was not subject to problems caused by weather conditions, whereas electrical equipment was more vulnerable in the field. A memorandum from the Air Defence Experimental Establishment of 26 April 1937 includes references to this subject in relation to the "Electrical Mark VIII Sound Locator."

"Instead of using flexible rubber tubes and stethoscopes, microphones are now fitted at the focus of the trumpets, and the electrical impulses produced are amplified by valve amplifiers. The listener now wears headphones which are connected by flex to the amplifiers. Each trumpet requires a microphone and each microphone a separate amplifier. Thus there are four amplifiers." The microphones were mounted in rubber to protect them from vibration, and provision was made for a quick reversion to stethoscope listening, for example in wet weather, when microphones might be damaged.

This type of equipment was in use by 1937. According to a report dated 30 April, a mobile sound locator, complete with microphones and electrical control equipment for use with a 90 cm searchlight, was collected from the Air Defence Experimental Establishment by the 1st Anti-Aircraft Battalion and towed to Blackdown in Dorset for trials. The President of the Royal Engineers Board outlined a programme of trials at Blackdown from August 3rd to September 7th 1937. He listed some of the matters to be covered. There was a need to "confirm or refute the disadvantage of telephone headset listening as compared with stethoscopes tubes, owing to the former admitting more background noise to the ear direct. The great advantage of electrical listening is the elimination of serious damage to listener's ear drums from gunfire or bombs etc near the locator." There was also a proposal to try out various methods of signalling between locator and searchlight in the event of a breakdown of the automatic system of searchlight control.

In March 1926, well before mobile sound locators came on the scene, Dr Paris, a colleague of Dr Tucker put in a patent application for "Sound Location with the aid of a Cathode Ray Oscillograph." He proposed to use the oscillograph for experiments in various areas, such as the analysis of aeroplane sounds in flight, the recording of propeller and exhaust sounds, the design of electrical sound locators, and meteorological acoustics. Experiments were carried out in 1929, and the idea of applying the oscillograph to sound locators was to assume considerable importance in the period leading to the Second World War.

A relevant letter, from the President of the Royal Engineers Board to Dr Tucker in January 1938, contains an early reference to a development of the mobile sound locator described as "Visual Indication of Sound." This was a method of providing a visual picture of the sounds detected by a locator. The signals from microphones mounted in the four trumpet collectors were amplified and led to a cathode ray oscillograph which provided the operator with a visual display of the sounds received.

Another matter of concern in January 1938 was the effect of gun blast on the ears of sound locator listeners. Major Lamb, Superintendent Air Defence Experimental Establishment, raised the matter with the Chief Superintendent of the Research Department at Woolwich Arsenal, and tests were carried out using guns in the forts of the Portsmouth defences. Major Lamb sent a report on the tests to the Royal Engineers Board on 27 January 1938. Blast pressure zones near the guns were classified in such terms as "the 7 lbs zone." The tests indicated that Sound Locator personnel should not be subjected to blast in the "7 lbs zone", but that the searchlight used in the tests, which was fitted with armoured glass, survived well in that blast zone. After the trials, it was suggested that the paraboloid trumpets on sound locators magnified the problem of noise for listeners, and that it was advisable to avoid directing the trumpets towards the mouths of the guns. This seems only common sense. People involved with guns are known to be afflicted with deafness in later years, a problem that would be greatly magnified for a listener at a sound locator in the immediate vicinity of a heavy gun.

A suggestion put forward in a memorandum of 28 April 1938 did not meet with much success, probably due to the tense international situation at the time. Abbreviations at the head of this memorandum make it difficult to decide who wrote it, and to whom it was addressed, but it was obviously from someone involved with sound locators.

"It is desired to exhibit a Sound Locator Mark VIII, Projector Mark V, and Generating Set 22KV Lister, on the Territorial Army Stand at Olympia for the Royal Tournament. We understand that it is possible to 'disguise' the course and speed sight and still be able to move the projector from the sound locator. We are therefore arranging for one Sound Locator to be sent to ADEE to have the necessary work done on it." There is no follow-up to this request in the associated documents, but it seems likely that the army would not be too keen to put a recently developed sound locator on public view, in particular the sighting equipment which was the heart of the system.

The Director of Scientific Research, Air Ministry, visited the Air Defence Experimental Establishment in the summer of 1938. Dr Tucker prepared some briefing notes for him, which included a general statement of the current position in relation to sound locators. It is evident that despite the introduction of new locators, many early types were still in use. Under the heading "Devices for Directional Listening" there is a statement that the Mark IIIx Sound Locator, "produced in 1923 is the present predominant equipment". The new locators mentioned were the "Mark VIII Paraboloid Locator with Automatic Course Finding Sight, co-ordinated with searchlight, and trailer mounted," and the "Mark IX, a Mark VIII with a more robust automatic course finding sight." Dr Tucker referred to the "greater sensitivity and accuracy" of the electrically equipped Mark VIII.

By the beginning of 1939, the Electrical Industry was co-operating with the Air Defence Experimental Establishment in fitting electrical equipment to Mark IX Sound Locators, including visual indicators.

A letter from EMI (Electric and Musical Industries) to ADEE on 9 March 1939 confirmed that the first Mark IX conversion was ready for inspection on "13th instant before this equipment is delivered to Biggin Hill." A reply on 14 March from "W.S.Tucker, Director of Research, Air Defence Experimental Establishment" confirmed that "Mr Friend and possibly Captain Bradshaw will be at your works at 11 o'clock tomorrow, March 15 for a preliminary inspection of the equipment before delivery is made to Biggin Hill."

Included in contemporary papers is a carbon copy of an "Inspection Note" from EMI (Electric and Musical Industries) which describes the work done by the firm: "One locator, Sound, Mark IX; Supply and fitting of Electrical Equipment for combined aural and visual observation." The cost quoted was £642.

The new equipment was not entirely satisfactory, and in May, Major W.H.G. Costelloe, Royal Engineers, Superintendent, Air Defence Experimental Establishment, Biggin Hill, complained about modifications which had become necessary in the equipment supplied by EMI. He suggested the Company should replace the equipment. "The elevation and bearing movements are noisy and detract from the performance of the locator whether used electrically or with stethoscopes."

A continuing problem for sound locator operators was the need to practise listening for aircraft sounds. It was not always possible to provide target aircraft, and various experiments were carried out in this area, in particular to find ways of training new listeners when no aircraft were available. Early in 1939, a commercial company produced a type of simulator for use in such places as Territorial Army Drill Halls. The device was box shaped, rather like a large refrigerator in appearance. Compartments at each side contained gramophone turntables, and the pupil sat facing one side of the machine, with the instructor seated opposite him on the other side. Both wore headsets plugged into the machine. The two turntables made it possible to play recordings of aircraft sounds which moved from side to side, enabling the listener to practise binaural skills. Unwanted sounds could also be fed into the system to create a more realistic effect. The instructor had control of the various parameters of the machine, and a printed record was produced of the pupil's efforts.

Another method of training was carried out at the airship base at Cardington in 1939, where a source of sound was carried by a tethered balloon, and the pupil listeners were seated on several sound locators in the area around and below the balloon.

It is clear from many reports of the period that aural methods of listening required much practice, and that the skills involved were not easily acquired. Some of the scientists in charge of research began to realize that in time of war, it might not be possible to train enough listeners to a satisfactory level of performance, and experiments were carried out in the late 1930s to find easier methods of operating sound locators which did not depend entirely on listening skills.

[1]Phons - A phon is a measure of the perceived loudness of a sound that corrects for the vibration sensitivity of the human ear by frequency.

CHAPTER TWENTY-FOUR

SOUND AND VISION

A sound locator listener, wearing his uncomfortable stethoscope or earphones required considerable powers of patience and concentration. The introduction of visual display equipment was a step towards improving the lot of such a crew member and enhancing the performance of the locator. Microphones, tuned to receive sounds in the wavelengths particular to aircraft engines, were mounted in the bases of the paraboloidal trumpets of a sound locator. The responses of the microphones were conveyed as electrical signals to a cathode ray oscillograph, where they were displayed as visual traces on a screen in front of the operator.

The Air Defence Experimental Establishment produced a relevant memorandum on 11 August 1939 marked 'SECRET', headed "Mark IX Sound Locator Equipped for Visual Following" "The application of the cathode ray oscillograph, to provide a visual equivalent to binauralling, has been developed by EMI (Electric and Musical Industries) and applied to Mark IX Locators. The visual method can at present deal effectively with average listening conditions, and that with a high degree of accuracy after a very short period of practice. Men often acquire great skill in their first lesson. It is possible to follow aircraft entirely by the visual trace on the cathode ray tube with greater accuracy than that obtainable by the ordinary method of binauralling provided that the background for listening is not excessive. With a high background, aural methods will probably have to be resorted to. It is probable that aural methods will have to be retained for noisy sites. The range of pick-up is better than with aural methods, and a beam can be exposed on a target at a lower angle of elevation."

The memorandum includes a technical description of the operation of a Mark IX sound locator with visual display equipment. "If the azimuth (horizontal bearing) paraboloids are turned so that they are 4 degrees off the direction of a sound which contains components throughout the band 250 - 1000 cycles per second, corresponding to wave lengths of about 4'6" to 1'2" (130cm to 36cm) , there is a phase difference of 180 degrees at the microphones for a frequency of 1000 cycles per second. This results in a horizontal cathode ray trace at that frequency."

A further point relating to the checking of a listener's performance was also mentioned in the secret memorandum. It was pointed out that "a locator fitted with the oscillograph gear would provide a convenient and otherwise unobtainable method of checking the performance of each listener. In such a case, the oscillograph would be under the observation of instructors only, the listeners listening in the usual way."

Visual display screens were also fitted to the 'Locator, Fixed, Mark I' already described, and the equipment can be seen in photographs of these locators dating from 1940, and in drawings in a 1940 handbook.

Under a sub-heading 'Following', the advantage of this type of equipment in tracking a target was described as "remarkably steady and very accurate. The steady following not only has its advantage on a Mark IX Sound Locator, but it would be an obvious advantage for Locators working in conjunction with RDF apparatus."

RDF was the term used to describe British radar in the early days. Various suggestions have been made as to the meaning of these initials, including 'Radio Direction Finding' and 'Range and Direction Finding'. Whatever the case, the title acted as a disguise, suggesting to possible enemies that radar was merely a branch of old fashioned radio direction finding, where bearings were obtained from broadcast radio signals.

Looking back with hindsight, there is certain irony in the fact that by the time these experiments in visual display on sound locators were taking place, cathode ray screens were already providing the essential visual displays at radar stations.

High ranking officers in the air defence system visited Biggin Hill (Map 1 - p.23) on 25 August 1939 to see a Mark IX Sound Locator with visual indication. These people included General Pile, the Officer in Command of Anti-Aircraft Defences, and Major-General Newton. As a result of their visit, an order was placed for the building of 6 pilot sets of equipment to be fitted to Mark IX Locators, followed by a proposal to build 1500 to 2000 production sets. EMI was asked to produce a good handbook "for use in the field."

Dr Tucker continued his efforts to avoid damage to sound locators when they were used in the field by unskilled troops. Some of them did not seem to understand that metal polish and emery paper were not suitable for use with delicate components.

For example, he sent out instructions from the Air Defence Experimental Establishment Biggin Hill on "Maintenance of Mark VIII Locators."

"The trouble would appear to be caused by unnecessary cleaning with metal polish. These commutators should not be oiled as they are stainless and do not rust. Cleaning with a dry rag is all that is required. The Line of Sight Pointer and the Commutator are of stainless steel and should never be oiled or cleaned with metal polish. They can always be cleaned with a dry rag. The clock springs should be kept oiled. The bevels should be kept lightly oiled. No part should ever be touched by emery paper."

Familiar names from the acoustic story at Biggin Hill and Hythe appear in reports from September 1939, when Robert Ferguson, one of Dr Tucker's colleagues is described as a liaison officer from the Air Defence Experimental Establishment, working with EMI on sound locator equipment. Both Robert Ferguson and Percy Rothwell are mentioned in documents dating from March and April 1940.

A memorandum about Ferguson's work at EMI from the Superintendent, Air Defence Experimental Establishment on 14 September 1939 contains the remark "as long as we are at Biggin Hill", suggesting that the eventual move of the ADEE to a new base was contemplated at that time. A report dealing with a conference at the EMI Works, Hayes, Chairman Dr W.S.Tucker, is headed "Air Defence Experimental Establishment, Bure Homage, Somerford, Christchurch, Hants" instead of the usual address at Biggin Hill. This is a preliminary hint of the eventual change of venue by the Air Defence Experimental Establishment. However, this did not happen at once, and a later memorandum of 14 October 1939 is still headed "ADEE Biggin Hill".

Mounting microphones in the bases of sound locator trumpets posed problems in field use, as the microphones were rather difficult to remove for servicing and repair, or for changing over to acoustical listening. Also, the fronts of the microphones were facing directly into the weather. In September 1939, Dr Tucker suggested mounting the microphones "facing the paraboloid, for ease of replacement when changing over from acoustic to electrical listening." This involved removing the microphone and fitting a "bell mouth" in the paraboloid. The report mentions that experiments had shown that a microphone would give good results in the reversed position, and that there were advantages in protecting it from the weather. Dr Tucker's idea was accepted, and EMI was asked to devise some protection for the back of the microphone when it was in position in the paraboloid.

As in other areas of acoustical research, Dr Tucker was closely involved in the development of sound locators. A memorandum relating to microphones and bell mouth fittings for the Mark IX Locator is dated 25 September 1939, and signed "W.S.Tucker, Director of Research, ADEE," and a copy of a letter to a colleague, written on his behalf and dated 31 October 1939, mentions that "Dr Tucker is away on duty" but "you will be a welcome visitor one afternoon to view the Electrical Locator."

Apparently, Press visitors to EMI in November 1939 got hold of more information than they should relating to visual indicating equipment. Lieutenant-Colonel M Luby, ADEE wrote to the President of the Royal Engineers Board from Biggin Hill on 23 November 1939, heading his letter "Subject: Security." He referred to a press cutting from the 'News Chronicle'. "Although the press article is somewhat inaccurate it appears to indicate that possibly rather more information than is wise, about a listening device which is not yet in service, was given to the correspondent concerned."

Sir Edward Fennessy, writing in 1997, recalled events in 1939 which relate to the use of sound locators at that time. He was involved at the radar research station at Bawdsey, Suffolk in the development of an electrical calculator used in plotting procedures which was to play a major role in the success of the system. This device needed large numbers of a particular electrical component made by Siemens which was in short supply. In order to get hold of a supply of this component, the Bawdsey researchers visited Sloane Square Underground Station in London where, on part of the platform screened off from the trains, equipment was in use which contained numbers of the component in question. This equipment was there for the purpose of co-ordinating bearings sent in from a ring of sound locators round London. The information enabled the central control station to predict the points and times at which the gun batteries should concentrate their fire. The Bawdsey team were able to claim that their work was of a higher priority, and to the dismay of the officer in charge, the necessary components were taken away. Edward Fennessy remembered that the man in charge at Sloane Square was a scientist named Hart. This could well have been Mr or in some references Dr Hart, a member of the Air Defence Experimental Establishment team at Biggin Hill.

Two letters about sound locators in 1940 are both amusing and instructive. The first, on 9 January 1940, was from "Phil Lithgow" (Major), "Searchlight Wing, School of Anti-Aircraft Defence, Shrivenham, Swindon, Wiltshire to Lieutenant-Colonel W.H.G. Costelloe, Royal Engineers, ADEE, Biggin Hill" on the subject "EMI Visual Equipment."

"Dear Cos,

I must apologize for not having spoken to you myself today. I am working far too many hours a day, and as I still have no telephone I simply cannot afford to spend three quarters of an hour sitting in someone else's office, doing nothing, while waiting to get a trunk call. I am still not a bit clear as to what is involved in teaching this equipment, nor what you want us to get laid on before your experts arrive."

Apparently two aircraft had been requested for flights to test the sound equipment, but only one was available. Lithgow went on to comment "two aircraft gambolling together in the heavens will probably prove impossible to provide. In my innocence I had thought that a few hours of advice and instruction would be ample for our needs. Yours aye, Phil Lithgow."

Lieutenant-Colonel W.H.G. Costelloe, ADEE, Biggin Hill replied on 16 January. After giving details about the syllabus and training in relation to sound locators, his letter ends: "It really is incredible that your great School which is, in fact, the Keystone of the whole arch of the Empire's Ground Anti-Aircraft Defence practice should have a call on only one Dragon Aeroplane. We deserve to lose the war. Yours"

In February 1940, the Air Defence Experimental Establishment at Somerford Grange, Christchurch near Bournemouth, was the scene of a demonstration to V.I.P's from the Admiralty and Army of a new design of sound locator, known as the "Naval Locator." In this device, trumpet type sound collectors were abandoned, and an array of 16 microphones was mounted on a frame, in two rows of 8 at right angles. One array allowed listening in azimuth, or the horizontal plane, and the other in elevation. This locator, officially described as a "time compensated array of microphones, followed by amplification and binaural listening" had been tested previously on HMS Glasgow in May 1938. In June of that year, a similar locator was tried out on land by the Army. Dr Tucker reported that the microphone locator had an accuracy and range "practically identical with a stethoscope locator." As in the case of land based locators, the idea was to couple the Naval Locator to a ship-borne searchlight.

On 8 February 1940, the V.I.P's had lunch at the Kings Arms, Christchurch before proceeding to Somerford at 1.30 p.m. The arrangements for the demonstration were outlined in an ADEE memorandum. "The party will assemble at ADEE Somerford for 1.45 p.m. From 1.45 to 2.15 p.m. a demonstration of the use of the locator will be given, with a loud speaker source of sound actuated by a gramophone record of an aircraft. This demonstration will include i) listening by telephone, and ii) viewing the visual indicator of the EMI equipment. The Visual Indicating Equipment consists of two cathode ray tubes. The images on the screens of these oscillographs, which are controlled by the locator microphones, become bright vertical lines when the direction of listening is accurate. 2.15 to 3.15 p.m. Weather permitting, a demonstration will be given with an aircraft flying at 150 mph (241kmph) at heights of 5000 to 7000 feet (1524 to 2134m) in the vicinity of the locator. Accuracy of following will be observed through binoculars which form a part of the sight. Radio communication with the aircraft has been arranged." Dr Tucker was present at these tests, probably as a scientist, not a V.I.P.

A De Havilland Dragon was flown as a target aircraft for the demonstration. Possibly because of their good lunch at the Kings Arms, the V.I.P's caused a few problems. "Owing to the nearness of the visitors to the microphones, the noise of their conversations seriously interfered with the sound picked up from the aeroplane. However, in six out of nine flights of average duration 2 minutes 40 secs, the target was located within 4 degrees for an average period of about 40 secs. The Admiralty officials were generally satisfied with the performance of the locator, but suggested that until other methods of location had been tried out, the experiment should be put in abeyance. In the meantime, in case it might be required in future, it should be retained intact."

Despite the demonstration at Somerford, various documents relating to multiple microphone locators indicate that the Air Defence Experimental Establishment decided that, on the whole, such devices did not offer much advantage over paraboloidal locators equipped with microphones. Dr Tucker collated numerous reports from Territorial Army units equipped with Mark VIII electrical sound locators, and it seems that the Mark VIII locator became a standard type used in the Second World War. There are also many references to the Mark IX locator in reports of this period. The Mark IX was similar to the Mark VIII except for detailed differences in equipment.

Just before the outbreak of war, an officer from the 26th AA Battalion suggested that "a general improvement to the Mark VIII Sound Locator could be made by fitting back rests to the Listener's Saddles." This sensible point refers to the very basic seats provided for the operators on sound locators. Sitting on a saddle with no back rest, wearing earphones, and straining to listen to faint sounds, was not the way towards successful detection of approaching aircraft. The point must have been taken up, as a photograph from the early 1940s, taken during a visit by the Secretary of State for War to an anti-aircraft battery at Hendon, shows a sound locator on which the seats have been fitted with back rests.

Various papers from early 1940 document the departure of the Air Defence Experimental Establishment from Biggin Hill to Christchurch. For example, a memorandum of 27 February 1940 is headed "Somerford Grange, Christchurch", and another on 8 March 1940 is stamped "Air Defence Experimental Establishment, Christchurch, Hants". By April 1940, the name of the station had been changed to the Air Defence Research and Development Establishment. At that time, experiments were in progress to develop radar control of individual searchlights. Obsolete A.S.V. (Air to Surface Vessel) radar equipment was mounted on a Mark IX Sound Locator. The sound collecting trumpets were removed from the locator, and aerials were installed, using the elevation and bearing sockets formerly occupied by the trumpets. The visual sight, and control gear linking the locator to the searchlight were retained. As in acoustic listening, two operators directed the locator in bearing and elevation by means of hand wheels. Each operator was provided with a cathode ray screen, and the radar information from the target was displayed as a spot of light which the operator had to keep on a marked position on his tube. A searchlight, electrically linked to its sound locator, was thus continuously aimed at the target.

The use of Mark IX Locators in this way was soon extended on a considerable scale, and eventually, radar equipment was attached directly to searchlights. Air Marshal Hugh Dowding of Fighter Command commented on this development. "A small Radio Location set was designed to fit to the searchlight itself, so as to get over the time lag which was such an insuperable obstacle to the use of Sound Locators. It is probable that if searchlights can substitute the speed of light for that of sound, they may take on a new lease of useful life."

In August 1940, Henry Tizard, one of the architects of radar as Chairman of the Committee for the Scientific Survey of Air Defence, visited Anti-Aircraft headquarters, where he was briefed by the Commanding Officer General Pile on radar gun laying sets which were coming into operation. By 1941, the Air Defence Research and Development Establishment at Christchurch had produced radar sets of great accuracy, working on very short wave lengths. This type of equipment was not only an aid to search-lights and guns, but was also used in coastal defence radar units. For example, such a set, operating near Dover in July 1941, was capable of detecting the movements of enemy ships in the harbour at Boulogne.

A letter written as late as 19 December 1942 contains a reference to the Mark IX Locator. Percy Rothwell, at that time based at the Radar Research and Development Establishment at Malvern, wrote to Dr Vick, another scientist engaged in Government work. "I heard from Dr Dutton of the Gramophone Company Ltd some weeks ago that the Mark IX Sound Locator was again in production. Mr Slatter asked whether other improve-ments suggested by the Acoustic Section here would now be considered."

The Germans also used acoustic sound detectors in the early years of the Second World War. General Josef Kammhuber was closely involved in the development of night fighter forces to combat Allied air attacks. His report covering the period July 1940 to September 1943 is quoted in the book *Fighting the Bombers* edited by David C. Isby. The report contains refer-ences to the use of acoustic detection devices. A belt of searchlights was established to cover the approach paths of bombers. Kammhuber stressed that to ensure good conditions for searchlight operation, the lights needed to be sited where "favourable conditions in respect of atmosphere and general suitability of the terrain were encountered, thus protecting the 'Horchgeraete' sound apparatus which operated on an acoustic basis, from the roar of the flak." He also mentioned that night fighters waiting for the approach of bombers were concentrated "behind the searchlight belt to prevent disturbance of the acoustical detection apparatus." Although Wurzburg radar sets were introduced in October 1940 to assist the control of night fighters, Kammhuber related that as late as 1943, when aluminium strips known by the code name "Window" were dropped during bomber attacks to jam the radar, he directed that "observations by eye and ear" should supplement the "reading of sets." During "Window" jamming "only the acoustic section was in action while the electrical part was switched off."

German sound locator 1937. Note crewman, probably the sight operator just visible behind locator, and tubing connected to earphones worn by listeners, suggesting acoustic operation

Further evidence of the use of sound locators by the Germans is provided by a photograph of a locator with its crew in the archives of the Royal Artillery Museum. The picture forms the cover illustration of an issue of the Munich Illustrated Press on 9 September 1937. There is a handwritten addition in ink at the foot of the illustration. "The monster ear of an anti-aircraft unit at the parade of the defence forces at the party congress." The locator has a large circular collector, rather like a searchlight in appearance, mounted on a substantial metal frame allowing rotation and elevation of the collector. Although no wheels are visible, the base looks as if wheels have been removed, and there are prominent adjustable feet. Two of the four crew members, wearing stethoscopes, are seated at steering wheels on the locator, and the others stand in front and behind the locator respectively. It appears from a ring of electrical contacts in front of one of the steering wheels and other cables in the scene that the locator is connected electrically to a searchlight. From previous descriptions of Mark VIII and IX mobile sound locators, it seems that sound locator developments in Germany and Britain had much in common.

Returning to the British Home Front, documents and photographs from the early years of the Second World War show that in spite of the spread of radar, sound locators were still in use at that time. Searchlight beams sweeping across the night sky were a familiar sight to many people who lived through that war. At the time, there was probably very little awareness of the efforts of listeners, seated on mobile locators, muffled up in greatcoats against the cold winter nights, straining to detect in their earphones the faint sounds of approaching aircraft. As they moved the control wheels, the collecting trumpets searched the sky, and the electrically coupled searchlight nearby followed the movements in unison. Periodically, a hostile aircraft was caught in the beam and anti-aircraft guns opened fire. On such occasions, the operators would have been too busy to reflect that they were direct descendants of those who manned primitive listening devices on the Western Front in the First World War.

CHAPTER TWENTY-FIVE

LISTENERS AND STETHOSCOPES

The successful operation of mobile sound locators and their associated searchlights depended to a crucial extent on the people manning the equipment. Operating a sound locator was no easy task, calling for qualities of patience, endurance, and extreme concentration. Similar responsibilities were the lot of observers at fixed sound mirrors, who were often known as 'listeners.' The early 15 foot (4.6m) sound mirrors, such as those at Joss Gap and Fan Bay, were hollowed out of chalk cliffs and faced with concrete. The later 20 foot (6.1m) mirrors at Hythe, Abbots Cliff and Denge were free standing concrete structures. Despite these differences of construction, listening methods were similar. Although various aspects of listening activities have already been covered in this account, at the risk of some repetition, a summary of what was involved will serve as a reminder of the problems faced by listeners at sound mirrors and sound locators.

In the early type of sound mirror the listener occupied an open air position in front of the mirror. He stood on a platform facing the mirror from where he controlled a trumpet shaped sound collector mounted on the end of a counterpoised arm. Rubber tubes running along the arm connected the sound collector to a stethoscope worn by the listener. He was able to direct the sound collector at any point of the focal plane in front of the mirror surface. The object of the exercise was to focus on the place where the loudest sound was heard. The listener's platform and the sound collector were mounted on a concrete pillar in front of the mirror. In later years, after the abandonment of the mirrors and the disappearance of the sound collectors and platforms, these concrete monoliths remained in front of the mirrors, puzzling viewers as to their original purpose (See p.69).

Dr Tucker provides further details of the task of a listener when describing operating procedures at the 20 foot (6.1m) Abbots Cliff mirror on its cliff top site between Folkestone and Dover. "The radius of curvature of the mirror is 15 feet (4.6m), and its aperture is a circle 20 feet (6.1m) in diameter. The focus may be located by a swinging trumpet pivoted about the centre of curvature, with its mouth directed towards the mirror, until it embraces the sound focus. The sound is conveyed to the ears of a listener by stethoscopes and when the adjustment is correct, the sound is a maximum. The listener searches by swinging the trumpet arm in bearing and elevation, and the direction of the trumpet, and therefore of the aeroplane, can be given in terms of angular bearing and elevation by observing horizontal and vertical scales. Troops operating these mirrors can find a target quite rapidly, and after the first indications the target can be followed with an accuracy of 2 degrees or less. A second similar mirror is in operation at Hythe 8 miles (13km) further along the coast to the south and west. These two mirrors are made of solid concrete with their axes inclined about 5 degrees to the horizontal, the most favourable elevation for the long distance aeroplane."

"This type of construction reflects no credit on the designers as it is very wasteful in concrete. A third mirror of the same diameter, but of different construction was designed by Lieutenant Francis and erected near Dungeness, at a further interval of 8 miles (13km), so that the three mirrors cover a sea front of about 20 miles (32km). The mirror is a monolith of concrete resting on the shingle and is commended as a good piece of design. The mirror and raft are reinforced with iron rods. The curved surfaces have the same dimensions as those of Dover (Abbots Cliff) and Hythe. The mirrors work together, getting first warning, bearing and tracks of aircraft, and from these their ground speed can be calculated. Readings are communicated to an officer at Hythe by telephone, and by means of a plotting board with arrangements for lag of sound correction, tracks have been plotted to within a quarter of a mile from ranges of 15 miles (24km) under favourable conditions."

It is obvious, from photographs taken at the time, that the listener at a 20 foot mirror, standing on his open platform, was in a very exposed position. There is no evidence in contemporary photographs that any sort of seat was provided for the listener, and it must have been tiring work. There are also documentary references to listening problems due to unwanted sounds such as wind noise. Some records mention shelters, constructed near the mirrors to protect listeners when they were not actually on the platforms.

Listeners at the circular type of mirror were often equipped with stethoscopes. These were connected to tubes which carried the sounds from the mirror surface to the ear. Although other forms of earpiece were used, the stethoscope, despite being rather uncomfortable, had a long innings. The particular properties of stethoscopes were outlined in a War Office manual of 1922. "The earpieces should be designed to exclude extraneous sounds, so that the listener can hear only the sounds collected by the trumpets. This demands an earpiece which fits closely into the orifice of the auditory channel."

A further point was made about the method of attaching the stethoscope to the sound collector by rubber tubing. This was essential in the case of a 20 foot (6.1m) mirror, where the listener needed the flexibility of the tubes in order that he could move freely on his platform as he directed the sound collector to various parts of the mirror surface. In the case of a 30 foot (9.1m) mirror, where the operator sat in a chamber underneath, a more comfortable form of earpiece was designed. Drawings in War Office publications show the stethoscopic earpieces suspended from metal arms overhead, so that there was no weight on the ears. During the period of acoustic research, there are frequent documentary references to the problem of providing the best ear attachments in the operation of sound mirrors. This was obviously a matter of importance; the whole system depended upon fallible humans, and a demand for lengthy concentration on sounds which were often faint and elusive.

Tests were carried out to see if the information supplied by a listener was accurate. A 1924 report describes the use of optical instruments to check listeners. In the Hythe system, two theodolites were used, one at the Acoustical Station on The Roughs, and one on Dymchurch sea front, 3 miles away (4.8km).

Dr Tucker commented on unsatisfactory features of the 20 foot (6.1m) mirrors, and described improvements in design which led to the introduction of 30 foot (9m) mirrors.

Dealing with the Hythe 30 foot mirror, he explained that "the aperture was increased to 30 feet, so that with the same radius of curvature of 15 feet (4.6m) the mirrors became hemispherical. This increase gives a larger angular field of operations, and it is found possible to cover an angle of 120 degrees as against 80 to 100 degrees with the earlier type. The sides of these hemispherical mirrors protected the swinging trumpet from wind and thereby reduced resonance sounds which hampered listening. The axis of the mirror was elevated to 30 degrees to the horizontal, so that a greater range of elevation angle could be dealt with, and accurate direction for aeroplanes closer in could be secured.

A further improvement was the provision of a listening chamber, completely enclosed, and protected from wind and local disturbing sounds. This chamber is supplied with windows, and the observer operates directly under the mirror. Bearing is obtained by a steering wheel directly coupled to the trumpet arm, while operation in elevation is secured by pedals operating the valves of a hydraulic pump, which by a system of levers moves the trumpet arm in elevation. The construction is a shell of concrete with face finished in cement. The reinforcement is expanded metal, built on curved angle iron to form a skeleton hemisphere, and the concrete is about 4 inches thick(10cm)." (See p. 88 & 90)

"A second 30 ft. (9.1m) mirror of more substantial design, was erected at Dungeness. The listening gear is nearly the same as that of the previous type. Its average range for all weather conditions was 11 miles, (18km) at times giving 17 (27km) or 18 miles (29km). These mirrors were operated by troops for 6 weeks in the summer of 1932. The mean range of the mirrors was about 10 miles (16km) under all conditions, and accuracy to an average less than 2 degrees were attained by the troops with a fortnight's training. The purpose of the these mirrors was essentially to plot the tracks of incoming aircraft, and during the coming season, (1933) their capacity to obtain heights of aircraft will also be tested."

The "more substantial design" of the Dungeness, or Denge, 30 foot (9.1m) mirror is evident when it is compared with the 30 foot mirror at Hythe. At Hythe, the listener's chamber, below ground level, must have been a rather claustrophobic working space. This arrangement was inevitable, as the lower rim of the bowl is very near the ground.

Hythe 30 foot mirror in the 1990s. The window frames of the underground listener's chamber can be seen beneath the lower edge of the mirror

At Denge, the bowl of the 30 foot mirror is mounted on a concrete sub-structure, which allowed the construction of a more spacious listening room under the bowl. The surviving lower walls of this box-shaped room are of concrete. From early photographs, it is clear that the missing upper part of the room was a wooden structure, fitted with windows facing out along the axis of the mirror, and it must have been a more comfortable working position than the chamber under the Hythe mirror.

Denge 30 foot (9.1m) mirror in the late 20th century. The sound collecting trumpet, mounted on the end of the horizontal arm which can be seen in this view, was directed in a search of the focal area of the mirror by a listener in the chamber under the bowl

The listener at a 30 foot (9.1m)mirror worked in better conditions than his colleague at a 20 foot (6.1m) mirror. He sat in a chamber underneath the mirror, facing in the same direction as the bowl. According to a contemporary War Office publication "the listener is seated so that his head is just above ground level, and when on duty in the day-time, he can keep a look-out through the windows at the base of the mirror." The windows of the listening chamber have long disappeared at the Hythe mirror, but they are clearly visible in photographs taken at the time of construction. The conical sound collector at a 30 foot (9.1m) mirror was on the end of a horizontal arm which was mounted at the focus of the bowl on a vertical metal column which passed down through the bottom of the mirror to the listener's position below. As in the case of the 20 foot (6.1m) mirror, the

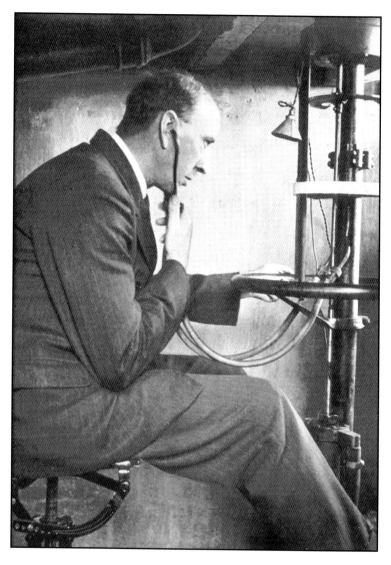

Mr Handford, c.1930, a member of Dr Tucker's team, Air Defence Experimental Establishment, at work in the listening chamber under the 30 foot mirror at Denge. He is wearing a stethoscope, and is using a hand wheel to control horizontal movements of the sound collector over the focal area of the mirror above him. Movements of the sound collector in a vertical plane were controlled by foot pedals just out of shot.

sound collector was connected by tubing to a stethoscope worn by the listener. Using the hand wheel and pedals, the listener could aim the sound collector at any point in the focal area of the mirror, and by means of graduated scales could give readings related to the loudness of the sounds in his stethoscopic earpieces. The corresponding bearings were passed to the control room by telephone. At the time of writing, the steps leading down to the listener's chamber, and the rusty remains of the lower part of the metal sound collector column, could still be seen under the 30 foot (9.1m) mirror on The Roughs at Hythe, and at the Denge 30 foot mirror, the vertical metal column, with a horizontal bar attached which formerly supported the listening trumpet, was still in position.

Steps leading down into the listening chamber under the Hythe 30 foot mirror

Suggestions for improving the design of the listener's position at a 30 foot (9.1m) mirror were mentioned in a report of the Royal Engineers Board of 21 November 1930. "The entrance to the listener's chamber could be improved by carrying the flank walls of the stairs upwards until they reach the back of the mirror. An entrance door at the head of the stairs could thus be formed, and the stairwell kept clear of drifting shingle." This reference to drifting shingle must relate to the 30 foot mirror at Denge, which was constructed just after the 30 foot mirror at Hythe. A 1935 report describes such an enclosed listening chamber as a "dungeon", and states that "listening rooms are infinitely preferable, as personnel are not tempted to use their eyes, but can concentrate on listening." This remark may be a reference to the fact that at a 20 foot (6.1m) mirror, the listener, in his open air position, could see the sound collector as he moved it over the mirror surface. In contrast, a listener in his chamber below a 30 foot mirror had to rely entirely on the sounds in his ears when aiming the collector. (See p.267)

In one respect, the listening methods at the early Joss Gap mirror were more advanced than at the later 20 foot mirrors. Written and photographic evidence shows that in addition to the use of trumpet collectors and stethoscopes, on some occasions, a listener, wearing earphones, searched the face of the mirror with a microphone attached to the moving arm instead of a trumpet (See p.44). No evidence has been found to show that this apparently more sophisticated method of listening was used at the later 20 and 30 foot mirrors, although microphones were the main listening medium at the 200 foot (61m) mirror. Microphones were also used in the flat disc receivers on Romney Marsh, and with mobile sound locators attached to searchlight units, making it somewhat surprising that greater use was not made of them with the circular type of sound mirror.

As the work of listeners at a 200 foot mirror has already been described in detail in relation to the mirror at Denge, a brief reminder is all that is required here. The main point is that there were two sorts of listeners at a 200 foot mirror. One or two people were stationed on the forecourt, just behind the front wall, using their ears to listen for sounds reflected from the surface of the mirror. Two way communication enabled forecourt listeners to draw the attention of those in the control room to particular sounds, and vice versa. In the control room behind the centre of the mirror, the listener on duty heard sounds picked up by microphones on the forecourt in the focal area of the mirror. The common objective of all listeners was to determine the bearings from which aircraft sounds were coming, and thus detect the direction of their approach.

The success of the mirror system depended not only on listeners, but also on good communications, and the efforts of staff in control rooms, both at outstations and headquarters. The sound mirror story up to the Air Defence of Great Britain Exercises in 1932 has already been covered in this account, but the system was tested again in the Summer Programme of 1933.

CHAPTER TWENTY-SIX

SUMMER 1933

The 'Summer Programme' for 1933 is described in the Minutes of the Royal Engineers Acoustic Committee. The two main objectives of the programme were "experimental, when it was hoped to advance the technique of long distance listening a further stage", and "tactical, when a party of RAF listeners would be trained to use the mirror system so that it could be manned by them in July." A later Minute has the comment: "During 1933, the Bowl mirrors have been operated successfully by a detachment of the RAF."

One problem with the mirrors was identified in the Minutes of a meeting on 7 February 1933, involving the Royal Air Force, the Royal Engineers and the Air Defence Experimental Establishment. The overall plan of defence involved patrols along the coast by friendly aircraft. But it was pointed out that when these aircraft passed in front of the mirrors, they filled the air with unwanted sounds, preventing the detection of hostile aircraft. The solution to this problem was a decision to use either friendly patrols or the mirrors, but never the two together!

A letter to Dr Tucker, from the Engineer in Chief of the Post Office Engineering Research Station at Dollis Hill in London, on 13 February 1933, reveals that help was given in the construction of microphones for use on the forecourt at the 200 foot (61m) mirror at Denge: "I am glad to hear you are now ready to make a start with the microphone manufacture, and I will make arrangements with Mr Ferguson for Mr W.H. Hatfield to go down sometime next week to give necessary assistance."

Proposals to use Wireless Direction Finding to check the performance of the acoustic mirrors were made in 1933. On 26 February, Dr Tucker wrote to the Superintendent, Air Defence Experimental Establishment, as follows: "It is essential for these experiments to have two Wireless Direction Finders capable of observing bearings on aircraft with short wave WT (wireless telegraphy). It is proposed to employ Direction Finders at the two stations Abbots Cliff and Dungeness, provided these stations offer no technical difficulties in DF procedure through their geographical positions. I am informed unofficially that such instruments may be in use by the Air Ministry, and if these could be rendered available they could be operated by our own trained staff. May application be made please for the loan of such instruments for these operations?"

Following this request, the Superintendent of the Air Defence Experimental Establishment wrote to the President of the Royal Engineers Board on 3 March 1933. "I have sent an officer to Farnborough to discuss with the Signals expert there the possibility of using long wave sets. He confirms your presumption that these sets are too inaccurate to use. He also ascertained that the short wave sets belonging to the Air Ministry would not be available in June."

Judging by a statement from the Royal Engineers Board on 21 March 1933, the Air Ministry was not very helpful: "It is improbable that these Direction Finding sets will be available for our use."

However, on 30 March 1933, a letter from the Royal Aircraft Establishment at Farnborough to Dr Tucker sounded more hopeful. "As discussed with your Mr Kemp on 27th inst. we have consulted Captain Nicholls who is responsible for shortwave Direction Finding in the Aldershot Command. We understand that this officer has one transportable shortwave Adcock suitable for the purpose and will probably be able to obtain delivery of another set of equipment in time for the June trials." The 'Adcock' was a type of DF set named after Frank Adcock, a researcher at the National Physical Laboratory.

In the event, DF sets were used in the 1933 Exercises, as detailed in a November report: "A new feature of the experiments was the attempt to employ Wireless Direction Finding in place of the visual method." Presumably, this is a reference to the use of optical instruments to check the accuracy of bearings obtained by the mirrors. The report goes on to say that DF sets were found to be helpful in conditions of poor visibility and that the sets were "useful adjuncts to the sound mirrors," although there was room for improvement in operating procedures. The DF sets were sited in the first place at Abbots Cliff and Denge, but the set at Abbots Cliff was subsequently moved to a site on the Hythe ranges, as it was found that more accurate results were obtained with both sets at sea level.

It is interesting to reflect that this use of Wireless Direction Finding to check bearings obtained with acoustic mirrors, occurred just two years before Watson-Watt and his colleagues, branching out from their background of radio experimental work, produced RDF.

Reference has already been made to the interpretation of these initials as 'Radio Direction Finding', but the essential difference between RDF and ordinary Direction Finding is that in DF, finding the position of an aircraft depends upon cross bearings obtained from listening to radio transmissions from the aircraft, whereas with radar, the position of an aircraft can be found without any co-operation on the part of the air crew, using radio waves, transmitted from a ground station and reflected back from the aircraft.

The Exercises in 1933 were preceded by 3 weeks of training from 26 June to 14 July. The training took place on five days a week from 10.00 to 13.00 hours, and from 20.00 to 01.00 hours. Aircraft used were described by type names as follows: No 9 Squadron of Virginias, No 32 Squadron of Bulldogs, No 25 Squadron of Furies, and no 210 Squadron of Southamptons which specialized in night flying over the sea. The Southampton was a twin-engined biplane flying boat, cruising at 80mph (129kmph) with its crew in open cockpits. The daylight flights were mostly Dover to Dungeness with "excursions" towards the Varne light vessel, and return courses along the lines Varne-Folkestone, Varne-Hythe, or Varne-Littlestone. At night, the aircraft flew to Cap Gris Nez and Calais, with return courses along the lines Cap Gris Nez-Dungeness, or Calais-Dungeness. Possibly due to the quieter conditions, maximum ranges obtained at night were considerable: 10 - 15 miles (16 - 24km)with the 20 foot and 30 foot mirrors, and 15 - 20 miles

(24 - 32km) with the 200 foot mirror. The report states that the listeners made "rapid progress" and that bearings were passed by telephone to the central plotting room at Hythe.

In his book A Test Pilot's Story Jeffrey Quill, famous as a test pilot of the prototype Spitfire fighter, wrote about his experiences as one of the air crew involved in the 1933 Air Defence of Great Britain Exercises. The year, 1933 coincided with the rise of Hitler to power in Germany, and at that time, much thought and effort was being devoted to the problem of identifying, locating and tracking incoming bomber aircraft so that an effective means for their interception and destruction by fighter aircraft could be established. Jeffrey Quill mentioned that the pilots were aware of attempts to track incoming aircraft by the use of acoustic sound mirrors. He described a 'periodic chore' carried out by aircraft from his squadron, when they were asked to patrol up and down pre-determined lines at various heights and engine settings for the recording of what he called the 'sound signatures' of their particular aircraft. This was to enable friendly aircraft to be identified, all other aircraft sounds being assumed to be 'hostile' during the exercises. He remarked that he thought it likely that the real purpose of those patrols was to see whether the sound mirrors could track the aircraft at all, and with what accuracy.

The fighter aircraft involved were in communication with an operations room at Upavon, Wiltshire which had a plotting table and land lines to the Observer Corps and Air Defence of Great Britain. Various types of aircraft such as Vickers Virginias, Handley Page Hinaidis, Boulton Paul Sidestrands and Hawker Hart day bombers made up the attacking force.

Jeffrey Quill commented on the value of the Air Defence of Great Britain Exercises in the 1930s. He believed that the Exercises highlighted the problems which would have to be solved if the country was to be defended against a determined air attack. He saw those problems as the location, identification and tracking of incoming enemy bomber aircraft, and the direction of our own fighter aircraft on to the bombers. He remarked that although wireless direction finding and sound locators were useful aids, the solution was in the hands of scientists working towards a more sophisticated defence system.

Participation by aircraft in exercises with the mirrors was not merely confined to the Royal Air Force. A document of May 1933 describes the activities of sea-borne aircraft. "HMS Courageous was in the vicinity of Dungeness on 9 May 1933, and it was suggested by the Admiralty that aircraft from there might co-operate with the Air Defence Experimental Establishment in an early warning experiment involving the strip mirror at Denge Beach. Two forces, each of 3 Fairy IIIF's approached the coast with Dungeness as their objective. The first raid was to start near Cap Alprech, bearing 118 degrees from Dungeness, and the second near Calais, bearing 80 degrees from Dungeness, the two flights crossed the coast line with an interval of about half an hour, the exercise was carried out between 18.30 and 19.30 hours in adverse weather conditions. The listening crew consisted of the loudspeaker operator, and two numbers (sic) patrolling the forecourt. The sound was picked up almost simultaneously by the loudspeaker operator and one of the outside listeners, but the direction was ill-defined. This was due to thc fact that the elevation of the aircraft was only 4 degrees when detected, and this was well below the acoustical horizon, so that definite bearings could not be expected. The first flight broke formation in a thunder-cloud bearing 118 degrees from Dungeness, and returned direct to the Aircraft Carrier without being detected. The second flight was prevented by low cloud from attaining a height greater than 2000 ft, and was not detected until 4½ miles from the objective - 5½ miles from the mirror."

Further particulars of Exercises in 1933 are given in a report headed: "Use of Sound Mirrors by RAF Personnel during the Air Defence of Great Britain Exercises in 1933." The report describes the manning of the mirrors, explaining that two officers and fifteen airmen operated four coastal sound mirrors in the Dover-Dungeness area. Five raids by formations and seven raids by night bombers were plotted. The mirrors used were at Abbots Cliff, 20 foot, Hythe 30 foot, and Denge, 30 foot and 200 foot.

Apart from descriptions of operational matters, the 1933 reports also contain domestic details. Apparently, RAF men involved with the mirrors had previously been stationed at Hawkinge, Kent, some distancc from the mirror sites. As a result, time was lost by the listeners in travelling to and from operational sites. A memorandum from the Director of Acoustic

Research, Hythe, to RAF Uxbridge, suggested it would be "advisable that the RAF detachment at Hythe should live in camps at Hythe and Denge if the best results are to be obtained. Tents and stoves for cooking can be provided by the Acoustical Research Section."

An unsigned memorandum addressed to the Director of Acoustical Research in September 1933 contains pointers to the future. Although it deals with matters of communication in the acoustic defence system, many of the ideas are recognizable as those put into practice in the control and reporting system which helped to make British radar so successful in the Second World War and the years which followed.

The memorandum is headed "An Outline Scheme for the Automatic Operation of Plotting Tables in the Air Defence of Great Britain." Various items are identified as desirable features of a communications system. There should be automatic operation of plotting tables from distant reporting centres, thus dispensing with human plotters. The simultaneous marking of the plot on more than one table from one operation at the sending centre, would obviate the need for human tellers passing information by voice communication, thus saving time. Plotting tables should be provided at the Home Office and Headquarters, Air Defence of Great Britain. Plots on the tables should remain for 5 for minutes only and then be removed automatically, instead of manually after 10 minutes. This idea was adopted in a manual system which lasted in RAF operations rooms until after the Second World War, when coloured plotting arrows were placed on the table in relation to coloured segments on a wall mounted clock, and removed accordingly.

The suggestion for automatic placing and removal of plots was very far-seeing, and it was not until the 1950s when plotting tables were abandoned, and information about aircraft movements was taken directly from radar display screens, that a truly automatic system developed.

CHAPTER TWENTY-SEVEN

AIR DEFENCE OF GREAT BRITAIN

Plans for the following year were already under discussion shortly after the Summer Programme of 1933. The records of a meeting of the Sound Location and Acoustic Committee of the Royal Engineers Board on 21 November, include proposals for 1934. In relation to the 200 foot mirror "the 1934 programme will include extension of the microphone system necessitated by the introduction of higher speed engines. Ten additional microphones will be provided together with the appropriate switch gear to supplement the 20 already in use."

During discussion at this meeting, it was pointed out that " the micro-phone equipment should be capable of dealing with the most difficult engines. Details of foreign engines must be studied." This last point is a reminder that successful operation of the 200 foot (61m) mirror depended to a considerable extent on an understanding of the acoustical properties of aircraft engines. If the sound characteristics of a particular engine were known, it was possible to tune the listening microphones to respond to the notes of that engine. Discrimination between the sounds of different engine types would be important in a war situation. If the detection equipment was tuned to respond to the sound of friendly aircraft engines, then at least, it could be assumed that other engine notes came from hostile aircraft.

This problem concerned Dr Tucker, and in January 1934, at a meeting between officers of the Air Defence of Great Britain and the Royal

Engineers Board, he requested the use of a squadron of aircraft with Rolls Royce Kestrel engines as "their notes give peculiar scope for study." The airfield at Hawkinge, only a few miles from the Hythe Acoustic Research station, was used from time to time by RAF aircraft participating in mirror exercises. Following Dr Tucker's request, Hawker Hart aircraft, with Rolls Royce Kestrel engines, were provided, but on this occasion, the aircraft were to be based at Manston in Kent, because Hawkinge was "not suitable for two squadrons equipped with a fast type of aircraft" over a long period.

Another aircraft in service with the RAF at this period was a variant of the Hart, the Hawker Hind, also fitted with a Rolls Royce Kestrel engine.

Hawker Hind light bomber, fitted with a Rolls Royce Kestrel engine.
This type of engine was the subject of acoustic tests by the Air Defence
Experimental Establishment. The aircraft is typical of those used by the
RAF in Air Defence of Great Britain Exercises in the 1930s.

In the light of subsequent developments, a letter of 10 May 1934 from Colonel Worlledge of the Royal Engineers Board to Dr W.S.Tucker, Air Defence Experimental Establishment, Biggin Hill, is of particular interest, not least in the personal style of the writing, and in the fact that it concerns radar pioneer Watson-Watt.

"Dear Tucker, I have arranged provisionally for Watson-Watt that he will come to see your Lympne outfit on Friday 25 May. He will be coming by car independently of me, and proposes to be at the Denge Station at 6.00 p.m. If he should be somewhere else at some other time, would you let him know? I will be coming down by the train reaching Littlestone at 17.15, bag in hand, prepared to stay, if flying conditions that day are bad, till Sunday." Colonel Worlledge's "Lympne outfit" is one way of describing the mirror system! He confirmed the arrangements in a second letter. "I will arrive at New Romney Station at 17.15 on Friday 25th. Watson-Watt is coming over in his own car to be at Denge at or about 18.30 that day. He is staying not far away, so will be able to go back home after the show." The reference to a "show" is another nice touch. Not long after these events, and through his friendship with Watson-Watt, Colonel Worlledge became involved in the development of army radar at the Bawdsey research station in Suffolk.

Correspondence of this period includes a letter, dated 11 May 1934, which contains a list of potential visitors to the Denge site, including a "Mr Rowe." A.P. Rowe was a scientific civil servant and Personal Assistant to H.E. Wimperis the Director of Scientific Research at the Air Ministry, who had himself visited the mirrors in 1932. Wimperis was the Air Ministry member of the Committee for the Scientific Survey of Air Defence, the Tizard Committee, overseeing the birth of radar, and Rowe was its first secretary. Rowe went on to play a vital part in the development of air defences in World War II, succeeding Watson-Watt as head of radar research. In his book 'Most Secret War', R.V. Jones quotes a remark made by A.P. Rowe in June 1934, when he warned the Air Ministry that "unless science evolved some new method of aiding our defence, we were likely to lose the next war if it started within ten years." Rowe's remark may have been prompted by his visit to the mirrors during the previous month.

It is clear from the letters quoted, and others, that a number of very important people visited the mirrors in the early summer of 1934.

On 16 May, the President of the Royal Engineers Board wrote to Dr Tucker at "The Roughs, Hythe" on the subject of visitors to Denge, where the 200 foot (61m) mirror was the focus of interest. "A party comprising at least seven officers, including the Air Officer in Command, Air Defence of Great Britain, and Colonel Wyatt, will be present for the evening performance on Friday 25 May. Most of the officers will be proceeding by air to Littlestone, and we shall let you know later what transport will be required for them. Accommodation for the night will be required for only three officers - the A.O.C. will not be staying the night."

The use of the term 'evening performance' in this letter has theatrical overtones, but it was justified. Visiting the 200 foot mirror for the first time was a dramatic experience. Apart from the strange activities of the listeners patrolling the forecourt or concentrating on their instruments in the control room, the mirror itself was a massive structure, emphasized by its lonely position on an expanse of shingle. Even at the time of writing, and in a state of decay, the almost sculptural appearance of the mirror creates quite an impression, particularly in certain lighting conditions.

A letter of the 17 May 1934 from: "HQ Air Defence of Great Britain, RAF Hillingdon House, Uxbridge" to "Dr W.S. Tucker, Air Defence Experimental Establishment, Biggin Hill, Kent 17 May 1934" contains further particulars of arrangements for the 'performance'.

"The Air Officer Commanding in Chief will be coming down to Littlestone aerodrome on Friday May 25th. He hopes to arrive by air at about 1800 hours, will examine the mirrors, remain and see the flying by day and by night and return to Northolt by air during the night. I have arranged for a touring car from No. 25 (F) Squadron, Hawkinge, to meet us, and they will provide a guard for the aeroplane while we are down there. Could you let me know where we could get some supper?"

In a second letter on 18 May, Dr Tucker was asked to make arrangements for five officers to attend the Exercises on Wednesday 30 May. Referring to the motor trolley which was used by the War Department as a means of transport over the Romney Hythe and Dymchurch Railway, Dr Tucker was asked "if the trolley is still out of order, will you please arrange for a train to the mirror from the Light Railway Company." It is clear from these letters that important visitors to the mirrors used various means of transport, travelling to the site by road or rail to New Romney, or by air to the small aerodrome at Littlestone. Arrangements were made for some of the V.I.P's to stay at Pope's Hotel, Littlestone.

A reference to the need for care in the selection of listeners occurs in an RAF letter of May 1934. "You are however relied upon to select intelligent airmen, since this is important work." Another letter from the same month concerns problems with the boat detailed to patrol the sea in the vicinity of the mirrors. The boat, a "pinnace", was necessary as a safety measure in the event of any forced landings in the sea by participating aircraft. It was fitted with a radio transmitter which was apparently "affected by sea water thrown over the bows."

In the run up to the Exercises, the Commander in Chief, Air Defence of Great Britain, issued orders relating to the manning of the mirrors. "The personnel selected will be required to report at RAF Station Hawkinge on Friday 22 June, in order to ensure that they are able to report to Mr Ferguson, Officer in Charge, Acoustical Station, Hythe, by 10.00 hours on Saturday, 23 June, to receive preliminary instructions, prior to commencing training on Monday 25 June." Training was to begin on that day with a lecture at the Hythe School of Musketry at 10.00 a.m.

Two non-commissioned officers were to be detached, one for the plotting table in the control room at Hythe, and one for duty at the 200 foot mirror at Denge. Also, an electrician with "knowledge of amplifiers and battery charging" was to be posted to Denge.

The acoustic team for the 1934 Exercises was as follows: at the Denge 200 foot (61m) mirror, 1 Officer, 1 NCO and 3 Other Ranks; at the Denge 30 foot (9.1m) mirror, 3 OR's; at the Hythe Control Room, 1 Officer, 1 NCO and 1 OR; at the Hythe 30 foot mirror, 3 OR's; at the Abbots Cliff 20 foot mirror, 3 OR's; or in total, 2 Officers, 2 NCO's and 13 Other Ranks.

Some of the documents of the period concern domestic matters. The detachment was to live in camps at Hythe and Denge. Cooking stoves would be available "but we cannot undertake to supply tents. Cooking utensils should be loaned from Hawkinge" and "tentage" should come from Headquarters. For transport, "Two Morris Light Tenders" would be provided to carry the personnel.

The records of the Acoustics Committee of the Royal Engineers Board include details of the automatic transmission of information between the various parts of the mirror system, and to RAF Uxbridge, in 1934. "Application for the provision of transmission lines to provide an effective automatic system for the mirrors at Abbots Cliff, Hythe and Denge has been made, and the purchase of the necessary apparatus is proceeding." Minutes of 20 November 1934, refer to "transmission of readings" and "the system installed at Hythe in 1934."

It appears from an Air Defence Experimental Establishment Report that only four mirrors were used in the 1934 exercises. This report gives further communication details. "The mirror system consisted of two thirty-foot (9m) mirrors at Denge and Hythe respectively, one twenty foot (6m) mirror at Abbots Cliff, and one two hundred foot (61m) mirror at Denge. For the 1934 operations, therefore, it was decided to ask for two new lines from the plotting centre completely separate from the main General Post Office trunk system, one running to the Denge thirty-foot mirror site, and the other to the Abbots Cliff site. When the new lines were asked for, it was decided to recommend the abandoning of the existing exchange line to the Abbots Cliff site, since this site was not normally used except in respect of operations involving its twenty foot mirror."

The telephone at the Abbots Cliff site posed particular difficulties. "Owing to the construction of the mirror, the listener himself was unable to operate it, so that it was worked by an assistant who also assumed the roles of visual observer and telephonist." Part of the equipment was "mounted inside the hut at the mirror site."

The 1934 reports of the Air Defence Experimental Establishment not only record the contribution of the mirror system to the Air Defence of Great Britain Exercises held in July of that year, but also contain human touches concerning people manning the mirrors.

Listeners at the 20 foot and 30 foot mirrors wore new headsets. These particular reports do not give details, but from sketches of the period, the headsets consisted of bands, attached to the stethoscope, and passing over the head, with the aim of taking the weight off the ears. The stethoscopes had proved to be so uncomfortable in use, that listeners tended to use one hand to support the stethoscope. The new headset left "both hands free for operating the hand wheel controlling the direction of listening, and for dialling messages for transmission to the plotting room." It was found that a man could listen and give accurate readings for about an hour, after which fatigue set in, and he began to show signs of impatience. Listening proved to be tiring work, and frequent changes of operator about every 40 minutes were found to be beneficial.

Although the use of stethoscopes may seem a clumsy procedure, these instruments were in use throughout the years of acoustic research, and were even available as late as the Second World War. At that time, operators of mobile sound locators attached to searchlight units were usually equipped with electrical listening equipment and headphones, but in the event of a power failure, they could change over to purely acoustic methods, listening to aircraft engine sounds conveyed from the trumpet collectors along flexible tubes, attached to the stethoscopes in their ears.

As in 1933, Wireless Direction Finding sets were used to check the performance of the mirrors in the 1934 Exercises. A memorandum of the time refers to "two Direction Finding Stations, at Denge and Hawkinge, for comparison of results."

One of the main reasons for the decision in 1922 to establish an Acoustical Research Station at Hythe, was its site on a route frequently used by commercial flights to the continent, thus allowing the possibility of testing the mirror system by observing civilian aircraft. It is apparent that this was still an important factor in 1934, as files relating to the Exercises carried out in that year contain detailed timetables of commercial flights by aircraft of many different companies for the period 30 April to 31 August. Flights by civilian aircraft were also a nuisance when they happened at the wrong times during Air Defence Exercises. There are references to this problem in documents of the time, usually in the form of attempts to explain shortcomings in the mirror system!

In a memorandum of 13 July 1934, Lieutenant-Colonel C.E. Ryan asked about the possibility of using the sound mirrors for the detection of coastal motor boats. "In certain cases it would appear that the mirrors are admirably situated for the purpose." He asked various questions about the ability of the mirrors to pick up sounds from coastal motor boats, the possibility of distinguishing the sounds of coastal motor boats from other craft, the length of warning to be expected, and whether or not this activity could be combined with anti-aircraft detection which he assumed would have the primary role.

Major Edwards, Superintendent Air Defence Experimental Establishment, Biggin Hill took up these points with the Royal Engineers Board on 27 July 1934. He suggested that experiments should be carried out in September if "a boat can be based at Dover and more under our orders. The idea appears likely to be possible, but the weather may interfere on some occasions." In the event, no motor boat was available in September 1934.

On 31 July, at the conclusion of the Exercises, the most senior officer involved wrote a letter of appreciation. It was addressed to "Dr W.S.Tucker, Director of Acoustical Research, The Roughs, Hythe" from "Headquarters, Air Defence of Great Britain, RAF, Hillingdon House, Uxbridge" and headed "Air Exercises, 1934".

"Dear Tucker,

I should like to take this opportunity of conveying my personal thanks to you and your staff for the assistance you rendered during the Air Defence of Great Britain Command Exercises in connection with the co-operation by the Acoustical Mirror System in the Hythe area.
Yours sincerely,

R. Brook Popham, A.O.C."

As is evident from VIP visits, the War Department branch from the Romney Hythe and Dymchurch Railway was still in use as a transport link to the Denge mirrors at this time. On 6 December 1934, the Secretary of the Railway wrote to the Officer in Charge, Shorncliffe asking: "With reference to the agreement made with the War Department in February 1930 for the provision of a siding from our line to the Air Defence Mirror at Greatstone, I should be glad to know how long this siding is likely to remain in force." He went on to say that if it was for 2 or 3 more years, he would be "prepared to have more elaborate repairs carried out which will materially add to the efficiency of the track." Dr Tucker was evidently consulted on this matter, and in a handwritten note to the Superintendent of the Air Defence Experimental Establishment on 13 December 1934, he declared that "the mirror must have a siding in order to carry on - I should say a period of 3 years is too low." In a reply to the railway, written on the same day, the Superintendent asked for the siding to remain "as long as the mirrors are in use." (See p.289) In his book on the history of the railway, W.J.K. Davies records that "the WD retained running powers over this line until after the war" and judging from reminiscences of long serving people on the RHDR the siding remained in position into the 1950s. It was subsequently removed and at the time of writing, most of the route has disappeared under housing developments. A short section of the track bed remains as a footpath to the Denge site.

The President of the Royal Engineers Board returned to the subject of using the mirrors for the detection of motor boats in a memorandum of 26 September 1934. He reported that in consultation with Dr Tucker, a decision had been made to postpone further experiments with motor boats until 1935. He also mentioned that the Denge mirror was closing down for the year and that the "electrical apparatus is being put in store." Presumably, the equipment at the other mirrors was also dismantled and stored, as it was vulnerable to both the effects of weather and interference by unauthorized persons.

Contemporary reports contain much information about the control system used in Air Exercises. A report of the Air Defence Experimental Establishment dating from 1934 includes a description of the reporting system relating to three mirrors: "20 foot (6.1m) at Abbots Cliff, 30 foot (9.1m) at Hythe, 30 foot at Denge. At each of these stations was a hut remote from the mirror itself, and in the huts were telephone instruments connected to the main General Post Office system." In another Air Defence Experimental Establishment report, there are references to the fitting up of a control centre for the 1934 Air Defence of Great Britain Exercises: "The frame itself was an important item, since the apparatus was to be installed in a wooden building." A later paragraph refers to "removal of apparatus to

Hythe on June 26th" and "Hythe installation completed on July 10th." There seems little doubt from these and other references, including anecdotal evidence, that the main control room at Hythe was in one of the wooden buildings on the site (See p.66 & 67).

The Hythe control room was an important centre during Air Defence Exercises in the 1930s. It was the collecting point for information received by telephone from the mirrors at Abbots Cliff and Denge, as well as the mirror on the site. By means of cross bearings from the various mirrors, it was possible to estimate the position of approaching aircraft. During Air Defence Exercises, the Hythe control room was in contact by telephone with a control centre at Faraday House, a General Post Office building in London. RAF personnel were involved at Faraday House, and a contemporary document gives particulars of four airmen detailed to act as tellers, under the supervision of Dr M. D. Hart, a member of the Air Defence Experimental Establishment. From Faraday House, information was passed on to RAF Uxbridge.

An unsigned memorandum from December 1934 contains hints of future developments in aircraft detection. The general style of the memorandum suggests it may have originated at the Air Defence of Great Britain headquarters. It is headed "Notes for Superintendent, Air Defence Experimental Establishment. "The ADEE is correctly named and allows for extension beyond mere guns and searchlights into wider regions of air defence from Air Defence of Great Britain point of view, including early warning, handling of Observer Corps, communications and accessories to Air Defence of Great Britain Headquarters. On the scientific side, other forms of radiation than sound may require investigation and development, and this must be co-ordinated with existing schemes. The staff capable of developing this work is within ADEE already." The last sentence was soon to become fact, when ADEE staff moved into radar research only two years later.

CHAPTER TWENTY-EIGHT

TROUBLE AT DENGE

Over the centuries, the lighthouse on the great shingle headland of Dungeness has assisted navigators passing through the English Channel. In the 1930s, this formerly remote and quiet part of the Kent coast was beginning to grow in popularity as a site for holiday homes. At Greatstone, south of New Romney, there was an expansion of building development, resulting in the inexorable spread of houses in a southerly direction along the coast towards Dungeness, passing close to the mirror site at Denge. The impact of this development, and the associated noise problems, were matters of increasing concern to those responsible for the sound mirrors, but it is apparent that the War Department and Air Ministry had little control over these events (Map 2 – p.64).

Surviving letters dating from 1931 onwards relate to the subject of land sales and building developments in the vicinity of the Denge mirror site. The Royal Society for the Protection of Birds, which owned land adjacent to the site, was particularly worried about the disturbance caused by the construction of buildings and roads. Dr Tucker described the problems in a report to the Royal Engineers Board on 17 November 1931.

"The site for the 200 foot (61m) mirror was chosen having full regard to the isolation of the position, and its freedom from local disturbing noises. Although this mirror is equipped with microphones which do not respond to any continuous sound outside aeroplane frequency, it is sensitive to any impulsive sounds which some ill-disposed person might be capable of creating, and would be considerably affected by car traffic. An important accessory of the mirror is the sentry listener who supplements the recorded loudspeaker aeroplane sounds by his own observations, and is thereby capable of eliminating motor driven craft and noises due to cars. The building of a car road past the front of the mirror would seriously impair its efficiency. There is no doubt that the extension of building and the erection of a road would very seriously reduce the value of the mirror both for experiment and as a means of defence."

An archive photograph shows the mirror site at Denge in the early 1930s including the hut used as a control room.

Plate IIA.   Front View of 200ft Mirror.

Top: Denge in the early 1930s before construction of the central control room in the 200 foot mirror. Below: Looking out over the forecourt with microphones in position. Leading away into the distance is the track of the 15 inch (38cm) gauge War Department branch from the Romney Hythe and Dymchurch Railway to the mirror site.

In a later picture, dating from 1934, the window to the new central control room can be seen in the centre of the mirror. Also visible in this view are the side screens erected to protect the microphones from side winds, and the 15 inch (38cm) gauge War Department branch from the Romney Hythe and Dymchurch Railway to the site.

There was a further reference to difficulties at the Denge site in a memorandum from the President of the Royal Engineers Board to the Under Secretary of State at the War Office on 20 February 1932. "It will be seen that development has already taken place within the listening arc of the mirror, but up to date, it has not seriously interfered with the experiment because the Holiday Camp goes to bed early, and also because ordinary conversation etc. does not affect the microphones. But should a band start up, matters would be different."

Denge 200 foot mirror in 1934. Note: Central control room window, War Department branch railway and side screens to prevent disturbance by cross winds

By 1932, the coastal road had advanced southwards to a point opposite the Denge mirror site, where it ended in a concrete car park. Dr Tucker wrote again to the Superintendent of the Air Defence Experimental Establishment on 15 September 1932 expressing his worries about what was happening at Denge: "Further development in this area would be fatal to the 200 foot (61m) mirror work."

The developer who owned the car park corresponded with the War Department on the subject of parking fees for military vehicles using the car park when on business connected with the mirrors. For a time, the War Department sought to avoid these fees, and there was a suggestion that a private car park could be constructed on the WD right of way to the mirrors. However, the Department's solicitors advised that this was not legal, as there was merely a right of passage in existence, and in the end, the developer succeeded in charging parking fees for War Department vehicles.

By 1934, the escalation of building and road development near the Denge mirrors was the cause of mounting concern. The Superintendent of the Air Defence Experimental Establishment referred to the problem in a letter to the Royal Engineers Board on 6 February. "It is reported that the road along the coast in front of the 200 foot mirror is being still further extended." This was a particular blow to the Royal Society for the Protection of Birds, as part of the land owned by the Society had been sold to a developer on the understanding that the coastal road would not be extended.

According to a letter from the President to the Officer in Charge, Eastern Command on 13 March 1934, the Royal Engineers Board did not think it worth a fight. "We agree that it is now too late to arrest development, and the best that can be done is to obtain another site, while and if such exists, and build there, when the development of the Lydd-on-Sea Estate drives us from the present mirrors."

Evidently at one point, the Royal Society for the Protection of Birds had considered the possibility of litigation against the developer. A letter from the Air Ministry to the Under Secretary of State, War Office, dated 9 November 1934 asserts that "the construction of a coastal road fronting the bird sanctuary and bearing heavy traffic would seriously impair the value of the mirror. The Air Council is of the opinion that it is desirable to support the RSPB in its action."

Nothing happened as a result of these suggestions, and Dr Tucker contin- ued to be very concerned about the possibility that the RSPB might sell all its land near the mirrors, thus allowing even more development. He put down his thoughts in a letter to the Air Defence Experimental Establishment on 15 January 1935. "The ruling given re the protection of the Dungeness Acoustical Mirror site is very disquieting. I have local information that the Society for the Protection of Birds is likely to be in need of funds, which may result in their surrendering the whole of the site surrounding our enclosure to building development. This would mean that the 200 foot mirror would cease to have either technical or tactical value, owing to local disturbing noise and building construction. If it is the policy not to maintain the site there is nothing more to be said. It might however be submitted that, if the full scheme of 200 foot mirror installations on the coast is still before Air Defence of Great Britain, the Dungeness site is a key position, alternatives for which may be difficult to find."

By early 1935, the Air Ministry had decided against any litigation in relation to the coastal road at Denge. The Secretary had been informed that whatever litigation might take place, the road would become a public road as "Kent County Council are strongly in favour of the road, and intend that it shall be provided for in town planning schemes when these are being prepared." A note of resignation on this subject also appears in a letter of 23 January 1935 from the President of the RE Board: "The concrete road against which we have protested is now a fait accompli." He went on to describe further problems. "In addition, there may soon be a broad gauge railway across the front of the mirror which will make access to our mirror awkward. Normal access is by petrol engined trolley on a light railway running to it from the coast road (See p.289 and Map 2 - p.64). If and when the line is built, we must ensure that our ease of access remains unimpaired. Our chief fear is that the combination of road and railway will upset the Bird Protection Society to such an extent that they will surrender the whole of the site to a building development company. The mirror would thus find itself in the middle of a town when it would be useless."

The "broad gauge" railway referred to was a proposed re-alignment of the standard gauge Southern Railway line to New Romney. Robert Ferguson of the Air Defence Experimental Establishment who was involved with the Denge mirrors, wrote to his Superintendent on 6 February 1935, giving good reasons for "objecting to the scheme proposed by the Southern Railway." His main reason was that "the crossing of the War Department track leading to the site by the Southern Railway is extremely dangerous."

This matter was important enough to demand a meeting of all concerned which took place at the Denge mirror site on 19 February 1935. Those participating included representatives of the Ministry of Transport, the Southern Railway, the Superintendent of the Air Defence Experimental Establishment, and Dr Tucker. They were transported to the site from New Romney station by the Romney Hythe and Dymchurch Railway. Eventually, the Southern Railway built a bridge to enable its line to pass over the narrow gauge branch to the mirrors in safety (Map 2 - p.64).

The 200 ft mirror seen through the bridge which carried the main line to New Romney over the War Department Branch Line - 2015

The 200 foot mirror was evidently in need of repair by 1935. Letters in February of that year between the Air Defence Experimental Establishment and the Royal Engineers mention a "need for re-surfacing, as the reinforcement is exposed in places, and cracks and excrescences are developing." There is a reference to minor repairs to the mirror in another letter of the same month, suggesting that some remedial work was done at this time.

Vandalism is not a new problem. On 21 May 1935, the Superintendent of the Air Defence Experimental Establishment reported that "on 23 April, the armoured plate window to the listening chamber of the Acoustical Mirror at Denge near Hythe was broken by a 0.22 bullet fired through the wooden shutter protecting the window." He requested immediate repairs.

By 1935, the problems of disturbance at Denge were becoming so pressing that thoughts turned towards the complete abandonment of the site. The RSPB (Royal Society for the Protection of Birds) was willing to sell the War Department some land further south, near the end of Dungeness Point. The land is described in a Royal Engineers Board document as "West of Dungeness Lighthouse. This area is at present almost completely free from development on the Southern side, and has a sea frontage on which only two buildings at present exist."

This new idea was not without its problems, as pointed out in a minute to the Royal Engineers Board from Dr Tucker on 17 May 1935. He explained that it was not just a question of abandoning the 200 foot (61m) mirror. "The Denge 30 foot (9.1m) mirror forms part of an experimental system comprising, in addition to the Denge mirrors, two other bowl mirrors at Hythe and Abbots Cliff. If the site of the 30 foot mirror (i.e. at Denge) be abandoned, the system becomes useless. It would be necessary to retain a small part of the site at Denge for the 30 foot mirror, since for technical reasons, this cannot be sited more than its present distance from the Hythe mirror."

Dr Tucker made further reference to the proposed move to a new site at Dungeness. In a letter to the Superintendent of the Air Defence Experimental Establishment on 31 October 1935, he commented on the new site: "The area shown gives what we consider to be the absolute minimum for the 200 foot mirror site." He mentioned two features which he considered desirable. The mirror should be far enough from the coast to avoid sea noises, and there should be a "clear arc of 90 degrees as far as practicable to the South. Both these are achieved by a mirror site as near the N.E. corner as is practicable for building purposes. A road in front would be disastrous." Dr Tucker also pointed out that it would be sensible policy to have the proposed new site in operation before the abandonment of the Denge mirrors.

Events were shortly to overtake the mirror system, and in fact, there was no move to a new site at Dungeness. Dr Tucker could never have imagined the eventual scale of building development near the mirror site. At the time of writing, the ruined mirrors, which formerly stood on a large area of open shingle, are completely screened from the sea by a mass of houses and a holiday camp. The remark by the President of the Royal Engineers Board that the mirrors might eventually be in the middle of a town is almost a reality.

CHAPTER TWENTY-NINE

AIR EXERCISE 1935

Despite all the problems at Denge, detailed plans were made to use the Hythe mirror system in the 1935 Air Exercises. A memorandum from the Acoustical Section, Biggin Hill, explained that during the Exercises, the control room would be at Faraday House, a Post Office building in London, and "for this purpose, the control room staff will proceed from Hythe to London in time to be on duty at Faraday Building at 18.00 hours on Monday, 22 July. An emergency control room staff consisting wholly or partly of Air Defence Experimental Establishment personnel will remain at Hythe in readiness to take over in the event of a breakdown in the Faraday Building Control Room."

It is apparent from reports of this period that the need for speed in passing information from mirror sites to control centres was a continuing preoccupation. Dr Tucker stressed the point in a 1935 memorandum. "Time is the most important factor in dealing with incoming raids, and this makes delays through telephony prohibitive. A system has been devised whereby the listener can dial his bearings in response to a control signal sent out from headquarters, and these bearings are displayed on an illuminated indicator panel. When the figures flash up, the locations derived from the mirrors can be plotted by strings of a plotting board which is specially ruled out and enables the officer controlling operations to make provision for lag of sound." A document of June 1935 gives much detailed information about the design of telephone circuits, plotting systems, and automatic reporting apparatus. Some of this equipment was tried out at the Hythe mirror site and control room.

The Minutes of the Acoustic Committee of the Royal Engineers Board include references to the automatic system for sending information from mirror sites to control rooms. Under the heading "Automatic Transmission of Readings" there is the entry "Application for the provision of transmission lines to provide an effective automatic system for the mirrors at Abbots Cliff, Hythe and Denge has been made and the purchase of the necessary apparatus is proceeding." Experiments with such methods of communication had already been carried out in the previous year, as shown by a minute of 20 November of that year, where, under "Transmission of readings" there is a reference to "the system installed at Hythe in 1934.

Minutes dated 10 October 1935 refer to "Bowl Type Mirrors, Transmission of Readings" "The apparatus was successfully installed in Faraday Building in time for the 1935 Air Exercises and controlled the Hythe Mirror System. Great credit is due to the Experimental Officer concerned - Dr M. D. Hart. Now that suitable moving-coil microphones are available, it is proposed to compare the normal listening trumpets and stethoscopes with one containing a microphone connected to an amplifier and a telephone headset. It is hoped that such a system will not only provide immunity from disturbing noises outside the range of aircraft noise frequencies, but will also help in the detection of gliding targets. In addition, the telephone headsets will make for greater listening comfort." It seems from this statement, that at the 30 foot (9.1m) mirrors, a return was to be made to listening methods first tried out many years before at Joss Gap, where the focal area of the mirror was scanned for sounds by either a trumpet collector or a microphone.

A further reference to the operation of the mirrors in 1935 concerns the 200 foot (61m) mirror. "The advance in Control Room technique makes possible the elimination of forecourt listeners where this is essential. These listeners cannot however be dispensed with when the mirror is required to discriminate between different sounds or to distinguish recognition sirens."

In a memorandum from Dr Hart to the Director of Acoustic Research in

December 1934, the problem of sending information via telephone lines over long distances was discussed. Direct current (DC) lines were not suitable for long distances, and quoting Dr Hart "one idea was to use DC lines for a short distance to a 'converting station', where a DC/AC conversion would enable AC (alternating current) transmission to a distant plotting station." A memorandum of 7 January 1935 suggested that "the DC-AC transmission would be tried in the first instance between one mirror and London. A mirror in the Hythe district was suggested for trial, and Folkestone Exchange for the 'converting station' " The General Post Office undertook to explore possibilities of provision and cost.

The use of the 200 foot mirror in 1935 is described in a report of that year. "The normal course of events in a raid over the Hythe mirror system is as follows:- aircraft approach from the seaward direction, and are usually picked up first by the 200 foot mirror at Denge. The bearing transmitted by this mirror gives sufficient information to the plotting centre operator to enable him to select zones in which one or more of the 30 foot mirrors should search. "

The manning of the 30 foot mirrors is also described: "The method of relief has been to employ a crew of two, both trained as listeners, when the spell of duty did not exceed four hours. They relieve each other in turn at approximate intervals of one hour."

In 1935, "all the mirror readings were transmitted by automatic apparatus direct to the Control Room in Faraday Building, and thence the warnings and plotted positions were telephoned to Uxbridge, and at certain times to the Observer Corps Centre at Manston." For the 1935 programme, special attention was given to training and preparation in connection with the "proposed mirror system of the Thames Estuary Defences."

Further information relating to activities in the summer of 1935 is contained in a paper headed: "A General Report on the Operations with the Hythe Mirror Installation as used by RAF Personnel during June and July 1935." "For the third year in succession, the Hythe Mirror system has been employed for the training of RAF personnel." The men involved were one Flight Sergeant, two Sergeants, and thirteen airmen, with three officers. The officers were Flight Lieutenant H. Burke, who also featured in the 1933

Exercises, Flying Officer A. T. Monks, and Flying Officer II.S.Lawes. "During the operations, F/O Lawes took charge of the 200 foot mirror, and F/L Burke shared with F/O Monks the responsibility of the control room at Faraday Building. Aircraft were provided by No 201 Flying Boat Squadron stationed at Dover Harbour." The timings for the experiments were "about three hours from 22.00 to 01.00 hours on June 24, 27, 28; July 1 to 5, 8 to 12, and 15 to 17." "The 200 foot (61m) mirror served as an effective sentry for the whole system. It is quite possible to man the 200 foot mirror with a watch of one listener and one telephonist only. The listener has the most tiring job, and one hour of continuous listening is about a maximum."

The idea of using motor boats as targets for the mirrors re-emerged in 1935. Letters from the Air Defence of Great Britain Headquarters suggested that such tests should be carried out between 6 and 31 May. On 15 February 1935, Dr Tucker wrote to the Superintendent of the Air Defence Experimental Establishment on the matter:- "the Officer in Charge, Motor Launch, should report at Hythe on May 7th (since the 6th is a Public Holiday) the place of meeting being the Hythe Acoustical Station, time to be specified later - probably 10.00 a.m. Operations will be confined to 5 days in the week (Saturdays and Sundays excepted) and will commence at 22.00 hrs extending over a period of about 2 hours. Wind and weather will effect the programme, which will be drawn up daily. Wireless communication, maintained by the RAF, should be ensured between the Motor Launch and Denge. The provision of a light on the mast-head of sufficient power would be required."

A memorandum from "Headquarters Coastal Area, Biggin Hill" laid down that "motor boat trials are to be conducted over the same period as trials with 'gliding aircraft' though at different times. The motor boat is to be used for safety purposes during the gliding trials." Presumably, the motor boat was to act as a lifeboat in the event of any aircraft making a forced landing on the sea.

Major Lamb, Superintendent of the Air Defence Experimental Establishment asked, on 26 July 1935, if local arrangements could be made for a suitable boat. Tests took place on 29 - 31 July. In August, some trials were abandoned because the boat was "broken down."

Despite such problems, experiments with a motor boat were carried out. In addition to tests using the sound mirrors, a 'Pilot Sound Locator' was used. Although not specified as such in the reports, this was probably a device similar in design to the pilot sound locators used by searchlight units. Some of the pilot locators were equipped with large horns, designed for detecting low frequency engine sounds. The locator used in the Hythe experiments was described in a contemporary document as a "two trumpet azimuth locator", meaning it could only search in a horizontal plane. The locator was mounted on a low pillar on a trailer, and hand wheel control was provided for searching in azimuth. According to the reports, there was no provision for height finding with this particular locator. Perhaps the unconscious humour of that statement in relation to motor boats passed unnoticed at the time.

In the event, the locator was a disappointment. "Trials have been continued at Hythe during May and June to include observation against a motor launch, in order to obtain data as to the efficacy of such a listening device for use by sentries guarding beaches. Wind and beach noise conditions were such as to make aural listening a failure, which was a foregone conclusion, as the apparatus uses a sound collector from which none of the disturbing background noises over a wide arc can be excluded or tuned out, while their high pitched constituents are magnified."

Apparently, good results were achieved by the mirrors in the 1935 Exercises, and "even the 30 foot (9.1m) mirrors approached ranges of 20 miles." A reference to the use of three mirrors at Abbots Cliff, 20 foot (6.1m), Hythe 30 foot (9.1m) , and Denge (30 foot) to obtain cross bearings, states that "all three mirrors provided bearings giving almost pin point intersections."

Records survive of tests made to check the listening ability of various men employed in acoustic experiments. Sounds of different frequencies were used in the tests, and the results were tabulated, showing details such as the sensitivity of each ear, and the response to notes of different frequencies. In one report, the men were listed as follows: "1 technical assistant, 4 soldiers, 2 sailors, and 1 RAF man." The technical assistant was described as "very good", two of the soldiers were classed as "good on low notes", and one soldier was "very good, except with the left ear on high notes." Officers were also tested. A certain Flying Officer was described as "poor for general listening and no sense of direction." He was also listed as "stone deaf in all tests." These remarks suggest that a particular type of listening was needed for acoustic mirror work, as this officer was reported to have good hearing when carrying out his flying duties.

As in other years, the 1935 reports are not confined to technical matters, but deal also with human problems. For example, a letter about personnel for the 1935 mirror trials directs that "two cooks should be provided, one for Denge and one for Hythe, to facilitate domestic arrangements which have been difficult in previous years." In another letter on this subject, an officer suggests that in view of the small number of men involved, it would be cheaper to station them all at Hawkinge for the duration of the exercises and transport them to the site as needed. This would then allow only one cook to be employed at Hawkinge. However, it appears that in 1935, the men were still stationed at the mirror sites, as a report of that year, dealing with Exercises using the mirrors at Abbots Cliff, Denge and Hythe states:- "The troops were encamped throughout the period at each of these places." Someone thought about the problems of men living in tents pitched on the shingle at Denge, and there is a written request for floorboards to be provided for the site.

The men at Abbots Cliffs mirror, in their cliff-top position, were exposed to the wind and weather. In 1935, the site was affected by storm damage. A letter of 27 September of that year from the Superintendent, Air Defence Experimental Establishment to the Royal Engineers at Dover, describes this incident: "A considerable amount of damage has been caused by the recent storm at the Abbots Cliff mirror. May the mirror platform and the latrine be repaired please?" The letter continues with a suggestion to make a smaller hut out of the remnants of the previous larger hut. This is another insight into the continuing need for economy in military spending in the period. (Map 1 - p.23)

*Abbots Cliff sound mirror on its exposed cliff-top
position overlooking the English Channel*

Reports of tests with two Heyford bombers, one 'silenced' and the other 'unsilenced' dating from 14 - 17 October 1935 give some idea of the operation of the 200 foot Denge mirror. The reports do not explain how the aircraft were' silenced', but it was probably some form of exhaust silencing.

"The course flown by the aircraft was from a point at sea approximately 5 miles off Dover, to the Denge mirror - a distance of about 22 miles. The aircraft followed each other over this course at intervals of 20 minutes."

The flights were mostly carried out at a height of just over 4000 feet (1219m), but some of the 'unsilenced' aircraft flew at lower altitudes, around 2500 feet (762m).

"In raids 7U and 8S the aeroplanes were followed visually by theodolite and the track plotted. The range of the unsilenced aircraft, when first heard, was 17 miles, (27km) and of the silenced aircraft 9.6 miles (15km)." These are not very impressive results at this date, considering that the courses flown by the aircraft were planned in advance, although there is no indication as to whether or not the likely approach direction of the aircraft was known to the listeners at the mirrors.

A report from Headquarters, Coastal Area, Biggin Hill, put forward some conclusions on experiments to check the dual role of sound mirrors in plotting both airborne and seaborne craft. In a paper headed "Ship Detection by a 200 foot Acoustical Mirror" dated 8 August 1935, three sources of information were listed. Firstly, "the experience of operators of the 200 ft mirror at Dungeness, extending over several years, during which the behaviour of the mirror towards the sound of steamers and other vessels has frequently been observed". Secondly, "observations made from the 200 ft mirror at Dungeness during tests with RAF Power Boats in May 1935." Finally, "observations made from the 200 ft mirror at Dungeness during tests with a motor driven fishing vessel in July 1935."

Other conclusions in this report were that ships could be detected by the 200 foot mirror at a range of 7 to 10 miles (11 to 16km), high speed power boats a range of 3 to 7 miles (4.8 to 11 km), and motor fishing vessels at a range of 2 to 4 miles (3.2 to 6.4km). "It appears that microphones are the most reliable source of information. The question of distinguishing between motor boats and aircraft is one that has not been fully considered, and would probably require ad hoc trials before it could be settled." Reading between the lines suggests that a new problem of discrimination had arisen, due to the fact that the sound of typical motor boat engines was not unlike that of aircraft engines.

On 21 August 1935, the President of the Royal Engineers Board, Colonel F.J.C. Wyatt commented on experiments carried out in July. "Provided the 200 ft mirrors (61m) are suitably sited for the purpose, they can fulfil the dual role, but the difficulties and operating techniques required when both enemy aircraft and boats are present have not been ascertainable with the meagre surface craft co-operation we have had. Our 30 ft (9.1m) mirrors are not well sited for ship detection but those planned for the Thames Estuary will be better placed. It is reasonable to expect a range of 2 - 3 miles

(3.2 - 4.8km) with the 30 ft. The estuary system could be defeated by a boat keeping well out from both coasts, and even for inshore targets, the mirrors are too widely spaced to permit of location by intersection of bearings. For narrower channels, 30 ft mirrors could be useful, though infra-red investigations are to be continued in the autumn."

Dr Tucker was still active in the Hythe area at this time, seeking ways to improve the microphone system in use with the 200 foot mirror at Denge. He sought advice from academic colleagues. Signing his letter "W.S.Tucker, Director, Acoustical Section", he wrote to the Superintendent, Air Defence Experimental Establishment on 3 July 1935: "I am anxious to consult Professor Fortescue on certain technical points connected with the microphone installation for long distance listening. Professor Fortescue was in intimate touch with the work as Professor at Greenwich Naval College, and is therefore familiar with the conditions of the Service. He is paying a visit to Folkestone on July 19th when I shall be in Hythe on duty, and I should like to discuss these problems on the spot. May I have authority please, to invite Professor Fortescue on this occasion." This request was granted.

In answer to various criticisms of the Hythe system from high-ranking officers, Dr Tucker explained that "the Hythe installation was laid down for experimental and not tactical purposes, and it has since developed into a training system, for which it is reasonably adequate." He referred to the siting of the mirrors, beginning with those on The Roughs at Hythe. "The site was deliberately chosen to be on the route of Civil aircraft for reasons of economy, and therefore was left particularly vulnerable to this class of disturbing noise. Moreover, the development of traffic and local building in the last 12 years has turned a quiet situation into an extremely noisy one. The same disability is overcoming the Denge site, as is common knowledge." Later, he gave details of problems in the training of RAF personnel during the 1935 Exercises due to interference from "Civil aircraft, and Service Aircraft not taking part."

Late in 1935, and continuing into early 1936, correspondence between the Air Defence Experimental Establishment and the Royal Engineers indicates concern at the visibility of the mirrors from the air, a matter raised in previous years. Aerial photographs were taken to illustrate the problem, and various schemes for camouflage were discussed. Dr Tucker referred back to his experience in this respect with the mirror at Joss Gap on the Thanet Coast in the First World War. After inspecting the photographs, he was not optimistic about the possibility of concealing the mirrors from aerial view.

The Royal Engineers referred to the great prominence, in aerial photographs, of the narrow gauge railway branch to the mirrors at Denge. Suggestions were made to remove this branch, using instead, a track from the New Romney-Lydd road to Belgar and Northlade farms, which could be used by War Department lorries. The Superintendent of the Air Defence Experimental Establishment replied to this idea with a statement that the W.D. railway branch must be retained as "essential". The Royal Engineers were however given permission to plant gorse bushes at Denge, and to soften the visual impact of the mirror with camouflage paint, at a cost of £50.

During a conference at RAF Uxbridge following the 1935 Exercises, there was evidently some adverse criticism of the acoustic system by the Air Officer in Command, Fighting Area. Dr Tucker commented in a letter to the President of the Royal Engineers Board on 19 August. Quoting the criticisms, he remarked that apparently, the A.O.C "had not found the Acoustical Mirrors of any use," but the A.O.C had also said that "when the Thames Estuary mirrors were completed, he was sure the result would be different."

Events which were to have a profound effect on all further acoustic work were taking place on the Suffolk coast in 1935. In July of that year, through contacts between Colonel Worlledge of the Royal Engineer and Signals Board with radar pioneer Watson-Watt, various members of the Board visited the Radio Research Station at Slough. They were very impressed with the work there, and also with developments at Orfordness (Map 1 - p.23) in the latter part of 1935. Discussions with the Air Ministry about participation in these developments, led eventually to Army radar.

A document from late 1935 makes it clear that Dr Tucker was aware of radar developments at that time. In a memorandum from the Air Defence Experimental Establishment, dated 4 November 1935, he used the code name RDF (Radio Direction Finding) and he must have seen radar in operation, as he referred to observations on "October 28th." In this memorandum, marked "SECRET", he made various comparisons between RDF and the 200 foot (61m) mirror. The heading of his paper implies the interesting possibility of a combined station at the Denge mirror site.

"Suggested Single Station Operation RDF and 200 ft mirror. The following properties of the systems are contrasted.

RDF provides ranges exceeding the 200 ft mirror, unless jammed, but at present there is no direction from a single station. The 200 ft mirror provides bearings with an accuracy of one degree on a crossing target, but not range.

RDF is jammed by atmospherics but not wind. The 200 ft mirror is jammed by high winds, but not by atmospherics.

RDF cannot record low flying aircraft. Under favourable conditions, the 200 ft mirror can detect aircraft at all heights, and can also get warning and bearing on ships.

RDF would, under quiet conditions give earlier warning and number of aircraft. The 200 ft mirror is effective over ranges which can be predicted and will not exceed a certain maximum, but would then give bearings, one for each target.

The two systems are, therefore, excellently adapted for giving complete information at one station. Mirror personnel get early warning and number of aircraft from RDF, hence, continuous watch is not essential. On approaching limiting range, mirror personnel get bearings; knowledge of the certain presence of aircraft giving confidence to the listener and better ranges that when not so aided. For complete sentry operations in bad weather, acoustical warning is given up to normal ranges in thundery weather. RDF gives radio warning in bad, windy conditions. The 200 ft gives accurate direction at ranges less than RDF can get ranges."

In this paper, Dr Tucker posed various questions about RDF, but there are no corresponding answers. The document looks like a record of something prepared by Dr Tucker which he intended to put to the people involved in RDF research. For example "is it admitted that ground obstacles or very low flying aircraft e.g.. Flying Boats, can come in undetected? It is presumed that the prevalence of local thunderstorms would put RDF out of operation. Would the system be immune from jamming from ground stations tuned in, as was observed on October 28th?"

Dr Tucker concluded his paper with some recommendations. There should be "provision of a single station RDF at Denge, to be manned by at least one Air Defence Experimental Establishment officer, previously trained." There would be "operations with training in situ one month prior to Air Defence of Great Britain exercises, and the equipment would be used in the Air Defence by RAF personnel entirely, with ADEE supervision. The site provides all the difficult conditions of a crowded civil aviation service, and jamming by local flying. Outgoing aircraft can be distinguished and ignored."

Some of these ideas emerged again in 1937. In January of that year, P.E.Pollard, a Scientific Officer from the Air Defence Experimental Establishment, working in the Army Cell at Bawdsey radar research station, put forward a proposal to combine radar with the 200 ft acoustic mirror. The object was to provide "in a simple manner a means of ship location and distant detection of low flying aircraft. The reinforced concrete mirror would act as an aerial reflector of the radar, and would produce a narrow beam capable of traverse." Nothing came of the suggestion, following a decision that it would be better to concentrate efforts on the production of self-contained radar sets.

The combination of acoustic and radar devices at one station is an interesting 'might have been'. In reality, it appears from reports of the time that the 200 foot mirror was closed down by 1937.

CHAPTER THIRTY

THAMES ESTUARY PLANS

Detailed plans exist from the early 1930s showing a serious intention to build a line of sound mirrors along the coast of England, extending from Norfolk round to Dorset. The overall idea was to place 200 foot mirrors at intervals of about 16 miles, (25km) and to supplement this main chain with 30 foot mirrors on the intervening stretches of coast. These plans bear a striking resemblance to those carried out at a later date, where gaps in the coverage offered by the fixed beams of the main radar stations, sited at intervals along the coast, were filled by smaller stations, equipped with rotating aerials.

Reading in a clockwise direction, starting on the coast of East Anglia, sites identified for the sound mirror chain were Yarmouth, Norfolk; Orford Ness and Felixstowe in Suffolk; Clacton and Tillingham in Essex; Grain, Warden Point, Swalecliffe, Reculver, South Foreland and Dungeness in Kent; Beachy Head and Selsey Bill in Sussex; St Catherine's Point Isle of Wight, and St Alban's Head in Dorset. The proposed site at Orford Ness was prophetic. The Ness had been an experimental establishment for many years, and in 1935, it was to be the place where the first significant break through in British radar occurred, when aircraft were picked up at ranges which soon rendered the acoustic system obsolete (Map 1 – p.23).

It is obvious that the construction of a chain of 200 foot (61m) concrete mirrors would pose a considerable logistical problem, a fact which concerned Percy Rothwell of the Air Defence Experimental Establishment. As the designer of the prototype 200 foot mirror at Denge he was well qualified to comment on the problem. In 1933, he drew attention to the great weight of concrete needed for the construction of such a mirror, and looking ahead to the construction of a chain of mirrors, he put forward a design for a "sectional mirror" heading his memorandum to the Royal Engineers Board "Proposed New Method of Construction of 200 ft mirror." The new design of 200 foot mirror would be constructed of "reinforced concrete units only 2 inches (5.1cm) thick, with stiffening ribs. The dimensions of the units would be 9 ft by 4 ft (2.7m by 1.2m). We should then have steel buttresses at approximately the same spacing as the concrete buttresses on the present Denge mirror."

Rothwell suggested a practical method for erecting the mirror. "The blocks are handled by light cranes operated by electric motors. Hooks or pins for attachment to the crane hooks are cast in the blocks. These must not protrude in such a way as to interfere with packing or storing, as it is intended that the new method of construction should have the advantage of allowing mirrors to be put in store until required in emergency." Rothwell described how the parts would fit together, using 'Tee' section steel supports. "The flange would be in the mirror face, and the slabs would be placed between the webs of adjacent Tees. In order to fix the slabs, holes would be cast in the end ribs of the slab, and the web of the Tee would be drilled so that the slabs could be bolted to the iron work."

In his memorandum Rothwell stressed that "schemes of Air Defence which include 200 ft (61m) mirrors will have to take into consideration sooner or later certain inconvenient features of the permanent structure, exemplified by the only existing 200 ft mirror at Dungeness." His list of inconvenient features began with "cost, due principally to the large quantity of shuttering required and its erection to very fine limits; piping or carting clean water in certain locations; and bringing machinery and large quantities of loose materials to necessarily very isolated spots."

Percy Rothwell also drew attention to "the impossibility of moving the mirror to a new site, necessary in peacetime owing to normal development of towns and industries, or in war, both for military and technical reasons;

the difficulty and length of time required in repairing the mirror if damaged by bombs or shells from a hostile fleet; the length of time taken for erection in emergency; the inconvenience to farmers or landlords, and expensive compensation in peace time; the difficulty of rendering inconspicuous to foreign aircraft and agents a scheme of Anti-Aircraft Defence employing large permanent structures in strategical positions; and the difficulty and cost of altering the height of the mirror if future developments demand it."

This formidable list of inconveniences made a good case for Rothwell's proposal that "in order to meet these disadvantages, a method of mirror construction using pre-cast reinforced slabs bolted in a steel framework is suggested. "

On 19 December 1933, a conference took place at the Air Ministry, chaired by Group Captain W. L. Welsh D.S.C., A.F.C. The subject was "Extended Experiments to be carried out for Developing the Acoustical Mirror Warning System."

The Minutes reveal that "Air Defence of Great Britain had submitted a scheme for the employment of a number of 200 ft strip mirrors and 30 ft bowl mirrors, to provide a continuous warning screen round the south-east of England from the Wash to St Albans Head." The first part of this plan was to develop a system for the Thames Estuary which "would require two 200 ft (61m) mirrors and eight 30 ft (9.1m) mirrors. The cost of this for mirrors alone was estimated at roughly £10,000." Other matters discussed included sites for the mirrors, and purchase or hire of the necessary land. Under "Maintenance" there was a decision not to provide housing for caretakers near the mirrors, as "the Army usually left their mirrors unattended for long periods."

Following this meeting, a letter from the Air Ministry to the Air Officer Commanding-in-Chief, Air Defence of Great Britain, RAF Hillingdon House, Uxbridge on 18 January 1934 explained that a Committee had been set up to "investigate and select the sites for the mirrors in the Mouth of the Thames." The duties of the Committee were "to select sites for two 200 ft strip mirrors, and four 30 ft bowl mirrors in the Mouth of the Thames for extended experiments during 1935 of the acoustical warning system," and "to decide on the system of communication to enable the information from the mirrors to be transmitted as rapidly as possible to Fighting Area Headquarters." The Committee was also asked to give firm estimates for the cost of the land required, the cost of building the mirrors, and the cost of the associated electrical equipment.

The Royal Engineers Board also held meetings concerned with the expansion of the mirror system. The Minutes of a meeting on Thursday 1 February 1934 refer to "proposals for the siting of acoustical mirrors on the seaboard of the Thames Estuary." The intention was that the Thames Estuary scheme would eventually form part of the whole coastal system from the Wash to Swanage.

Dr Tucker was soon active in this matter, and it is recorded in the Minutes that he carried out a reconnaissance of possible sites. Details are included relating to the siting of new mirrors. "The original outline of the Wash-Swanage scheme prepared by the RE Board in January 1933, included a double (220 degrees arc) mirror at North Foreland. The proposal was to install a standard 200 ft mirror (110 degrees arc) further to the West at Reculver and not at North Foreland, for the reason that the noises in the Margate area would prevent the vital co-operation with the complementary mirror on the other side of the Estuary at Clacton. It will therefore be necessary in the eventual scheme to place a similar mirror at North Foreland to cover the East and South aspects of the Kent Coast. This was agreed to. It was agreed to recommend two 200 ft (61m) mirrors and seven 30 ft (9m) mirrors." Conservative ranges were given for the mirrors as 20 miles (32km) for the 200 ft mirrors, and 10 miles (16km) for the 30 ft mirrors (Map 1 - p.23).

"Linked up with the general lay-out was the question of the position from which the system should be controlled. Everything pointed to the selection of Grain for this purpose." A glance at a Kent map suggests that the Isle of Grain, at the mouth of the River Medway opposite Southend, roughly in the centre of the proposed system, was a logical site for a headquarters. "From Grain, there would have to be communications forward to each site. At Clacton and Reculver there would probably be a form of sub-control at the 200 ft mirrors controlling the 30 ft mirrors also sited at these places. The Royal Engineers Board agreed to place Dr Tucker at the disposal of Air Ministry for the purpose of pointing out the selected sites." (Map 1 - p.23)

Dr Tucker's conclusions from his reconnaissance of the mirror sites must have been passed to higher authority. On 15 February 1934, a report on the subject was submitted with a covering letter from the Air Defence of Great Britain to the Air Ministry. The main factors governing choice of sites for the "Thames Estuary Mirror System" were outlined. These were "avoidance of inhabited areas, avoidance of railways and main roads and freedom from sea noise."

"Provision is made for seven sites in all. Of these, the two outer sites nearest the mouth of the Estuary will accommodate one 200 ft and one 30 ft mirror. The remaining five 30 ft mirrors will be disposed approximately 7 miles (11km) apart to give overlap of course plotting." The sites chosen on the north side of the Estuary were "Clacton, Tillingham and Asplins Head" and on the south side "Grain, Warden, Swalecliffe, and Reculver. Of these, Grain serves as a final sentry linking up with the North and South systems."

The report contains various comments about the sites. At Clacton, there was concern that "some local disturbing noise is to be expected from motor traffic on a new road from St Osyth to the beach about one mile (1.6km) east of the site." Noise was also seen as a possible nuisance at Asplins Head, where there could be "disturbance to the listeners from traffic on the road, and in particular from the noise from the telegraph wires." This problem was also identified at Grain. "Some restrictions would probably be necessary to prevent campers and others creating disturbing noises in the summer." (Map 1 - p.23)

A file of contemporary documents contains detailed maps of the proposed mirror sites, together with verbal descriptions. The site at Asplins Head in Essex was "on Foulness Island near New Burwood." The site at Warden Point, for a 30 foot mirror was "slightly NE of Mud Row on the cliffs to the right of Drapers Point." Reculver was to be the site of a 200 ft (61m) and a 30 ft (9m)mirror, "West of Knock Point and East of the Church Ruins, longitude one degree thirteen minutes east, latitude fifty-one degrees, twenty two minutes, thirty seconds." There is also a map showing the land required for the mirror site at North Foreland. It was near Crescent Road and North Foreland Avenue, very close to the old Joss Gap site. A large map shows all the sites with overlapping areas of coverage.

The Agenda for the RE Board meeting on 22 February 1934 included the following questions. "Will the same officers and other ranks to be trained at Hythe in 1935 be available as instructors and crews for the Thames Estuary System in 1936? As the Thames Estuary project will require 3 officers, cannot three be trained this year?"

A letter and memorandum from the Royal Engineers Board to the Air Officer Commanding the Air Defence of Great Britain on 9 April 1934, dealt with the control and reporting system for the Thames Estuary System:

"It is recommended that the main plotting centre for these mirrors (Thames Estuary) be situated at the General Post Office South, Carter Lane, adjacent to the Toll Exchange."

Carter Lane is a street in the vicinity of St Pauls Cathedral, London. The memorandum continued with reasons for the siting of the plotting centre.

"A single main plotting centre as opposed to several centres each serving groups of mirrors will enable intersections to be obtained between any two mirrors, in particular, if one be North and the other South of the Thames. There are no GPO cables across the Thames Estuary, so that GPO communications between two mirrors one North and one South of the Thames will of necessity pass through Toll Exchange, so that this place is the best centre of gravity from the line point of view."

An old problem, familiar to those with experience of the Denge site, was also raised in this memorandum.

"Building developments have resulted in a revised arrangement for the 200 ft mirror and the 30 ft mirror originally proposed for the Clacton site. The 200 ft has had to be moved to Frinton, and the 30 ft has had to be sited further West." (Map 1 - p.23)

Several other points were mentioned, including high land prices, and the need for fencing of the sites. Cost was a recurring theme. The memorandum ended with a suggestion that the Dungeness (Denge) 200 ft and 30 ft mirror designs be used as models for the Thames Estuary system.

By the Spring of 1934, it appears that although the R.E.Board had approved Percy Rothwell's proposals for a sectional 200 foot mirror, there were no proposals for immediate action. On 3 May, a memorandum from the President confirmed that he liked the idea, but "as the Thames Estuary project is in effect a large scale test and examination of our early warning devices, we do not wish to prejudice the issue by having one of the 200 ft mirrors constructed in this way. We think, however, that the first extension to the system would afford a good opportunity to erect such a mirror."

Dr Tucker was soon involved in discussions about the proposed sectional mirror. On 28 May 1934 he wrote to the President of the Royal Engineers Board on the subject. "I am prepared to say that a mirror constructed in sections will be acoustically satisfactory if the panels are rigid, and if the joints are sealed with some material such as cement which will prevent transmission of sound through the mirror."

Various proposals for new 200 foot mirror sites must have been put to Dr Tucker at the time, as he went on to make some interesting comments. A site at Sandgate, just west of Folkestone, would be "too near for tactical purposes, a distance between 200 ft mirrors of 16 miles (26km) being desirable in general." He was obviously referring to the fact that the proposed site at Sandgate was too near the existing 200 foot mirror at Denge (Map 1 - p.23).

"A site at the North Foreland would make a natural extension of the Thames Estuary installation. On the other hand, the Denge site is not unfavourable for a second mirror facing South." This last point seems to make light of the problem of building developments near the Denge mirror, but it may relate to discussions about a mirror site on an unspoiled area further south near Dungeness. Dr Tucker continued by commenting on another proposed site. "If a site near Abbots Cliff be chosen, the two experimental 200 ft mirrors could yield intersections and work together. Money would also be saved by this choice, as a direct telephone system will be available." Abbots Cliff is the correct distance from Denge in terms of the proposed spacing of a chain of 200 foot mirrors. It also had the advantage that a 20 foot mirror was already on the site, thus saving the need to acquire new land.

Dr Tucker also mentioned other factors in relation to the site at North Foreland. "The site at the North Foreland will obviously be a necessary tactical site if the mirror system is to be extended. At my last survey, no thought was given to the Golf Links area, as it was not known that any part of it would be available. If the extension round the Kent coast is contemplated, I think another visit should be paid, with a view to selecting a most favourable site."

On 24 September 1934, Percy Rothwell had a meeting with "Mr Fay, Assistant Director of Works and Buildings, Air Ministry." His report mentioned the control cabin to be attached to the 200 foot mirror. "I mentioned the essential requirement of silence and view in the listening chamber, and the difficulties of effective ventilation and weather proofing consistent with these requirements." On the subject of the forecourt of the mirror, he reported that "some remarks were made about paving of the forecourt. I said the essential requirements were tidiness, the necessity for avoiding maintenance and the growth of herbage which might set up noise in a breeze. I agreed that tarmac would be quieter to the tread than concrete." Dr Tucker had reservations about the forecourt, and in a covering note, dated 3 October he commented "I am not disposed to agree to tarmac as an alternative to concrete."

The Royal Engineers Board wrote to the Air Ministry on 8 October 1934, in relation to Rothwell's mirror design. "In view of the greatly reduced cost of the sectional design, we recommend that it be used in the case of the mirror proposed for Reculver. In the improbable event of some acoustical shortcoming becoming evident after the construction, we foresee no difficulty in converting the wall into a solid block according to the standard design which it is recommended should be used for the Frinton mirror." The various sites mentioned on the Essex coast make a logical chain from south to north, starting at Asplins Head, then Tillingham, and on over the River Blackwater estuary to Clacton and Frinton (Map 1 - p.23).

A letter from the Secretary of the Air Ministry to Air Defence of Great Britain Headquarters in late 1934 draws attention to problems at that time. "Owing to the difficulties in finding sites, and in obtaining Treasury Sanction for the scheme, (which sanction has even now not been received) and numerous other delays, I cannot hold out any hope that the mirrors will be completed until after the end of June 1935."

By 17 December 1934, there was better news in another letter from the Air Ministry to the Officer in Command of the Air Defence of Great Britain. "I am directed to inform you that approval has been given for the purchase of the land required, and for the work to proceed, in connection with the proposed acoustical mirror system for the Thames Estuary, on the basis of two 200 ft mirrors and seven 30 ft mirrors."

The success of the Thames Estuary scheme depended not only on the design and siting of sound mirrors, but also on the associated network of communications. Dr Hart, a member of the Air Defence Experimental Establishment with a particular interest in communications was closely involved in that aspect of the project.

He pointed out that "the extension of the distance between mirror and plotting centre from about ten (16km) to about eighty miles (129km) introduces new problems in technique. In particular, it will not be possible to use DC (Direct Current) signalling methods, and recourse will have to be had to AC (Alternating Current) methods. The adoption of AC signalling will preclude the use of the methods adopted in 1934 for outward signalling from the plotting centre to the mirrors. Some experiment will be necessary on these lines. In order to design a plotting centre for the Thames Estuary scheme, it will be necessary to know how many simultaneous raids should be capable of being dealt with. It might be possible to arrange for a party line from two or more mirrors, thus effecting economy in lines." However, he could see a problem with this, in the "the impossibility of speaking to one of the party line mirrors without interfering with the communications to the others. The question of the unique case in which a 30 ft (9.1m) and 200 ft (61m) mirror are situated at the same place will have to be considered, that is whether one or two pairs of lines should be provided."

As suggested in connection with the Hythe system, one solution to the problem of long distance communication was to use DC lines for a short distance to a 'converting station', where DC/AC conversion would enable AC transmission to a distant plotting station.

The need to connect plotting stations with control centres over long distances was to arise again only a few years later, when the radar defence system was established. There seems little doubt from documentary evidence, and memories of people involved, that the experience gained in the area of communications during the acoustic years was of value at a later date.

CHAPTER THIRTY-ONE

THAMES PROJECT ABANDONED

A letter from the President of the Royal Engineers Board to Dr Tucker in December 1934 stated the position adopted by higher authority at that date in relation to the Thames Estuary Scheme.

"We have heard from the the Air Officer, Commander in Chief, that it would be premature at this state to put in hand the provision of signal apparatus for the Thames Estuary system. They are to tell us when the time is ripe. Accordingly your work under this head should be directed towards completing all the necessary particulars required for preparing a scheme on paper when called for. Your own system is to be maintained, and the records kept in such a form that when the provision of further apparatus is required, the work can be put out to tender." The phrase "your own system" is clearly a reference to the existing group of mirrors in the Hythe area.

The time seems to have been 'ripe' by 28 January 1935, as the President of the Royal Engineers Board asked Dr Tucker to submit "an outline of a scheme of Automatic Transmission of Readings, so that necessary arrangements with the Post Office may be initiated. Accordingly, please let us know when we may expect an outline of the project showing the lines required and the arrangements necessary for housing displays, apparatus and plotting rooms."

Dr Tucker replied on 31 January, outlining what was required for the "Acoustical Mirror Transmission System." He listed essential requirements for "the production of the Estuary Scheme." These were "a plotting centre in London to deal with the four Hythe mirrors (a room in a London exchange); a converting centre to convert from DC (direct current) to AC (alternating current) which involves space on racks in the Folkestone Automatic Exchange; lines between Folkestone and the Plotting Centre; a temporary display board, and a plotting board, experimental in character, which would have to be made by the Air Defence Experimental Establishment. Trials for this equipment should be predicted for the end of July 1935. This work is of such magnitude that it demands immediate decisions and authority to proceed at Biggin Hill without delay."

The immediate cost of the work concerned Major R.G. Lamb, Superintendent of the Air Defence Experimental Establishment. He wrote to the Royal Engineers Board about the matter on 1 February 1935, suggesting that as the work was in connection with the Thames Estuary Scheme, the expense would be a "fair Charge" against the Air Defence of Great Britain.

Early in 1935, a memorandum on the subject of communications was posted from Royal Air Force Headquarters, Air Defence of Great Britain, to the Air Ministry. Dr Hart of the Air Defence Experimental Establishment received a copy of the memorandum headed "Acoustical Mirror Warning System" on 4 February 1935. "All acoustical mirrors to both north and south of the Thames Estuary to be connected to a mirror operations room. The exact location of such an operations room will be governed principally by the suitability of the land-line facilities in the area. All land-lines between mirrors and the mirror operations room to be suitable for automatic working, the automatic apparatus concerned being developed by the Air Defence Experimental Establishment under the supervision of Dr Hart. Lateral communication between mirrors will not be required. Speech circuits will be arranged between the mirror operations room and Fighting Area Headquarters Operations Room. Owing to the necessity for co-ordination of reports between mirrors, to allow for sound lag and other considerations, the development of automatic apparatus to cope with the varying factors involved is highly desirable. Much work has already been carried out by the ADEE. Experimental equipment was installed at Littlestone (Denge) last year which functioned satisfactorily. The total cost of the automatic equipment for the complete Thames Estuary organization of two 200 ft (61m) and seven 30 ft (9.1m) acoustical mirrors, with necessary apparatus in the mirror operations room, is estimated at approximately £10,000."

A report of a meeting held at the General Post Office on Friday 15 February 1935 was also concerned with practical details of the communication system. "Existing War Department private lines are to be used for the Abbot's Cliff-Folkestone circuit, and for one Denge-Folkestone circuit. The existing Abbot's Cliff-Hythe (Roughs) circuit will be broken at Folkestone Exchange, and the existing Denge-Hythe (Roughs) and Abbot's Cliff-Hythe (Roughs) circuits will be joined at Hythe (Roughs)." Although rather difficult to follow, the overall idea was to integrate communications between the three sites in the Hythe system into the main telephone network, and thus make them part of a larger scheme to cover the Thames Estuary.

The minutes of a meeting of the Air Defence of Great Britain devoted to the "Thames Estuary Project," held on 22 February 1935, contained further details, and demonstrated the state of planning reached by that date.

The Air Defence of Great Britain hoped to be "self supporting in the matter of mirror listening and operating by 1936. Graduates from the 1935 training might still be available for use in 1936." Presumably, 'graduates' means people trained on the Hythe system. "The principle of having an officer in charge of the Control Room was accepted. Shortage of qualified staff might make this difficult. Training of an officer might be possible at Biggin Hill, and another during the 1935 exercises."

"For 1936, two wireless operator mechanics would be required" and there was to be further co-operation with the Post Office Research Department "in the quest for a reliable method and technique." This last point refers to the land line connections between various parts of the system.

Under "Transmission Experiment, 1935", the Minutes continued "the Hythe four mirror system to be used, with Headquarters at Faraday Building, to devise a method of working for the Thames Estuary Project for 1936. The General Post Office would hire out lines, relays, and DC-AC (direct current to alternating current) converting equipment to provide interconnections for the Denge-Hythe-Folkestone-London circuit. Estimated cost £250, for equipment to be used again on the Thames Project, and a GPO charge of £200. This amount was being expended entirely on Air Ministry account, and Air Defence of Great Britain proposed to tell the Air Ministry this."

The minutes included some references to "operational details." A minimum of 3 raids was to be dealt with at a time. "Simultaneous speech and dialling facilities between mirrors and control room should not be provided until proved to be essential. For the present, speech would be restricted to non-dialling periods. The question of the siting of the Thames Estuary Control Room is to be a matter for future consideration."

Dr Hart met an official of the General Post Office Telephone Department in January and February of 1935 to discuss communications in the mirror system, including matters related to the Thames Estuary Scheme. Apparently the room in a London Post Office building, probably Faraday House, which had been used in previous years as a control centre for the sound mirrors could not be spared, and 'other possibilities' were being explored. The proposed connecting lines between Folkestone and London were discussed in relation to costs. There would be no difficulty in accommodating the extra lines in the Folkestone telephone exchange, but the idea of having teleprinters on the circuit was abandoned.

The proposed sectional mirror for Reculver still figured in correspondence between Major R. G. Lamb, R.E., Superintendent of the Air Defence Experimental Establishment at Biggin Hill, and the Royal Engineers Board on 8 March 1935.

"Sectional Mirror for Reculver. The centre of curvature of the mirror is 7 ft above datum, this height being necessary to clear the front wall screening the listeners. Two ventilators only are required in the listening chamber in order that the surface may be disturbed as little as possible, and its resonant properties remain unaffected as far as possible. The position of the access gate should be decided later." This correspondence ends with a request for clarification in relation to the Thames Estuary Scheme. "Will you confirm that the Air Ministry are preparing drawings for the remaining mirrors."

Evidently Dr Tucker's request for control room facilities was considered carefully by the Post Office, but there seems to have been a somewhat grudging allocation of space, and it is apparent that the Post Office did not wish the mirror experiments to get in the way of normal business. Mr B.L. Barnett of the General Post Office wrote to Dr Hart at the Air Defence Experimental Establishment on this topic on 12 April 1935. Marking his letter 'secret' he continued: "Dear Hart, I am writing to confirm the provisional arrangement made to let you have the use of part of the Old Central Exchange switch room in Faraday Building (North Block). We will endeavour to let you have the room by the middle of May, and we can let you use it until the end of August when we shall require the space in connection with an extension of the Trunk Exchange."

Major Lamb, Superintendent of the Air Defence Experimental Establishment, was concerned about delays in the construction of equipment to transmit mirror information to control rooms. He wrote to the President of the Royal Engineers Board on 3 May 1935, referring to the experimental programme planned for July 1935. Major Lamb pointed out that "any delay in this years work must be reflected in the provision of the equipment for the Thames Estuary Scheme in 1936." Included with this communication were blueprints showing the arrangement of lines at Lydd and Folkestone Exchanges which connected the sites at Denge, Abbots Cliff and Hythe. Hythe Exchange number 67227 was connected directly to Faraday Building. Dr Hart was much involved with this work, and copies of some of the papers were also sent to Mr Ferguson at Hythe.

In a memorandum of 29 May 1935, Dr Hart, who was in charge of the control room at the GPO Faraday Building, referred to the subject of preserving secrecy during the acoustic experiments. "It has been thought desirable, both from the General Post Office and our points of view, not to emphasize the connection with the Fighting Services of the experiments in question. In this regard it is pointed out that there are working in Faraday Building not only GPO personnel, but also Contractor's men who have presumably signed no declaration under the Official Secrets Act. Actually the connection with the Fighting Services is known only to three or four GPO personnel. To the remainder, the experiment is a General Post Office engineering experiment and, as such, excites no interest. It is therefore suggested that all Service personnel visiting or using the room should wear plain clothes, and that in the case of RAF operating personnel, they be instructed not to disclose their connection with the RAF."

By June 1935 the Air Ministry had apparently accepted responsibility for the project, and was directly funding the "The Thames Estuary Acoustical Mirror System."

A memorandum from Headquarters, Air Defence of Great Britain, Uxbridge, to the Secretary of the Air Ministry on 17 June 1935, headed "Manning of Acoustical Mirrors" gave details of the potential involvement of over 500 people. The figures indicate that the business of creating an acoustic early warning system on a considerable scale was being taken very seriously at that time. Under a sub-heading "Thames Estuary, Denge and Hythe", the staffing was listed against the various types of mirror. "200 ft (61m) mirrors total: 45, 3 crews of 5 x 3 Reliefs; 30 ft mirrors (9.1m) total: 60, 10 crews of 2 x 3 Reliefs; Control Rooms: 24, 2 crews of 4 x 3 Reliefs." The complement was to include "6 Officers or well educated non-commissioned officers", making a total of 129 people. Under a second sub-heading "Remainder of Scheme for South East Coast", the staffing details were "200 ft mirrors, total 315; 30 ft mirrors, total 24; Control rooms, total 60; the personnel to include 15 officers or N.C.O's, Total 399."

In July 1935, passes were issued for entry to Faraday Building from the Air Officer in Command, Fighting Area, Uxbridge. As Dr Tucker was at various times in charge of a team which included Dr Hart, he was classified as 'known to Dr Hart' and allowed in without a pass. In the same month, the Superintendent of the Air Defence Experimental Establishment sent a report to the Royal Engineers Board, adding a note that "the report contains, with complete detail, the principles, construction and operation of the Automatic Reporting Apparatus for the Hythe Installation, and with certain modifications, it will be applicable to the Thames Estuary Installation."

Visits by VIP's to Faraday Building were "on the cards", but a note of 10 July 1935 recorded that "a preliminary trial of this apparatus on 9 July was not successful."

A further point, relating to RAF personnel at the Faraday Building, occurs in a letter written by Major Lamb on 17 July 1935. "With reference to Dr Hart's letter, dated 29 May 1935, it has been found impracticable for the rank and file of the RAF who will man the automatic apparatus at Faraday Building to wear mufti, as the personnel familiar with its operation are not in possession of mufti." It is hard to imagine that these men did not possess civilian clothing. Perhaps the meaning of the statement is that the 'mufti' was at home, and not immediately available.

After the experiments at Faraday Building in July 1935, some of the equipment was dismantled and sent to Biggin Hill. Letters of thanks were sent to various GPO people at Canterbury and Faraday Building and the Post Office research centre at Dollis Hill.

At about this time, it looks as if some of those involved in the Thames Estuary Scheme were informed about current radar experiments. A note scribbled on a file by an officer with an illegible signature on 27 July 1935 reads "we might not use the mirrors at all in the end, according to latest information, as the scientific committee hopes to evolve something better." At the time of this note, radar research had been in progress at Orford Ness on the Suffolk coast since 13 May 1935, and in those few months, impressive results pointing to 'something better' had already been achieved.

An important meeting of the Royal Engineers Board was held on 2 August 1935 to consider the "Communications and Electrical Requirements of the Thames Estuary Acoustical Mirror System." The Air Defence Experimental Establishment was represented by Drs Hart and Paris, two colleagues of Dr Tucker who was not present on this occasion. The minutes of the meeting recorded the decision that the "mirrors are to be completed by June 1936". On the subject of communications "proposals for transmitting observations from the mirrors were outlined and illustrated by reference to the 1935 Hythe-Dungeness system, using the control room in Faraday Building."

Much of the discussion revolved around matters concerned with the central control room in London, and the arrangements provided for the mirror system by the Post Office. From the lack of any further documentary references, it appears that the idea of a control room at Grain on the south side of the Thames Estuary was not pursued. The Minutes of the Royal Engineers Board, under "Conclusions and lessons learnt" contain a statement that the best place for a control room was near a terminal of trunk telephone lines. Another conclusion was that " when the experimental stage is over, the vulnerability of Faraday Building is to be considered." At this distance in time, it is not apparent what 'vulnerability' means here; it could mean vulnerability to air attack, but it is more likely to be a reference to the security problems posed by the siting of a control room in a building inhabited by people who had nothing to do with the air defence system.

The Minutes include further points about the control room. It was needed for preliminary experiments early in 1936, and there was a suggestion that the control room should be "three times the size of that used in 1935. This experimental room is probably needed until the autumn of 1937." Various other requirements for the control room are listed, including a decision that "Dr Hart was to have a pied-a-terre in Faraday Building so that he could continue the work." There is also a reference to future plans. "It was possible that the system would require to be operated in 1936, and it was probable that this experimental stage would last until the Autumn of 1937."

A drawing of transmission lines, marked SECRET, and headed 'Acoustical Mirror System Thames Estuary Dialling Circuit Requirements' is included with the Minutes. The drawing shows two networks of lines, north and south of the River Thames. On the north side, London is connected to mirror sites at Clacton, Frinton, Tillingham and Asplins Head, with Converter Stations at Clacton and Southend. On the south side, lines connect London to mirror sites at Grain, Warden Point, Swalecliffe and Reculver, with Converter Stations at Chatham and Canterbury.

Despite all this planning, progress was brought to a halt by a letter from the Air Ministry to the Officer in Command of the Air Defence of Great Britain on 15 August 1935. "I am directed to inform you that the construction of the acoustical mirror system in the Thames Estuary has been suspended temporarily until about the end of September 1935, when a further communication will be sent to you after the position has been further reviewed."

This letter was followed by another on 23 September 1935, with bad news for those attempting to develop the mirror system. "It has been decided, in view of the possible development of alternative methods of detection, to suspend until the end of March 1936, all work on construction of the acoustical mirrors in the Thames Estuary. It is realized that the decision will render it impossible in any event to complete the scheme until some time in 1937. If it is decided to adopt an alternative method of detection, it is hoped that some of the sites already acquired for mirrors may be found suitable."

It is now clear that the Air Ministry based such decisions on the knowledge that by September 1935, radar researchers working on the Suffolk coast were achieving substantial results. A note by a Wing Commander, Air Operations, with an illegible signature, but written "on behalf of the Air Marshal, Air Officer In Command of the Air Defence of Great Britain" on 1 October 1935, also refers to possible new methods.

"For the time being, we can only await results of trials with alternative methods of detection, but in the Spring of 1936, we must find out whether the intention is to continue with acoustical mirrors, because if it is, we will have to train more people in 1936 to man the mirrors in 1937. All this must be very discouraging for Dr Tucker and his party. He asked me about it when I saw him at Biggin Hill the other day, and I was unable to enlighten him. I shall be seeing him again on Thursday 10 October at an RE Board Meeting, and will let him know then of the postponement of the construction programme, in case he should not have already been told by the RE Board, whose responsibility it is to keep him informed."

Despite the depressing news from the Air Ministry, a meeting of the Royal Engineers Board in October 1935 still devoted time to discussions about the importance of a central control room, and recorded a decision that the Army and the RAF should use the same system of reporting. This is a clear pointer to the future, when both the Army and the RAF were involved in the control and reporting system developed in the radar years.

Colonel R.S. Rait Kerr, President of the Royal Engineers Board wrote to the Superintendent of the Air Defence Experimental Establishment on two occasions in November 1935 with further bad news for those involved with the Thames Estuary Scheme. The gist of his correspondence was that "the War Office has now heard officially from the Air Ministry to the effect that they do not intend at present, or in the near future, to proceed with any further work on the communications required for a Thames Estuary System, as far as the type of transmission we installed for them at Faraday House this year is concerned. The Air Council has considered all the repercussions consequent on a suspension of the work, and has decided to suspend all action until the end of March 1936."

On 28 February 1936, Dr Hart wrote a memorandum on communications, probably as a result of his experience in the Thames Estuary project. He looked in particular at the subject of plotting, and his paper included references to sound locators, and also contained pointers to the future control and reporting system developed for Fighter Command.

"Plotting might be defined in essence as the determination in three dimensions of the position of raiding aircraft, including if necessary, other attributes of the raid, such as notably, the number of aircraft taking part. The information acquired must be transmitted to the place where use is made of it in time for such use to be effective."

The memorandum highlighted the importance of establishing the height of raiding aircraft, in order that the defending fighters might be scrambled in time to climb to interception altitude. This far-seeing document ended with a discussion about techniques of combining information from several listening posts, including reference to the use of "4 paraboloid" locators.

The Thames Estuary scheme was finally abandoned in May 1936. Apparently, Dr Hart had been asked to appear before the Committee for the Scientific Survey of Air Defence, often known by the name of its chairman, Henry Tizard, to explain the proposed communications system for the Thames Estuary project. A letter from the Headquarters of Number 11 Group, Royal Air Force, signed by Air Vice Marshal P.B. Joubert de la Ferte, CMG, DSO on 13 May 1936, must have been a disappointment for Dr Hart.

"Dear Hart,
I am sorry to say it has been finally decided not to ask you to come before the Tizard Committee to explain your scheme for communications. Mr Tizard does not think that his Committee is the appropriate place for this. He is, however most anxious that you and Watson-Watt should get together so as to avoid any overlapping of effort."

Watson-Watt was at that time leading his team in radar research at Bawdsey Manor on the Suffolk coast, where impressive ranges were being achieved.

References to an obsolete mirror in the Thames Estuary area occur in a letter from Major Boreham, who was involved with Joss Gap during the First World War. Writing to Dr Tucker in 1936, he recalled their common experience with the mirror. "I hope Joss will come back. It was most useful and most accurate, in spite of its somewhat crude collector. It was personnel that mattered in those days." Some time later, he wrote again on the subject with various suggestions for use of the Joss Gap mirror. Dr Tucker was not enthusiastic in his reply. "The mirror is regarded, I believe, as an encroachment, and only the Commander, Royal Engineers, Dover can advise as to whether they still retain any interest in it. I should think they would be glad to be clear of it." It is clear from Dr Tucker's discouraging reply to Major Boreham that there was no further use for the Joss Gap mirror. This was confirmed in a letter from the Air Ministry to the Commanding Officer of the Air Defence of Great Britain on 14 May 1936. "It has been decided not to retain the mirrors at Fan Hole, Joss Gap and Warden Point as it is understood that these mirrors are of an obsolete type, having been superseded in design by thirty foot mirrors." At the time of writing, the processes of natural cliff erosion and demolition have ensured that there are no significant visible remains of the obsolete mirror at Joss Gap, but the remnants of the Warden Point mirror are the still to be seen on the Isle of Sheppey. Collapse of the cliffs and wave action had resulted in the broken fragments of the mirror coming to rest on the beach at Warden Bay (Map 1 - p23 and illustration p30). The mirrors at Fan Hole were buried in the 1970s, but have recently been uncovered, restored and opened to the public by the National Trust (Epilogue - p409).

A more important sentence in the Air Ministry letter signalled the end of the Thames Estuary Scheme. "The suspension of the work on the acoustical mirror system in the Thames Estuary will be continued until the end of October next, when the matter will again be reviewed." In the light of the rapid success of radar, it is not surprising that there were no further developments in the Thames Estuary scheme, and the idea was abandoned at this time. Although nothing came of the project, plans for the building of mirrors in parts of the British Empire were to lead to one final development in the sound mirror story, and a sea voyage for Dr Tucker.

CHAPTER THIRTY-TWO

MALTA

Hotel Osborne stands in a narrow street in Valletta on the Island of Malta. The upper rooms command a fine view of the fortifications of this old walled city, built in the 16th century by the Knights of St John. The way to the hotel, climbing the steep streets from the Grand Harbour, passes near the Auberge de Castille, also built by the Knights as an inn, or place of rest and entertainment for members of the garrison. Close by are the two great bastions of St John Cavalier and St James Cavalier, guarding the entrance to the city. These historical remains, together with visible evidence of the effects of the Second World War, are reminders that Malta has been under siege more than once over the centuries.

Dr Tucker stayed at Hotel Osborne in March 1933. Like many before him, he was concerned with the defence of Malta, and as a representative of the Royal Engineers Board, his principal contact in Valletta was The Chief Royal Engineer, who was based in the Auberge de Castille. The objective of Dr Tucker's visit was to survey sites for several 200 foot sound mirrors. With a Fascist regime in power on the Italian mainland and Sicily, there were fears of a threat from that direction, and mirrors defending the approaches to Valletta and the Grand Harbour were regarded as a priority.

Colonel, later Brigadier A.P. Sayer of the Royal Engineers Board, who was to play a considerable part in the development of Army radar by the end of the Second World War, accompanied Dr Tucker on the reconnais-

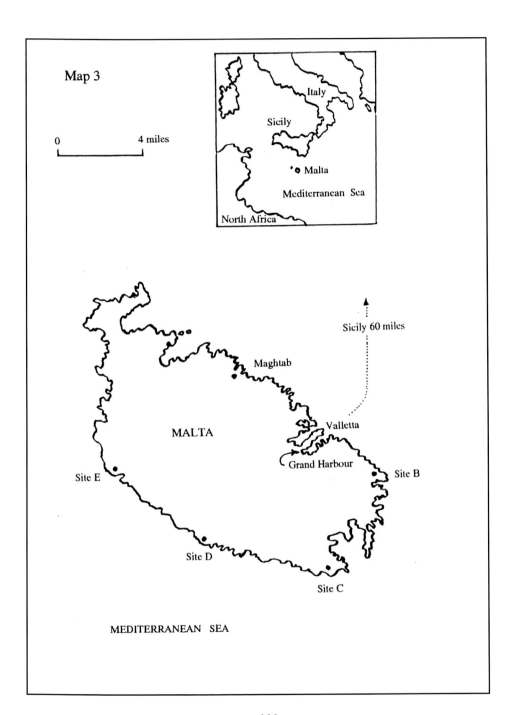

Map 3

0   4 miles

Italy

Sicily

Malta

Mediterranean Sea

North Africa

Maghtab

Sicily 60 miles

MALTA

Valletta

Grand Harbour

Site E

Site B

Site D

Site C

MEDITERRANEAN SEA

sance, which also included a visit to Gibraltar. Their report strongly recommended that "nothing should be sacrificed in the performance of these mirrors for the sake of a few pounds; every second of warning that is obtainable is of the utmost importance in a place like Malta where, on the Valletta side at least, no geographical assistance in range can be obtained." This last point was amplified in the report.

"Up to date, the mirror system has been considered almost entirely from the point of view of the defence of Great Britain, or of London only. A stage has now been reached where the mirrors have been proved, where definite results are assured." Discussing the difference between Great Britain and Malta, it was pointed out that in Great Britain, the idea was to site mirrors distant from an important centre such as London, in order to give early warning of the approach of aircraft. This was not possible in a small island such as Malta, where, for example, mirrors could not be placed in advance of Valletta, and thus "the length of warning obtainable is dependent on the range of the mirrors alone."

According to the report, observers in suitable positions on Malta, might pick up an attacking aircraft at a distance of 5 miles. Given an approach speed of 140 mph, that would give about 2 minutes warning. With a mirror, it was claimed that the pick-up range would be 20 miles, allowing a warning of 8 minutes. These figures were based on actual experience in England. Estimated costs were quoted, such as "Mirror, £2,100, Hut £150, Land £150 max, Electrical equipment £400." The estimated total cost of a mirror was put at £3000. The report stressed that mirrors guarding the approaches to Valletta should be constructed as a priority.

Malta was not the only overseas site at which mirrors were to be constructed, and reconnaissance visits were made to other parts of the British Empire at this time. During their trip in 1933, Dr Tucker and Colonel Sayer spent 9 days in Malta and 6 in Gibraltar, where they selected several sites for 200 foot (61m) mirrors. "Mirror No.1 Windmill Hill Flats - aspect South West, between Buffadero and West Batteries; Mirror No. 2 Europa Advanced Road, aspect South East - on a flat terrace North East of Governor's Cottage Farm; Mirror No. 3 Ferdinand's Battery Road, aspect North West; Mirror No. 4 North Front - aspect North East."

The report on the Gibraltar visit drew attention to the "population of 18,000 nearby" which would be a "detriment" to listening, and also to the possibility of trouble with "wind and sea noise".

Colonel Sayer was involved in another reconnaissance in December 1934 when he visited Singapore with Dr Paris, a colleague of Dr Tucker. A system of 8 mirrors was proposed, or failing that, "5 at least." Sites were chosen at "Lunchoo, Pengerang, Bedok, Blakang, and Mati." The report of this visit drew attention to potential noise problems not previously encountered. Observations discovered a noise level of 55 decibels due to crickets, birds and frogs at a distance. Not far from the village of Plintong, the cricket noise level was 61 decibels. An observation near a pool found frogs making noises at a level of 86 decibels, which would pose difficulties in the use of sound equipment, particularly at night. A suggestion was made that it might be possible to train operators to listen "through the noise made by crickets which is very distinctive and not very disturbing."

Despite the plans for mirrors in Gibraltar, Singapore and elsewhere, the main focus in the initial stages was on Malta. Before selecting any mirror sites, aircraft were used in tests of listening conditions on the island with the unaided ear. As a result of these tests, Dr Tucker decided to draw a "frontier line" 5 miles (8km) off the coast around the island.

Under "Selection of sites for the 200 ft Acoustical Mirrors for long distance listening", Dr Tucker made the following points:-

"There must be adequate overlap of the listening sectors up to the effective ranges of the mirrors, and an ultimate listening frontier which forms a continuous line about Valletta as centre. At the rear of the mirrors, there should be rising country capable of screening the mirror and its microphones from sounds of aircraft approaching from behind the mirror, and in front of the mirrors, there should be a view down to within a degree or two of horizon level - if not actually to that level. Rising ground at either flank is useful also as serving to protect the mirror from lateral disturbing sound. Under no circumstances should the mirror have a view of the breaking sea. This fortunately can generally be realized owing to the cliff structure of the shores. Sound screening of breaking seas is also more certainly secured by rising ground in the form of a slight slope reversal between the mirror and the cliff edge. Careful consideration should be given to the selection of a site well protected from wind."

As a further aid to the choice of sites, an aerial survey flight was made around the coast at an altitude of 2000 to 3000 ft.

A surviving map shows the five sites chosen for 200 foot mirrors on Malta. Each site was given an identification letter:

A	Maghtab Map reference:	412302 Bearing:	20 degrees E of N
B	Zonkor	533229	60 degrees E of N
C	Ta Karach	492153	138 degrees E of N
D	Ta Zuta	370196	193 degrees E of N
E	Tal Merhla	316243	259 degrees E of N

Reading in a clockwise direction, the mirror sites are in a rough circle round the island, starting with Site 'A,' west of Valletta, to Site 'B' east of Valletta, Site 'C' on the south-eastern corner of the island, Site 'D' on the south coast and Site 'E' on the south-west coast (Map 3 - p.330).

The reconnaissance report recommended that "the installation of five mirrors at the sites chosen be adopted in the following order of priority:- First priority: - Mirrors on Sites 'A' and 'B'; Second priority: - Mirror on Site 'C'; Third priority:- Mirrors on Sites 'D' and 'E'."

It is clear from this that mirrors 'A' and 'B' were important because they defended the approaches to Valletta and the Grand Harbour from the direction of Sicily.

Dr Tucker's report gave detailed descriptions of each of the five sites. Site 'A', at Maghtab, was described as "three and a half miles north west of Valletta, and one mile back from the north east coastline. It forms the western flank defence of Valletta. The listening axis is 19 degrees east of north. This site is on agricultural land, on ground a few hundred yards from a steep bluff which extends behind the mirror for more than a mile on either side. The bluff protects the mirror from sounds in the rear and from the southerly winds, and its flank also screens off the direct sounds from Valletta. A slight reverse slope in front of the mirror protects from the sea noise throughout most of the sector, although breaking sea is visible several miles in the North Easterly direction."

The report contained a reference to the use of mirrors 'A' and 'B' to obtain cross bearings on aircraft approaching Valletta. "Sites 'A' and 'B' give flank intersections 5 miles (8km) from Valletta and overlap giving a triangular area whose base extends over a 13 mile (20km) front at a range of 20 miles (32km)."

It is evident from Dr Tucker's report that the 200 foot mirror at Denge, near Dungeness in Kent, was regarded as a prototype for the Empire system. "In the matter of construction it is urged that no deviation from design on that adopted at Dungeness be contemplated. The dimensions of the mirror and its curvatures, vertical and horizontal, have been derived with the greatest care, based on tested physical principles."

Searchlight units near Valletta were equipped with sound locators at this time, and Dr Tucker pointed out that observers at such locators "would be helped by longer range warnings such as could be provided by a sound mirror." In his view" the best mirror for the purpose is the 200 ft concrete strip mirror."

Dr Tucker quickly addressed some of the practical problems involved in setting up a mirror system on Malta. The estimated cost of a 200 foot mirror had risen to £3,300, and samples of stone quarried locally in Malta were sent to the Building Research Station late in 1933, resulting in a favourable report on the quality of the stone on 3 February 1934.

Details of the setting out and construction of a 200 ft mirror were sent to Malta from Kent, under the heading "A.W. Letford, C. of W., Lydd" on 14 July 1934. The points made in these instructions were obviously the result of experience in building the Denge 200 foot mirror, under the supervision of a Royal Engineer officer from Lydd, only four years previously.

A brick or concrete pier about 18 inches (46cm) square and 8 ft (2.4m) above the foundation level was to be used as a datum point. When striking out the radius, the advice was that it was necessary" to employ several men to keep the tape absolutely straight when checking." Piano wire was found to be more satisfactory.

Although some of the terms used are slightly obscure to a layman, it is clear from the instructions that great care was to be taken with the casing used to form the concrete mirror surface. "The casing must be wrought, fronts cleaned off, and the whole well soaped or lime washed. No undue forces should be applied when removing the casing in order to avoid the danger of fracture. All concreting to be done from the front. Concrete to be carried up inclined running boards which need to be firm to avoid spoiling the casing. Top edges should be bull-nosed to avoid noise over the sharp angles. Ideally the concrete should be laid continuously. If constructed in sections, care is needed at joins. Slump tests to be made frequently to check that the contractor is not making the concrete too wet." The final instruction was to "photograph the work". The 'inclined running boards' mentioned in these instructions can be seen in a photograph of the construction of the prototype 200 foot mirror at Denge in Kent. (See p.100)

The ambitious plans to construct a ring of mirrors around Malta were not carried out, and in the event, only one mirror was erected. This was at Site 'A' at Maghtab, north west of Valletta. (Map 3 - p.330) According to a letter from the President of the Royal Engineers Board to Dr Tucker at the Air Defence Experimental Establishment, work was in progress in the autumn of 1934.

"Malta 200 ft mirror: In order that we may arrange our programme of summer experiments for 1935, we should like to feel assured that the staff earmarked to install the electrical apparatus in your 200 ft mirror, now building, will be able to carry out and complete the work prior to mid April 1935 at the latest. Will you please let us know when you expect to be ready for the installation of the instruments to commence, and also when you expect to have the constructional work completed."

Dr Tucker must have contacted Colonel C.W.Bushell, the Chief Engineer, Malta, who replied to the RE Board on 11 November 1934.

"The present position with regard to this mirror is that the site has been acquired, and soil cleared down to rock level. The approach road and water supply are complete, and constructional stores have arrived. Tenders are being called for in about three days time. I propose to include one or more English firms with special experience of Malta, and work may not therefore start until the middle of December. Allowing three and a half months at least for construction, I am of the opinion that April 1st is the earliest date that we shall be ready for the installation of the electrical apparatus, and I do not feel certain that I can guarantee that date."

The President of the Royal Engineers Board wrote to The Chief Engineer, Malta on 29 December 1934. His letter stated that the electrical instruments were ready "but as it will not now be feasible to install and test them in Malta before our summer programme in May, this part of the project will have to be postponed until after mid June. As soon as you can give us a firm date for completion of the structure, we shall conclude our arrangements. Meanwhile, the Air Defence Experimental Establishment officers concerned have been warned to prepare to leave England early in June."

A lengthy letter from the President of the RE Board to the Chief Engineer Malta on 25 February 1935 included details of the people involved.

"Malta 200 ft Mirror. We are now arranging for the officers who will commission the mirror to embark early in September. Installation of apparatus: three weeks will be spent on this work. Local assistance will be required as under:- Wireman, 3 weeks; Mason 3 days; Carpenter 6 days; Labourer 4 weeks. We suggest that the Foreman of Signals, who will have to maintain the mirror equipment, should assist in its erection and so become familiar with its details. The following personnel could be trained after completion of the installation of the apparatus:- one officer, two NCO's, three sappers. Time required: six weeks. In this connection, we would like to offer you an officer vacancy on a course we are running for the RAF at Dungeness from 24 June - 19 July. Aircraft required should consist of at least one Flight for the period, and a Squadron should be available for at least three flights during the exercises. Day and night flights should be practised during the programme. Assuming that the full programme is carried out, accommodation will be required for 9 weeks for the two officers. These will be Mr Ferguson, Grade 'C', whose status is roughly that of a Senior Captain, and Mr Handford, Grade 'E', whose status is approximately that of a Senior Warrant Officer, Class I. It is important that these officers be economically housed as they both have heavy home expenditure."

Methods of personal address at this period, when professional people tended to use surnames, results in frequent documentary references to 'Ferguson' or 'Handford', but no use of first names, and rare use of initials.

Mr Ferguson is sometimes given his initial 'R', and he has been named Robert by those with memories of the period. In the case of Mr Handford, such enquiries have produced no result.

The difference in status between the two Air Defence Experimental Establishment officers is reflected in a reply from the Chief Engineer, Malta. "Accommodation can be arranged as follows:- Mr Ferguson can be a member of the Royal Artillery Mess at Tigne, living in single officers quarters, or he can live in a hotel for approximately 50 to 60 shillings (£2.50 to £3.00) a week, full board and lodging. Mr Handford can live in a hotel for about 50 shillings a week." Mr Ferguson was apparently not keen to be billeted with the Army, and a further letter on the subject from the Royal Engineers Board informed the Chief Engineer Malta that "Mr Ferguson would like hotel accommodation arranged for him at the rate quoted. Mr Handford is making his own arrangements for accommodation."

The choice of these two particular officers from the Air Defence Experimental Establishment to go out to Malta was logical, as both Mr Ferguson and Mr Handford had already played prominent parts in the development of the prototype mirror system centred on the acoustic research station at Hythe in Kent.

A request in March 1935 from the Director, Acoustic Section to the Superintendent Air Defence Experimental Establishment, touched on practical details which were to cause a little difficulty. "The officers concerned would like to be informed what their subsistence rates will be during their stay in Malta." Further correspondence of 2 April, 24 June, and 22 July 1935 referred to arrangements for the passage by sea for Messrs. Ferguson and Handford, and the question of their allowances was still under discussion.

An undated copy of a letter to the Chief Engineer, Malta, from Colonel Edwards, President, Royal Engineers Board, headed '200 ft Mirror' contains the sentence "we are told that construction is now complete." Judging by correspondence in August 1935 about final details of the visit to Malta by Messrs Ferguson and Handford to install electrical equipment, it is possible to deduce that the structure of the Maghtab mirror was completed by the summer of 1935.

As the time approached for their visit to Malta, the two officers returned again to matters of detail. On 7 August 1935 Major Lamb, Superintendent of the Air Defence Experimental Establishment wrote from Biggin Hill to the President of the Royal Engineers Board.

"Messrs. Ferguson and Handford have raised the question of kit allowance for the visit to Malta. Mr Ferguson states that he will be put to the extra expense of buying trunks and hot weather kit, and estimates his expenses at £15. Mr Handford estimates his additional expenses at £3 for trunks. Whilst I have every sympathy with the claim, and forward the request, I feel that the utmost which they can press for is the cost of extra trunks, which I assess at £3 each, as the winter climate in Malta is not so oppressive as to call for special clothing." Major Lamb also wrote to Ferguson and Handford. "Will you please note that you will proceed to Malta, travelling overland on 30 August 1935."

The Royal Engineers Board informed the Air Defence Experimental Establishment that the officers should make their own arrangements with the P and O Steamship Company and claim a refund on the relevant form. In a reference to tickets for the journey to Malta, these were to be sent direct to the officers concerned at Hythe and Biggin Hill respectively. Finally, on 21 August, a memorandum to the Command Paymaster, Eastern Command dealt with the request for additional expenses. "A grant of £3 each to Mr Ferguson and Mr Handford has been approved, to cover expense of hot weather outfits during their forthcoming visit to Malta." Army red tape had at last been overcome with this grudging acknowledgement that Malta has a warm climate.

CHAPTER THIRTY-THREE

THE MAGHTAB MIRROR

Messrs Ferguson and Handford arrived in Malta at the beginning of September, 1935. In a handwritten letter from the Chief Engineer's office in the Auberge de Castille, Valletta, Mr Ferguson put down his immediate thoughts, addressing Dr Tucker by his military rank.

"Dear Major Tucker,
 2 September 1935
We arrived last night about 11.50 p.m. I saw the mirror this morning and it looks a good job; the stone work round the forecourt is absolutely perfect. The chamber has been altered in length, also it is higher; it is beautifully finished - the shelving downstairs has not been started. This will be put in hand tomorrow. Excuse rough note, but I wanted to get a line off to you. We had a pleasant and enjoyable trip, though rather expensive. Kindest regards."

Mr Ferguson wrote to Dr Tucker again on 10 September, also from the Chief Engineer's office. It is evident from his remarks that the previous concern of the two officers over hot weather clothing expenses was not misplaced.

"It is very hot, the temperature of the sea being 84 degrees Fahrenheit on Sunday. Handford is quite fit, and everything is going along nicely." The letter continued with a progress report on the fitting of equipment to the 200 foot (61m) mirror. Items covered included "fastening signal lamps to the forecourt wall and putting up cable-run for signal lamps. The mirror axis is being checked, before having the bearings painted. I have recommended the purchase of additional land in front of the mirror, in order that a fence may be erected. I have been introduced to the Commanding Officer at the RAF Aerodrome, and willing co-operation has been promised. It is estimated that the installation will be ready for preliminary trials by the 24th September. Sixteen men are to be trained for operating the mirror. A few

The control room and listening chamber behind
the 200 foot sound mirror at Maghtab, Malta

lectures will be given to the whole party, but it is proposed to split the party into small groups for the actual training. In a further letter from Chief Engineer's office, on 16 September, Mr Ferguson drew attention to problems with the control room on the back of the mirror. It was necessary to eliminate outside noise from this room as far as possible, making doors and windows something of a nuisance. But there was also a need for adequate ventilation, especially in a warm climate. Ferguson reported that the need for "additional ventilation of the control room is receiving attention. At the moment, no-one could exist for more than half an hour."

Despite Dr Tucker's instructions before the construction of the Malta mirror that the design should conform exactly to the prototype 200 foot mirror at Denge, there were some departures. One of these was the fact that the feet of the supporting buttresses protruded slightly at the point where

Buttresses projecting in front of the face of the 200 foot mirror at Maghtab, Malta

the front of the mirror face met the forecourt. These protrusions must have had some negative effect on the acoustical performance of the mirror. Mr Ferguson mentioned the point, remarking that listening in the forecourt appeared to be a little more difficult than at Denge. "The supporting buttresses are exposed to a height of 1 foor 7 inches (48cm) above the apron, this seems to be bad. The axis of the mirror is 20 degrees, not 19 degrees, so I have had to get new numbers engraved for the control panel - fortunately, I insisted on having a check. My letters may appear a little disjointed, but this is unavoidable as I have to use any office available."

Mr Ferguson continued: "This morning, I gave a preliminary lecture on the mirror at Valletta. The installing of the gear will be completed by this weekend, and test flights should begin on Monday morning. Graham Carter introduced me to the General the other day, and he expressed a wish to see the mirror in operation. PS. We are both keeping fit, but badly eaten up by sand flies etc."

The latter part of this letter indicates that the Maghtab mirror was ready for operations by September 1935. This is confirmed by a letter from the 'Officer Commanding Troops, Fortress Headquarters, Valletta, Malta' to 'The Under Secretary of State, The War Office, London SW1' on 21 September 1935, which included various details. The installation of instruments and training was proceeding, and plans were in hand to erect barbed wire and palisade fencing for security and wind shielding. "A caretakers quarter is to be built, with a window from which the forecourt will be visible. The approximate cost of the caretaker's quarter is £460. Meanwhile, a night watchman has been engaged and provided with a temporary hut."

In a letter to Dr Tucker on 28 September, Robert Ferguson explained his methods of communication at that time. He made use of the Chief Engineer's office in the absence of any other base, and although he was offered a typist, he chose to write in person in order that he could speak his mind without causing offence to the mirror people in Malta. This letter also gave the date on which tests began at the Maghtab mirror.

"The installation was brought into use for tests on the 23 September 1935. The machine, a IIIF, operated from 9.0 a.m. to 10.40 a.m. at a height of 8000 ft (2438m) and a distance of from 8 to 12 miles (13 to 19km); the courses selected were parallel to the coast. The system worked effectively. Similar flights took place on the 24th from 19.00 to 21.00 hrs. Morning flights also took place on 25, 26 and 27 September." The designation "IIIF" in Robert Ferguson's letter refers to a Fairey IIIF naval seaplane of the period. A map which survives with these letters shows tracks of an aircraft involved in a test on 30 September 1935. The aircraft was a "Scapa Flying Boat, height 7000 - 10,000 ft (2134 - 3048m), time- 5 p.m. to 7 p.m."

Written on the map in red ink is a note that "the Flying Boat was heard throughout the period of the exercise with ease on the loudspeaker, accurate bearings being recorded acoustically."

At this period, workmen were still doing a few final jobs on the mirror, such as "covering the cable along the trench wall which feeds the signal lamps; putting bearing numbers on the trench wall; ventilation of the listening chamber; packing the lookout window; installing lights in the three rooms."

During these activities, someone at the War Office raised a question with the Air Defence Experimental Establishment about the suitability of the 200 foot (61m) Malta mirror for detecting coastal motor boats. (CMB's.) As usual, the query was handed to Dr Tucker, who briefed Major Lamb, Superintendent of the ADEE as to his reply to the War Office. "Dr Tucker states that the Malta mirror is most suitably placed for CMB detection, as the cliffs give good screening for sea noise. A coastal motor boat under the cliffs would probably not be heard, but at ranges out to sea quite satisfactory records should be obtained."

By 30 September 1935, the President of the Royal Engineers Board was in correspondence with Dr Tucker at the Air Defence Experimental Establishment on the subject of the length of stay in Malta of Mr Ferguson and Mr Handford. It appears that the people at Malta had asked ADEE to allow Mr Ferguson to stay for another two months, but that "Mr Handford should return as soon as Mr Ferguson can spare him."

Replying on 2 October, Dr Tucker strongly deprecated the recall of Mr Handford, giving as his reason that Mr Ferguson and Mr Handford were equally expert with the mirror. Also, Ferguson had not been "quite fit". This had not interfered with his work up to that point, but provision needed to be made for emergencies, and Ferguson could not do all the work alone. In any case, Handford was not needed urgently at Biggin Hill. The mirror work was important, and "the extra expense of Mr Handford's stay in Malta should not be a serious argument in a matter of such vital importance."

Dr Tucker's view obviously prevailed, as Colonel C.W.Bushell, OBE, Chief Engineer, Malta, was advised by Colonel F.J.C.Wyatt, President RE Board that "we have no objection to your keeping Ferguson and Handford until you are confident that your trained crew can carry on unaided."

During October, Mr Ferguson sent in various progress reports from the Auberge de Castille, Valletta, Malta, addressed to the Director of Acoustical Research, Air Defence Experimental Establishment, Biggin Hill.

In the period 30 September to 5 October, flights were made by "Scapa Flying Boat" and "IIIF'" machines. On 4 October 1935, with a "Scapa Flying Boat, the range exceeded 20 miles (32km)."

On 10 October "the Boat was completely observed acoustically up to 20 miles. (32km) The General Officer in Command, the Chief Engineer, and Staff Officers were present for an hour and expressed their appreciation and interest. Sapper observers performed all operations throughout under the supervision of Handford and myself."

Reports for the weeks ending 19 and 26 October included summaries of results, and show, in some cases, good plotting of aircraft movements. Theodolites and telescopes were used to check acoustic plotting. On October 31st "the Scapa Flying Boat operated from 17.40 to 19.30 hrs at heights from 10,600 to 11,200 ft. (3231 to 3414m) Visibility moderate, acoustical ranges 30 to 36 miles (48km to 58km)."

A letter to Dr Tucker, headed "R.Ferguson, Chief Engineer's Office, Malta, 2 November 1935" indicated further successful tests of the mirror. Ranges of "25 to 35 miles" were achieved "this last week. I do not think there is anything to grumble about. The second Flight this week was carried out at 10,600 to 11,200 feet (3231 to 3414m), and the ranges were all over 30 miles (48km), the maximum being 36 miles (58km) if not more. Also the bearings were absolutely OK. I took no part other than walking round - the same applies to Handford. Handford is very fit and very keen - most helpful and full of cheer. Kindest regards to Mrs Tucker and Beryl (Dr Tucker's daughter). How did the Denge tests go?"

The performance of the Malta mirror as reported by Mr Ferguson is superior to that of other mirrors recorded in contemporary documents. Perhaps listening conditions on Malta were more favourable than those in the vicinity of the 200 foot mirror at Denge.

Apart from his duties at Maghtab, Mr Ferguson visited the other sites chosen for 200 foot mirrors on Malta. He had reservations about Site 'C' on the south east corner of the island, and suggested an alternative position. He also wrote to Dr Tucker asking for a ruling on the question as to when he and Handford should return to the UK. He ended his letter on an optimistic note. "The whole programme of training has been very successful and the mirror is doing its job exceedingly well as you will see from the results."

As a result of his correspondence with Mr Ferguson, Dr Tucker, wrote to the Superintendent of the Air Defence Experimental Establishment on 4 November 1935 with a query about the Maghtab mirror. "Reports from Malta relating to the 200 ft mirror continue to be favourable up to October 26th, and training is proceeding satisfactorily. Can a letter be sent asking by what date the handing over of the mirror at Malta may be expected."

The Superintendent replied to Dr Tucker's query on 8 November. "We are expecting a report from Malta any moment now; meanwhile, we have already asked for early warning if there is any question of retaining Ferguson and Handford beyond the original 12 weeks."

Ferguson continued to send progress reports to Biggin Hill. On 9 November 1935, he referred to a problem of aircraft operating at the wrong place and time. "It will be observed that morning training is largely spoiled owing to the presence of other aircraft carrying out exercises in the neighbourhood. An attempt is being made to minimize the trouble." Flying was hampered by bad weather, but on November 15, "the Flying Boat operated from 14.30 to 16.00 hrs. Heavy thunder showers curtailed the programme; visibility bad, acoustical ranges 21 to 26 miles."

At this point, in November 1935, the two ADEE officers were thinking of returning home. Ferguson referred to this in a letter to Dr Tucker. "We both feel that no further useful work can be done by staying longer, and as a Trooper is leaving Malta on 17 November, I have decided to allow Handford to return. I propose returning after the trials or before if you desire it."

Dr Tucker replied on 25 November. "I expect to see Handford in a day or two, so shall be nearly up to date with your news." He mentioned in his letter that the War Office had asked for Ferguson to call at Gibraltar on his way home, to advise on a noisy engine room in the Rock. In discussing this,

Dr Tucker observed that "the whole enclosure would behave like an organ pipe."

Judging by a letter from the Chief Engineer Malta to Dr Tucker, Air Defence Experimental Establishment, the two officers from ADEE created a good impression.

"Royal Engineers Headquarters Office, Auberge de Castille, Valletta, Malta. 11 December 1935.
"Dear Dr Tucker,
Mr Ferguson is leaving here on the Rawalpindi today, and I wish therefore to write to you and express my appreciation of the work both he and Mr Handford have done here. Mr Ferguson was really excellent, not only was he untiring in supervising the training of the crew, but proved himself most successful and tactful in dealing with the RAF, and was able to undertake all detailed arrangements for the Aircraft. The Mirror and Instruments seem to be working excellently. I am submitting a long official report.

Yours sincerely,
C.W.Bushell, Colonel,
Chief Engineer.

Following the return home of his colleagues, Dr Tucker wrote a full report on the Malta mirror for the Superintendent of the Air Defence Experimental Establishment. This report, dating from 16 January 1936, gives a useful summary of events up to that point.

"The electrical gear was installed during the first 3 weeks in September 1935. The work entailed fitting up 30 transformers, wiring 30 microphone circuits and 19 signal lamp circuits, the erection and spacing of microphones and signal lamps in the forecourt, and installing a Control Panel, Amplifier and Loud Speaker in the control cabin."

"Training commenced on 24 September 1935. Flights were arranged as far as possible to take place daily. A crew of two were trained during the first weeks flying for visual observation with the theodolite. Six Sappers reported daily for training and instruction, this being two more than the normal, recognized crew. From the 24 men originally detailed for instruction, 7 were found unsuitable after a few days training. It is considered that a crew of 4 can be trained in 16 flying hours. The observations were generally made during the afternoons or between sunset and dusk. The maximum range observed was 37 miles (60km), the minimum range observed was 21 miles (34km). The average range observed was 25 miles (40km) The maximum bearing error was plus or minus 2½ degrees. Flying boats were largely used for the range tests, as they were not restricted for distance from the coast."

A 24 hour test was carried out to find out the best way of manning the mirror. According to the report "16 men and 1 NCO is an excessive number. 12 men and 1 NCO are considered sufficient. Two forecourt observers are not efficient. They will persist in talking and patrolling together. Forecourt observers should be relieved every half hour. Control room observers can perform for 1 hour without fatigue. A crew of 4 on a 4 hour watch would be made up of one control observer, one forecourt observer, one visual observer on top of control room for daylight work with telescope, and one telephonist. The forecourt and visual observer should relieve each other at half hour intervals. The control observer and telephonist should relieve each other at intervals of one hour."

Dr Tucker made various comments about the construction of the Maghtab mirror.

"The forecourt need not be smoothed to anything like the extent carried out at Maghtab - this would reduce cost. The exposed parts of buttresses in front of the Mirror is a bad feature and breaks the continuity of the surface. The control cabin wall is curved to the shape of the mirror in the inside at the look-out window. This should be made rectangular.

A rubber floor should be fitted in the control cabin and also in the test room downstairs. Noises are transmitted to the cabin where a high factor of reverberation exists. A platform should be erected above the control room at a sufficient height to give all round visual observation. A central pillar is required to accommodate a telescope. The platform should be enclosed by a wall 4'6" (1.4m) high to give the observer protection."

Tests using a telescope were also carried out at the 200 foot (61m) mirror at Denge in Kent. The telescope, trained on an aircraft as it became visible, was used to check bearings previously given by the mirror. Unfortunately, doubts were cast on the efficiency of the mirror when, in some cases, aircraft were sighted before detection by acoustic means.

Dr Tucker also commented on matters related to training in Malta. He asserted that "training cannot be effectively carried out when aircraft are continuously operating at Ghallis Rocks i.e. diving in front and circling round the mirror. If the speed of aircraft increases to 250 mph (402kmph) which is generally assumed, the warning time is likely to be 6 minutes. This is based on the average range of the Maghtab mirror."

An Appendix to the report included lists of men trained, with comments. For example, Sapper Marriott was given a classification of 'B', and assessed as 'Fit for Control' and 'Keen'; Lance Corporal Chambers was classified 'C' and 'Fit for Control' but 'Not Keen'. Sapper Byers did not do well. He was classified as 'E', 'Not yet Fit for Control' and 'Not reliable'.

Although there was some success in mirror operations during the period when Messrs Ferguson and Handford were in charge, things did not always go well after their departure, as can be seen in a letter from 'L. Manton, R.E. Headquarters Office, Auberge de Castille, Valletta, Malta, to Colonel F.J.C.Wyatt OBE, MC, President, R.E. Board, Regents Park Barracks, Albany Street, London NW1, on 19 February 1936.'

"Dear Wyatt,
On 5 February 1936, we put up a pair of Scapa Flying Boats in order to demonstrate the Sound Mirror to General Sir Cyril Deverell. It was a failure. I enclose the report on the failure and should be very glad if you can help us." The letter suggested a need for "a device by means of which we can train the crew, without an aeroplane."

The attached report gave details of the problem. "The mirror was manned throughout both flights. The flight between 10.30 and 11.00 hrs. was not detected and it was assumed that the flight had not taken place. There was no acoustic detection of the flight between 12.00 and 12.30 hrs. until the aircraft were practically overhead. Even when the aircraft were within sight, listeners in the forecourt were unable to detect their sound, even when directed to the point where sound should have been strongest. Their sound was not heard at all in the control room. From the result of the mirror trials held in the Autumn it has perhaps been assumed that the satisfactory results then obtained were typical of what could be expected from the mirror throughout the year. Results on February 5th have shown this assumption to be wrong."

Dr Paris, writing on behalf of the Acoustic Section sent a memorandum to the Superintendent of the Air Defence Experimental Establishment giving possible reasons for the failure in Malta. The aircraft were flying at 2000 ft (610m) and he pointed out that "it is not unusual in Great Britain for the sound of aircraft at this height to be cut off at a range of a few miles by an acoustical horizon. Although an acoustical horizon will account for the failure of the forecourt listeners to hear the sound until the aircraft were very close, it does not explain why their sound was not heard at all in the control room, even when the aircraft were practically overhead. We feel that this indicates that the microphone circuits must have been at fault. There is no satisfactory way of training forecourt listeners apart from the use of aircraft."

Dr Tucker was also concerned by unsatisfactory mirror reports. He was anxious that unskilled officers, for example in Malta, did not blame the mirror for failures which could be attributed to unfavourable conditions, or unsatisfactory operation. Officers were advised to "ensure that targets fly in the sector of the mirror, and to eliminate as far as possible interference by other aircraft, speed boats etc. in the vicinity of the mirror. They must bear in mind that the mirror is designed for early warning, consequently the interval between the warning and the arrival of the aeroplane within range of the defences is the essence of the matter."

There were signs of doubts about the effectiveness of an acoustic early warning system in a letter from Malta on 20 June 1936. It was addressed to 'The Under Secretary of State, The War Office, London SW1' from "His Excellency, The Governor and Commander-in-Chief, Fortress Headquarters, Valletta, Malta."

The letter opened with a statement that the total cost for providing the first mirror on Malta was estimated at £4,500. It continued by drawing atten-tion to the fact, already mentioned in various reports, that the defences would have to cope with aircraft speeds of 250 mph (402kmph), and estimated that in those circumstances, the Valletta mirror would give about 6 minutes early warning. There were further references to problems caused by friendly aircraft flying near the mirror.

The most important points came at the end of the letter. "I have heard it stated that the acoustic mirror is not the correct solution to the problem of 'earliest possible warning' of the approach of enemy aircraft. If this is so, and there is any likelihood of the correct solution being arrived at soon, I do not recommend any more mirrors to be constructed." The final point made was that if there was nothing better, then "construction should go ahead on a second mirror on the SE side of the vital Valletta area." It appears from his letter that the Governor may have been aware of developments in radar at this time.

In July 1936, Colonel Colbeck, President of the Royal Engineers Board commented on the letter from Malta. "Our main contention is that for 2 years or more nothing better than the mirror is likely to reach a practical installation stage, consequently we suggest putting in more mirrors now to cover the interim period. Our view is that these mirrors will probably be of considerable value in any case, to supplement any other system of long range detection that may be developed." Colonel Colbeck was soon to be involved with such a new system of early warning, as by 1937 he was in charge of Committee 'D' of the Royal Engineers Board which dealt exclu-sively with radar.

Three officers visited the Maghtab mirror on 5 May 1937 by which time it seems to have been abandoned. A report of the visit, with an illegible signature, describes the state of the mirror at the time.

"I visited this mirror with Colonel Hunter and Captain Cowie. The condi-tion of the mirror is excellent. Slight cracks have occurred in the control room, due it is thought, to the large night-to-day temperature changes. There is no ventilation in the control room. The camouflage painting on the front is excellent. The unclimable fence is not a serious obstacle to sound, as the ground falls away rapidly in front, and the fence is well below the level of the mirror angle.

The electrical gear has been dismantled as there was some trouble due to the damp winter and lack of personnel. Several officers have lost faith e.g. Major Baillie, but others agree that the mirror has not yet been tried out over a long enough period, chiefly owing to lack of troops. Major Edwards agrees that ranges up to 35 miles have been obtained on occasions, and on other occasions, notably when the Chief of the Imperial General Staff visited the mirror, the mirror was useless. There was no opportunity to fit the new amplifier, but the amplifier with complete instructions was handed over to Captain Cowie." After this report, no further documentary evidence was found relating to events at Maghtab.

The Maghtab mirror remained in excellent condition at the turn of the 20th century, enjoying a kind climate, and a protected site inside a radio compound. The Malta mirror is a copy of the 200 ft (61m) mirror at Denge except for one difference, described by Mr Ferguson in 1935. The buttresses, which look similar at the back of the mirror, protrude slightly at the front of the mirror, at the point where the foot of the mirror meets the forecourt. These protrusions are like small vertical triangles, sticking out about 1' 7" (48cm) as Ferguson described. The main mirror is made of concrete, but the wall at the front of the forecourt is made of local Malta stone, covered with a skin of cement, which has come away in places, revealing the stone underneath. The wing walls appear to be of the same construction. The forecourt is in excellent condition, and it is similar in design to the Denge forecourt, with a lower area towards the front where the microphones were mounted.

One interesting difference between the Maghtab and Denge mirrors is that at Maghtab, at a point on the centre line and axis of the mirror, located some distance ahead of the front forecourt wall, there is a small concrete pillar, hidden in bushes at the time of writing. On top of this low pillar, and in the exact centre of the top face, is an indentation. This must be where an instrument was sited when the pillar was used as a datum point for setting out the mirror. Various figures are inscribed on the concrete pillar. These could well be mathematical factors used when siting the mirror. Presumably, such a datum point would also have been necessary at Denge, but it does

Forecourt of the 200 foot mirror at Maghtab, Malta
*The control room, with a window in the mirror face as at Denge, is made of local
stone. On top of the control room is another open topped enclosure, rather like the
bridge of a ship, on which it is likely, from documentary evidence, that a visual observer
with a telescope was stationed, with the object of checking the bearings observed aurally
by the listeners. From that position, there is a splendid view along the axis of the mirror.
As described by Dr Tucker at the time of his reconnaissance in 1933, the site of the mirror is below a ridge, some distance from the sea, although looking along the axis from
the top of the control room, the coast and sea are clearly visible.*

not seem to have survived. Instructions about the pillar were sent to Malta
from the Royal Engineers at Lydd at the time of the setting out of the
Maghtab mirror.

In the absence of further documentary evidence, the story of the Malta
sound mirror seems to end around 1937. It is time to return to Hythe, where
doubts about the future of an acoustic early warning system were also beginning to cloud the horizon.

View along the face of the 200 foot Maghtab mirror from the top of the control room. The cables are not part of the original structure.

View towards the sea from the hills above Maghtab, Malta. The 200 foot mirror can be seen in the middle distance and an early watch tower on the headland. In this late 20th century scene, extensive building works have taken place since the construction of the mirror in 1935.

Maghtab 200 foot mirror. View along axis from the top of the control room. Note the excellent condition of the front wall and flooding in the lower part of the forecourt. Coastal watch towers dating back to the days of the Knights of St John can be seen from the telescope position on top of the mirror and also from the hills behind the site. There is a parallel on the Kent coast in England, where Martello towers, built at the time of a potential invasion by Napoleon, can be seen from the site of the Acoustic Research Station on the Roughs at West Hythe. The face of the Maghtab mirror is painted with lines and colours, and according to the people in Malta, these are intended to represent the typical local environment of small fields, bounded by stone walls.

CHAPTER THIRTY-FOUR

DOUBTS

During the period of experiments with the 200 foot (61m) mirror on Malta, there was also concern about the future of the prototype 200 foot mirror on the south-east coast of England. On 22 January 1936 Colonel Colbeck, President of the Royal Engineers Board sent a memorandum to the Superintendent of the Air Defence Experimental Establishment drawing attention to problems at Denge on the Dungeness peninsula. He was concerned about proposals to buy land "90 acres, to the South West of the present site, the property of the Southern Railway" on which to build new mirrors (Map 2 - p.64).

"Pending a decision from the Air Ministry as to whether the mirrors are required or not, we cannot make a case for the purchase of land from an operational point of view. At the same time, the site is essential for experimental purposes, and if the site is built over, the experimental value of the mirrors will, we are now informed, be practically nil. In the circumstances, it is felt we might risk waiting another year. It is of course possible that someone will offer to buy the site at short notice, but could not we arrange with the Southern Railway company to give us first refusal? In another year, the whole question of the necessity for mirrors will, we hope, be settled."

The memorandum continued: "It is by no means certain the 200 foot acoustical mirrors will be adopted for Air Defence of Great Britain purposes. The Air Ministry have not yet committed themselves on this point. We understand that the view prevailing at the moment in that Department is that such mirrors will form no part of their air defence scheme."

The Air Ministry had evidently decided by this time that there was no place for acoustic mirrors in an aerial defence system. In relation to proposals to move to the new mirror site at Dungeness, the Air Ministry's response was "we therefore suggest postponement." It seems probable that this decision was related to the early success of radar.

The War Office, advised by the Royal Engineer and Signals Board, was also aware of the potential of radar. In February 1936, reports were coming in from Dr Paris, at that time on detachment from Biggin Hill to Watson-Watt's radar research team at Bawdsey. He used the code word 'Cuckoo' to refer to radar.

"We have now made a further study of 'Cuckoo'. The method has so far been devised entirely for long range detection i.e. for ranges up to 130 km depending on the height of the aerial. There is no immediate intention to develop it for short range location, unless the Army wishes and is prepared to finance it, but its application to Fortress Defence makes it essential. As a mere sentry, it will be adequately developed by the Air Ministry, but it remains for us to supply the missing links to bind it to the defence system."

Dr Paris recommended that "we should co-operate with the Air Ministry in developing 'Cuckoo' as a sentry in fortresses and studying the possibility of linking it to the Defence System." To accomplish these objectives, he proposed various areas of research including: "a) the application of the present method for short range location; b) method of getting elevation; c) technique for instantaneous translation of oscillograph pattern into co-ordinates of a point in space and continuous following of that point as it moves at a speed of 250 mph; d) conversion of this translation into instrumental control of searchlights and guns; e) investigation of some method (e.g. direction finding) of monostatic working in order to avoid the well known disadvantages of the two station method (the only method possible now)."

This report included a suggestion that there should be study of "methods of allying with existing acoustical instruments e.g. 200 ft mirror."

Dr Tucker continued to express his concern about the mirror site at

Denge. On 11 February, 1936, he wrote to the Superintendent, Air Defence Experimental Establishment, heading his letter "Dungeness Acoustical Mirror." After discussing the problem of encroachment by buildings and roads, for which he provided sketch maps, he concluded: "Two air photographs are attached which show the rapid development in building which is taking place along the concrete road and light railway, and emphasizes the need for some rapid action if the mirror position is to remain useful for experimental purposes." Correspondence in May 1936 concerns the need to keep the foreshore in front of the site "free from boats, huts etc. to avoid disturbance to work with the mirror."

Despite his worries, Dr Tucker was actively involved in planning a programme for 1936. In a letter to the Superintendent, Air Defence Experimental Establishment on 13 March, he discussed "Operations at Hythe in May and June 1936." He stressed the importance of co-operation between the Services. "The administrative details of this programme involve the assurance from RAF that they will keep to their programme as regards supply of the Heyford Bomber, and that equipment for microphones (for the 200 foot mirror) and modifications of the 30 foot mirrors will be through the workshops."

In an accompanying memorandum, Dr Tucker outlined his proposed programme for 1936, involving use of the airfield at Hawkinge near Folkestone. "One Heyford Bomber should be available from May 4th till June 12th inclusive. It should be stationed at Hawkinge and should carry out flights by day over the sea. Ranges of from 15 to 20 miles (24 - 32km) would be required out to sea." Part of his programme would be the testing of "a new microphone system of 20 triple resonated microphones capable of receiving on a wide frequency band at Denge outstation." (Map 1 - p.23)

It is apparent from Dr Tucker's memorandum that there was no place for the 20 foot mirror at Abbots Cliff in his plans for 1936, and it was probably abandoned by that time. "Experiments with the 30 foot mirrors; two of these will be in operation: Hythe and Denge. The mirrors will be equipped for altitude and azimuth listening, involving two listeners per mirror. Information of bearing and elevation will be transmitted by automatic telephone and display to the Hythe office." There is also a reference in this memorandum to "Recognition of Aircraft." "The recognition siren will be installed in an aircraft - a Wallace from Biggin Hill, or a Heyford Bomber - and observations of range as observed by the 200 foot mirror and possibly the 30 foot mirrors will be made, as before, accompanied by visual observation."

The idea of mounting a recognition siren on an aircraft may be related to the unsolved problem of distinguishing friendly from hostile aircraft. The reference to "visual observation" suggests that in 1936, optical methods of checking the performance of listeners were still in use. In fact, in March 1936, there is correspondence between the Royal Engineers and the Air Defence Experimental Establishment about acquiring a telescope for "identification purposes." Approval to purchase such an instrument was given on 30 March 1936.

The RAF was losing interest in the mirrors by 1936, and operations must have been carried out entirely by Army personnel or members of the Air Defence Experimental Establishment in that year. A letter to the Establishment from the Commanding Officer, Air Defence of Great Britain on 18 March states: "It is confirmed that no training of RAF personnel is to be carried out at Hythe this year." However, the RAF did supply aircraft for the Exercises: "No. 7 (Heavy Bomber) Squadron, Heyfords, has been provisionally earmarked for the co-operation required at Denge during the period 1 May to 15 June 1936."

The overall acoustic story is for the most part based on documentary evidence, and it is inevitable that the passage of time has put first hand accounts of the earlier period of acoustic research beyond reach. However, the recollections of two scientists, Humphry Smith and Hugh Roberts, both with memories of the 1930s, serve to illuminate activities at Biggin Hill and Hythe in the later years.

Humphry M. Smith was appointed to the Air Defence Experimental Establishment at Biggin Hill in 1934, where his colleagues included people already featured in this account, including Rothwell, Hart, Young, and Handford, with Dr Tucker as Director and Dr Paris as his Deputy. Ferguson was in charge of the ADEE outstation at Hythe. It was the accepted practice that members of the scientific staff at Biggin Hill would from time to time be called upon to assist in exercises with which they were not normally associated, and Humphry Smith was involved twice for a few weeks in exercises at Hythe and Denge. During the Air Defence of Great Britain Exercises in 1935, he relieved Maurice Hart at the London control centre in Faraday House.

Radio investigation of the ionosphere was a topic of discussion at meetings of the Physical Society, and as a member of the Society, it was no surprise to Humphry Smith when he heard in 1935 of the successful reception of echoes from an aircraft. It was obvious to him that the use of radio would render the various acoustic techniques obsolete, so when some of the people from the acoustic field, including Dr Paris, moved into radar research at Bawdsey, he requested a transfer to that station. As he was required to finish the projects on which he was working at Biggin Hill he was not released at that time. Subsequently, in 1936 he left the Air Defence Experimental Establishment and took up scientific work at the Royal Observatory.

Hugh Roberts was well qualified to take part in acoustical experiments, having being apprenticed at Metropolitan Vickers, and holding an MSc in Physics and Electrical Engineering. He joined the Air Defence Experimental Establishment at Biggin Hill in 1936, where colleagues included Humphry Smith and Percy Rothwell, with whom he worked on acoustic projects. He described the Director Dr Tucker as a gentleman in the Edwardian mould, but also one who was very specific and did not mince words.

According to Hugh Roberts, there was no permanent staff at the Hythe Acoustic Research Station when he was working there in 1936 - 37. People involved lived in the surrounding neighbourhood. The official approach to the station was by a road, winding over the top of the escarpment. Power for the station was provided by an engine driven generator. The road and the engine house both appear on a contemporary map, and at the time of writing there are visible remains of these features at the site. Hugh Roberts lodged in a house at the foot of The Roughs and climbed the hills each day to the station where Ferguson was in charge. His main work was in experiment and design with such equipment as hot-wire microphones. There was a good workshop on the site, and an expert mechanic assisted the scientists by making up special pieces of apparatus. Although he was not directly involved in Air Defence of Great Britain Exercises, Hugh Roberts recalled that the main building at the Hythe site was divided into sections, and one of these areas would be used as a plotting centre. There were no problems with security. People respected the place as 'secret', and the staff took

The 30 foot mirror at Hythe from below, a scene which must have been familiar to scientist Hugh Roberts as he climbed the hills to the Acoustic Research Station in the late 1930s

secrecy very seriously.

The original 20 foot (6.1m) mirror at Hythe was obsolete by 1936, but it was still used for test purposes. Hugh Roberts recalled that local noise and adverse weather could create difficult conditions for the listener. Listening at the 30 foot mirror was also hampered from time to time by noise interference from wind and rain. In relation to the method of operating the 200 foot mirror, he could not recollect any employment of listeners in the forecourt, and it seems likely that by the late 1930's, listening at the 200 foot (61m) mirror was by electrical methods only. He took part in experiments with various types of hot-wire microphones at the 200 foot mirror, and recalled that much of the work was devoted to tuning the microphones to pick up aircraft sounds of particular frequencies. He remarked that there were great efforts at that time to prove the efficiency of the 200 foot mirror, possibly because those responsible were already aware of the early success of radar.

Hugh Roberts had memories of the transport system between the sites at Hythe and Denge. A petrol-engined vehicle was in use on the Romney Hythe and Dymchurch railway, and due to excessive speed on the part of some drivers, there were occasional derailments at the sharp curve where the War Department branch to the Denge mirrors left the main line.

Contemporary photographs of listeners at work are very rare. One such photograph shows a listener in the chamber under the 30 foot mirror at Denge. Hugh Roberts identified the operator as Handford, who worked with Ferguson at Hythe, and subsequently went out to Malta with him to supervise the fitting of electrical equipment to the 200 foot mirror (see p.267).

A number of the workers in the acoustic field subsequently moved into other areas of research, including Hugh Roberts. He was not alone in expressing a view that although the acoustic early warning system became obsolete in the middle 1930s, some aspects, in particular communications, pointed the way towards a control and reporting system which was to assume great importance in the radar years.

A present day visitor to the site at Hythe might be puzzled by several vertical concrete blocks standing in positions once occupied by the huts of the Acoustic Research Station, familiar to scientist Hugh Roberts and other members of Dr Tucker's team. The blocks must date from a period after the closure of the station and demolition of the huts. A possible explanation for these curious objects occurs in a letter from a former radar expert Dr Ernest Putley. He visited the site in 1943 when involved in the development of Type 16 radar used to control air operations over France including those on D-Day. He writes "There were only three Type16s along the south coast, but one of them was located at Hythe. I had to check the setting up of the Type 16s to ensure their performance would be at its best for D-Day. The Hythe radar station was located on the high ground behind Hythe." The grid reference given by Dr Putley coincides with the site of the Acoustic Research Station at Hythe. Describing the equipment of the Hythe site, he continues "In addition to the Type 16 it also included Types 12, 13, and 24." It seems likely from Dr Putley's letter that the concrete blocks at the site of the Hythe Acoustic Research Station are the remaining foundations of radar equipment from the Second World War.

CHAPTER THIRTY-FIVE

FINAL DEVELOPMENTS

With hindsight, it is hard to imagine that Dr Tucker was unaware of radar developments by 1936. Nevertheless, despite whatever doubts he may have felt at the time, he carried on with acoustic experiments. Copies of his report on sound mirror exercises in the summer of 1936 were sent to both the Superintendent of the Air Defence Experimental Establishment and the President of the Royal Engineers Board.

Much of the report was concerned with technical details about the use of new microphones at the 200 foot Denge mirror, and apparatus for automatic switching between the various microphones. Although not very illuminating to a layman, this technical report is useful, because it indicates that as late as 1936, careful experiments were carried out at Denge to improve the performance of the 200 foot mirror.

In anticipation of a growth in holiday traffic, the Southern Railway decided to re-route its New Romney branch line to bring it nearer the coast. This development took place in 1937 and the railway, formerly running behind the mirror site at Denge was re-aligned to pass in front of the mirrors. As feared by people from the Air Defence Experimental Establishment during initial discussions in 1935, there were problems at the point where the Southern Railway standard gauge line crossed the War Department narrow gauge siding from the Romney Hythe and Dymchurch Railway to the mirrors. On 11 February 1937 Robert Ferguson of the Establishment wrote to his Superintendent on the matter: "It has been reported to me by Saunders this morning that the Southern Railway line is now crossing the W.D. track to the mirror. In order to get across, application has got to be made to the District Engineer, Southern Railway, for permission."(Map 2 - p.64)

Southern Railway bridge over the War Department siding looking away from the mirror site towards the sea. The line of the W.D. line extends beyond as part of a walkers' track.

This was not a very satisfactory arrangement for the mirror personnel. It appears that a proposal made early in the life of the Southern Railway project, to build a bridge over the War Department siding, was carried out at this time. The Southern Railway Divisional Engineer wrote to the Air Defence Experimental Establishment describing the overbridge to be built, which involved raising the Southern Railway line and lowering the W.D. siding. He said that there would be no problem in the interim about W.D. trains crossing the Southern Railway, but asked for some notice to be given. The new Southern Railway line, with a bridge over the W.D. siding, was eventually opened to New Romney on 4 June 1937. Although the Southern Railway standard gauge line was closed many years ago, the bridge, carrying a rough shingle road over the course of the W.D. narrow gauge line still existed, on a private site, into the 21st century. The trackbed of the W.D. branch remained as a footpath, followed by many walkers on guided visits to the sound mirrors.

The new Southern Railway line in front of the Denge mirrors was on the whole regarded by the mirror people as a negative development, but there is a slightly surprising footnote to this affair in a memorandum by Dr Tucker in April 1938, where the railway is seen in a positive light. Dr Tucker's subject was the problem posed to the operators of mobile sound locators by the increasing speeds of aircraft. He suggested that "Denge, ancillary to Hythe Acoustical Station" would be a good site for experiments related to this problem, using an experimental locator on a fixed pedestal, equipped with paraboloids of the type fitted to Marks VIII and IX sound locators. "The station is well sited for privacy and military protection, a situation which has been improved by the railway now intervening, its embankment serving not only for cutting off sound, but also limiting access."

Returning to 1937, on 3 March, the indefatigable Dr Tucker wrote to the Superintendent, Air Defence Experimental Establishment with further suggestions for improving the performance of the 200 foot (61m) mirror at Denge. With reference to the wall along the front of the forecourt, he suggested that the "height of the forecourt wall be reduced to 8 inches (20cm) above ground level to improve the acoustic properties of the mirror. The present high wall forms a large reflecting surface which frequently causes repeated reflections." This change was sanctioned on 19 March, but judging by the height of the wall, about 5 feet, (1.5m) when seen in the 1990s, the work was not carried out.

There seems little doubt that at this time, the success of RDF, or radar, was making life difficult for those engaged in acoustic research. On 17 March 1937, Dr Tucker wrote a "Secret Memorandum from Director, Acoustical Section, Biggin Hill" about the relationship between the Air Defence Experimental Establishment and Tizard's Committee for the Scientific Survey of Air Defence.

"The following statement is prepared to report on the difficulties arising through the operations of the Tizard Committee. In view of the high speeds of aircraft which are to be anticipated, the Tizard Committee started on the general assumption that sound is so severely handicapped by 1) its low velocity relative to light, and 2) its heavy attenuation in the atmosphere, that alternative methods not so handicapped will inevitably replace the use of sound. The first reactions to this attitude are shown in the removal of the mirror installations from the Air Ministry programme, and in the attitude of the Committee towards the other experiments involving sound which are subject to the handicaps above quoted."

Dr Tucker continued by commenting on the sources of information used by the Tizard Committee in relation to acoustics work. One of these was "through Mr A.P. Rowe, the Secretary of that Committee, who has also been a member of the Acoustics Committee over a period of years. Of late years however, Mr Rowe's contact with our activities has been very limited. A statement of the acoustical work in hand was made by me at a meeting of this committee. The statement occupied only one hour, or less, and naturally could not be a detailed one."

Various other points were made by Dr Tucker, including "unsatisfactory questionnaires" and "informal discussions, lacking any official authorization." In the autumn of 1936 the Tizard Committee had asked for tests of height finding using two sound locators. These were arranged at some inconvenience to the ADEE, but "it was not found possible by the members of the Committee to attend any demonstration."

It seems obvious with the benefit of hindsight, that acoustic work was undergoing a process of marginalization, following rapid and successful developments in the field of radar. Dr Tucker was evidently not happy with the state of affairs at the time, as demonstrated by the ending of his memorandum. "Under the present regime, our contacts with the Committee are vague, and such activities as we have pursued have, in general, only been authorized in an indirect manner."

In correspondence of late 1937, there are pointers that experimental work at the 200 foot Denge mirror had been closed down. On 21 December, the Superintendent, Air Defence Experimental Establishment wrote to the Air

Ministry about the disposal of redundant equipment. The Air Ministry in turn approached the War Office to enquire if any of the equipment would be of use to the Observer Corps. "The equipment in question consists of 12 microphones from the 200 ft acoustical mirror at Denge with a separate transformer, amplifier, loudspeaker, small switchboard and batteries for each unit, the total cost of the apparatus being assessed at £240." The ADEE was authorized "to recover such of the components as may be of use." The only other known 200 foot mirror, at Maghtab in Malta, was also virtually abandoned by 1937.

The Director of Scientific Research visited the Air Defence Experimental Establishment at Biggin Hill in the Summer of 1938. In the briefing notes prepared for him in July by Dr Tucker, there is a list of Establishment personnel at that time, including various people who have appeared in this account: "Mr M.D. Hart, Mr P. Rothwell, Mr R.H.Ferguson, Mr Friend, Mr H. Roberts, Mr A. Reading, and Mr Handford. "

By 1938, it seems that the Kent mirrors were not in regular use. Dr Tucker, as Director of Research, wrote to the Superintendent, Air Defence Experimental Establishment on 28 September, at the time of the Munich Crisis. "I would like to submit that, for the present emergency, some use should be made of the coastal acoustic mirrors at Hythe and Dungeness. The gear is in working order as far as aural methods are concerned, and the electrical equipment could be installed at short notice (24 hours). The installation would give an extra 10 miles of warning on the coast observations at least, and would assist in confirming further observations received in that area. Reporting might be made through Observer Corps channels. The only provision necessary would be the re-installation of the telephone. Lines already exist."

In addition to his scientific work, Dr Tucker was concerned with matters of personal importance in 1938. On 15 and 18 July, he was in correspondence with Brigadier A.P. Sayer, President of the Royal Engineer and Signals Board on the subject of his pension, and the date of his retirement. Brigadier, formerly Colonel Sayer, had visited Malta with Dr Tucker in 1933, when they were looking for sites for 200 foot mirrors on the island.

Dr Tucker was due to retire as Director of Research at the Air Defence

Experimental Establishment on 17 February 1939, but following his request, an extension of service was approved on 11 August 1939, and he was allowed to continue for an extra year up to 17 February 1940.

CHAPTER THIRTY-SIX

LAST DAYS OF THE MIRRORS

Despite optimistic comments about its contribution to Air Defence Exercises in the 1930s, later reports indicate that time was running out for the Hythe sound mirror system. Although there had been some success in tracking slow-moving biplanes, the increasing speed of more advanced aircraft, and the short ranges achieved by the mirrors, cut early warning times down to an unacceptable level. The problem of distinguishing between friendly and hostile aircraft had not been solved, and listening activities were increasingly affected by growing levels of noise in the general environment.

Looking back from the 21st century, it may seem strange that acoustic experiments were continued into the late 1930s. Results were often discouraging, but it is worth remembering that until the development of radar, there was no alternative early warning system. Another important factor was the growing and widespread fear of air power.

The Italian General Guilo Douhet was a believer in the invincibility of the bomber aircraft. He wrote a book in 1921 entitled Command of the Air, putting forward a theory of air power and its potential. Douhet's theories influenced the design of air force training manuals used in America, where General 'Billy' Mitchell was a leading advocate of air power. Writing in 1920, Colonel J.F.C. Fuller, a British military thinker, stated that "Fleets of aeroplanes will attack the enemy's great industrial and governing centres." Colonel Basil Liddell Hart, the noted military historian, wrote in 1925: "A modern state is such a complex and interdependent fabric that it offers a target highly sensitive to a sudden and overwhelming blow from the air."

Air Marshal Trenchard, sometimes referred to as the "Father of the Royal Air Force", also believed in the dominance of the bomber aircraft. In a memorandum to the Chiefs of Staff in 1928 he stated that "Air power can pass over the enemy navies and armies, and penetrate the air defences and attack direct the centres of production, transportation and communications from which the enemy war effort is maintained."

It is possible that efforts to devise an acoustic early warning system were spurred on by the fact that in the 1920s and 30s, because of spending cuts and a general feeling of pacifism at large, the armed forces had been run down to a level which left the country defenceless. Basil Collier, in his book The Defence of the United Kingdom gave a sombre picture of this state of affairs. He pointed out that after the end of the First World War, armaments ceased to be an asset and became a burden, which from social, financial, and economical points of view could no longer be supported.

The newly established Royal Air Force suffered very badly from the post war cuts, and by the early 1920s, it had been reduced to such an extent that it was hardly effective either in an offensive or defensive role. Although possibly said in jest, there were comments that the Royal Air Force was small enough at the time for pilots to know to each other, as in a local flying club. The ground-based defence forces suffered from similar drastic cuts and economies.

In the political arena, the post-war government under Lloyd George based estimates for military spending on what became known as The Ten Year Rule, an assumption that there would be no major war involving the British Empire during the following ten years.

By 1932, it was becoming apparent that it was time to abandon the Ten Year Rule. International relations were deteriorating, and although the country faced an economic crisis, the leaders of the fighting forces pressed for rearmament. In 1934, influenced by events in Germany, the British Government adopted a scheme to expand the air forces, which was upgraded in 1937 in the light of increasing alarm about German rearmament. Max Hastings in his book Bomber Command wrote that "in the last decade before the Second World War, it is no exaggeration to say that the threat of aerial bombardment and the difficulties of defence against it became a public obsession in Britain and France." Stanley Baldwin made a famous remark in a speech to the House of Commons on 10 November 1932. He came close to the theories expressed by Douhet when he said: "I think it is as well for the man in the street to realize that there is no power on earth that can protect him from being bombed. Whatever people may tell him, the bomber will always get through." When seen against such a background, attempts to develop an acoustic early warning system make better sense.

The success of radar by 1939 must have influenced the decision of the Royal Engineers Board to convene a meeting on 8 May. Dr Tucker was present, and the main business was the final abandonment of the mirror system. According to the minutes: "The President referred to the decision of the GS (General Staff) to abandon the mirrors, and the consequent relinquishment of the Denge site. He referred to discussions in June 1938 when no final decision had been made. At that time, the equipment was withdrawn to Hythe, but was capable of replacement at short notice. After discussion, it was agreed that there were no valid grounds for opposing the General Staff decision. It was agreed that the 200 foot (61m), 30 foot (9.1m) and 20 foot (6.1m) mirrors should be destroyed before disposal of the area."

There were also suggestions that demolition of the mirrors would provide an opportunity for experiments with explosives. The aim was to assess what effect the reflecting properties of a mirror would have on the blast from a charge exploded at the focal point.

A letter written in May 1939, from Colonel W.H.G. Costelloe, President of the Royal Engineers Board, to "M.D.Hart Esq", probably Mr or Dr Hart of the Air Defence Experimental Establishment, mentions that "it is now as good as settled that the Hythe-Denge mirror system should be 'wound up'." This is followed by suggestions for disposal of the electrical equipment to the Post Office.

On 16 May 1939, the President of the Royal Engineers Board was in touch again with the Superintendent of the Air Defence Experimental Establishment about the abandonment of the mirrors: "Will you please make arrangements now to salve all small stores, fittings etc. at Denge, and remove them to Hythe for disposal, if not otherwise required." On the same day, Dr Tucker wrote a memorandum at Biggin Hill referring to the possible use of the redundant sound mirrors for experiments with explosive charges, ending with a statement that "preliminary trials of an exploratory nature can be carried out at Dungeness, where three large concrete sound mirrors with apertures of 200 ft (61m), 30 ft (9.1m), and 20 ft (6.1m) respectively are available for such work. They are shortly to be destroyed." A week later, Dr Tucker suggested that the telephone equipment used in the mirror system might be of use to the General Post Office. In a further letter to the Royal Engineers Board on 21 June 1939, he suggested disposal of the automatic telephone relay installation to the GPO.

The suggestions made in 1939 to use the mirrors for experiments with explosives were followed up. On 24 January 1940, Dr Tucker sent a report to the President of the Royal Engineers Board headed "Experiments to investigate the nature of the disturbance produced by explosions in large, concave, concrete reflectors." These experiments were carried out at Denge "prior to the employment of explosives for demolition of concrete sound mirrors." The work involved comparing charges blown up in free air, with charges placed "in the bowl of the hemispherical concrete mirror at Denge beach on 16 January, 1940." A charge was also exploded at the focus of the 200 foot (61m) mirror. Various points were made in this report about the directive effect of the mirrors on the explosions. There was mention of "cracking of the mirror surface."

The experiments with explosives at Denge were carried out by Dr Tucker in the last weeks of his career as a Government scientist, but it seems that the instructions of the General Staff in 1939 to destroy the Kent mirrors were never carried out. Dr Tucker may well have been glad that the mirrors, which were reminders of a lifetime spent in acoustic research, were not ultimately destroyed. At the time of the Munich Crisis, he had produced a memorandum outlining his ideas for reactivating the sites, and it is quite possible that despite the introduction of a radar based early warning system, he thought the mirrors might be useful in the future.

By the beginning of the 21st Century, five of the six mirrors in the Hythe system were still in existence, and the sixth mirror was only lost through natural causes.

The 20 foot (6.1m) mirror by the coastal path at Abbots Cliff remained in good condition although without its pillar. This mirror, on a high cliff overlooking the English Channel, with views of Folkestone harbour in the background, enjoyed the most commanding site in the Hythe system

Abbots Cliff sound mirror with Folkestone Harbour pier in the distance

At Hythe, on the hills to the west of the town known as The Roughs, the foundations of the acoustic research station and its approach road could be traced on the ground (see over).

373

Site of Hythe Acoustic Research Station in 1976. Note 20 foot mirror and its pillar. The footings of the control room can be seen in the foreground. The vertical concrete blocks standing in the footings may be the remains of a radar installation which occupied the site in World War II. The 20 foot (6.1m) mirror, formerly standing against the escarpment, collapsed face downwards in the later years of the 20th century, burying the pillar in the process.

Hythe 20 foot mirror in 1993 collapsed face downward

View towards the English channel from behind the Hythe 30 foot mirror.
Note Martello towers on the coast. By the beginning of the 21st Century,
the 30 foot (9.1m) mirror remained standing, but the passage of time,
exposure to weather, and vandalism were taking their toll

The 20 foot, 30 foot and 200 foot sound mirrors at Denge before the restoration project of 2003. By the 1990s, the three mirrors at Denge were almost surrounded by water due to gravel workings. The 20 foot (6.1m) mirror was out of plumb because of undermining of its foundations, and the pillar supporting the listening gear had disappeared

The 20 foot mirror at Denge, out of plumb due to undermining of foundations

By now the 30 foot (9.1m) mirror was decaying, and rusty metal reinforcement was showing through the concrete in places. The metal pillar which formerly supported the sound collector was in position, although rusted away at the lower end where it entered the listening chamber. The concrete lower part of this chamber was exposed at about head height, as was the flight of seven steps behind the mirror which formerly led down into the chamber (see opposite).

*Rear view of the decaying circular mirrors at Denge. On the left, behind the
30 foot mirror, can be seen the concrete casing of a flight of steps down
into the former underground listening chamber*

The lower part of the listening chamber was originally below ground level; the wooden upper part, with its windows looking out along the axis of the mirror, had not survived. The shingle upon which the mirror stands had sunk by several feet since the mirror was erected, thus exposing the foundations which were formerly below ground level.

It is evident from a report of 26 January 1937 by F.W.Eastes (probably from the Air Defence Experimental Establishment) that the 30 foot (9.1m) mirror at Denge was already in poor condition by that date. Describing a visit to the site the previous day, he found the "whole of the listening gear mechanism seized; all exposed parts rusted up", and recommended that the complete mechanism be taken to Biggin Hill for overhaul. He set down his requirements for this job as: "One fitter and two labourers from Biggin Hill, one derrick, one three ton lorry, and three days of good weather."

The Denge 30 foot mirror before restoration. Note former underground listening chamber exposed by lowering of ground level since 1930. A section of the listening gear has survived

Returning to the 1990s, the Denge 200 foot (61m) mirror was also in a state of decay. Some of the concrete buttresses behind the mirror had almost flaked away, leaving the iron reinforcement rods in full view. The remains of the collapsed listening room lay on the ground behind the mirror; the former window of this room remained as a hole in the centre of the mirror. The foundations of the mirror had been undermined and exposed at one end, leaving it jutting out over the encircling water. The forecourt was in fair condition, although parts of the forward end, often called the 'trench' in contemporary documents, had subsided. A few sections of the front wall were still upright, but much of the rest had collapsed. A flight of steps which formerly led down to the forecourt from the wing wall was in mid air, suggesting that, as in the case of the 30 foot mirror (9.1m), the ground level was several feet lower than it was in the 1930s.

By the early years of the 21st century, the three mirrors were suffering from over seventy years of wear and tear by weather and vandals. At the time of construction in the years 1928 to 1930, foundations were laid directly in the shingle with no supporting piles, and over the years, ground levels had fallen away, leaving the foundations exposed. There was a large hole through a buttress behind the 200 foot (61m) mirror displaying twisted reinforcement rods completely separated from the concrete. Despite this depressing picture, subsequent events at Denge were to lead to a better future for the mirrors.

Denge in the 1990's showing the 200 foot mirror, forecourt and ruined front wall.
Note the former control room window in the face of the 200 foot mirror,
and the 20 foot and 30 foot mirrors in the background

A view at Denge in the 1970s, showing water already encroaching on the mirrors

CHAPTER THIRTY-SEVEN

Dr TUCKER LEAVES THE STAGE

Dr Tucker's final year as Director of Research at the Air Defence Experimental Establishment was running out by the time of the explosive experiments at Denge in early 1940, and he was again in correspondence with the War Office asking for a further extension of service. It is obvious from his papers that he did not wish to relinquish his scientific work, and that he considered he had something to offer in a time of national emergency. His wishes were not granted, and in a letter to the Superintendent of ADEE on 15 August 1939, he wrote "Would you please notify the President of the Royal Engineer and Signals Board that I have duly received the statement that my appointment terminates on 17 February 1940."

On 17 August 1939, Henry Tizard, Chairman of the Committee for the Scientific Survey of Air Defence, wrote to Dr Tucker. After mentioning the appreciation of the Committee for Dr Tucker's help, he continued: "It seems to me that the work you have been doing at Biggin Hill is even more extensive than I thought." His letter ends: "I am extremely sorry to hear that you are leaving. It seems such a pity that you should be severed from the work at this stage."

Brigadier Sayer, President of the Royal Engineer and Signals Board wrote to Dr Tucker on 7 September 1939 about arrangements for handing over to a new Director, and the impending move of the Air Defence Experimental Establishment to Christchurch, on the south coast near

Bournemouth.

"The general idea is that you shall remain as Director ADEE Biggin Hill, while Black is appointed right away as Director (or probably Superintendent of Research) ADEE Christchurch. It will mean that you and he will have to work together; he will have to learn the full Biggin Hill activities, and it would be better to do this, if possible, before they move out. If they have partly gone, you will at least have to get him into the picture of general aims and immediate objects. At Christchurch, he will assume control of the Experimental Research work, with you in the background to help and advise. He will have to get right into the picture of our RDF (radar) work, and I think with Forshaw or Butement, he should put in a bit of time at Bawdsey to see the Air Ministry side of this work, the Experimental CD set (a centimetric coastal defence radar set) and its possibilities, and if they are still there, make contact with Rowe and Co."

Sayer explained that his letter was a "put you in the picture" communication. "I doubt if Biggin Hill will be closed down completely and abandoned before December, but that will remain to be seen. You will not move to Christchurch, though of course you will be visiting as and when necessary. I hope you realize my object in writing to you privately on this matter, and I am sure you also realize that I am relying on you to help and put Black into the picture as completely as possible so that he can keep the whole show going in the efficient way you have trained and taught it."

Realizing that his services were soon to be dispensed with, Dr Tucker wrote to the Royal Society on 14 September 1939, including a C.V, and asking for his name to be put on the Central Register of those offering themselves for National Service. He was hoping to use his scientific skills towards the war effort. In addition to these problems, he was also in difficulties over his pension entitlement, which was adversely affected by bureaucratic confusion at the time he left the world of education to join the Service. Brigadier Sayer wrote a letter to the authorities on his behalf, but received the reply that "no departure from established practice can be contemplated."

In October 1939, Dr Gough, Ministry of Supply, replied to Dr Tucker's request to be allowed to serve in some new capacity. He was advised to take up University work. In the light of his experience and qualifications, it is not surprising that University work was not Dr Tucker's idea of National Service. He wrote: "It will be very difficult for me to sit back and do nothing at this critical time, and my desire to be of service is not put forward from motives of a lucrative appointment, but one in which I could pull my weight. I would be prepared for more action now, but I have received no encouragement in this direction, and my age is a definite bar." Dr Tucker was in fact only 62 years of age, by no means too old to serve in a time of national emergency.

On 31 October, Dr Gough wrote again. "Dear Tucker, I quite realize all the difficulties you are up against and your desire to be actively engaged in work of national importance after you leave the Air Defence Experimental Establishment. I now hear from Brigadier Sayer that it is unlikely that the transfer of personnel from Biggin Hill to Christchurch can be completed until early in 1940, and may not even be completed before 17 February 1940." His letter ended by inviting Dr Tucker to call for a discussion.

As the date of his retirement approached, Dr Tucker received many letters from military and civilian colleagues. On 3 February 1940 Professor T. Graham Brown wrote from the Physiology Institute, Cardiff. "My Dear Tucker, I was very sorry to have your letter of January 24, and to hear that your connection with the War Office will so soon be severed. As you know I have watched your admirable work during the past 10 or 12 years, and I would like to take this opportunity of telling you how very much I myself appreciate all that you have done for the Country."

On 9 February, Dr Tucker wrote to Colonel Sylvester Evans, Superintendent, Air Defence Experimental Establishment, Biggin Hill with a request "to convey through you a special message to all my old friends in the ADEE. Although inevitable, the breaking of this association is being very keenly felt by me, and I cannot let the occasion pass without wishing them all a very happy future in their new activities, and a continuation of that same spirit of co-operation and support for my successor and for yourself. May the ADEE flourish."

On 14 February W.G.Costelloe, a former President of the Royal Engineers Board addressed Dr Tucker as "Dear Director of Research."

"I write to express the very sincere hope that one of your F.R.S. (Fellow of the Royal Society) friends - A.V. Hill or Tizard or Bragg, has co-opted you in such a way as to give you full scope for continuing your work of the last 20 years in the way you would wish." He ended "may your health and vigour be unimpaired, and may your wife make a great recovery, so that your years of retirement from official life may indeed prove to be the happiest of a long life."

On 16 February 1940 Brigadier Sayer, President of the Royal Engineer and Signals Board wrote: "I want to record how much I regret your departure and the loss of your valuable experience as a help and guide in those parts of our work with which you have been so closely associated for so many years." He expressed the wishes of the Board for good fortune in the future, and ended by saying that he and W.S.T. had become friends, not merely just Service colleagues.

Dr Tucker finally retired from the Air Defence Experimental Establishment on 17 February 1940. On the 19th, his successor Dr D. H. Black wrote to him from the new base of the ADEE at Christchurch, expressing thanks for the presentation of technical papers to the ADEE library. Three days later, he wrote again with thanks to Dr Tucker for his help in the hand-over period:

"I appreciate how hard it must have been to you to hand over your 'family' to the care of another, and a rank outsider at that."

A letter arrived in April from the Professor of Physics at Cardiff, signature illegible, but probably from Professor J.H. Poynting.

"My Dear Tucker, I went right up in the air at your news; that they should drop the man who knows most in all the country about these things just when every bit of experience is of the greatest value is atrocious. I imagine that dammed Cambridge clique that is making a racket of industrial science had a hand in the business. What I have heard of the appointments of University men in Government jobs doesn't thrill me much. Some of them will hardly win the war for us."

On 13 May 1940, Dr H. J. Gough, Director of Scientific Research, Ministry of Supply wrote again to Dr Tucker:

"Thank you for your letter of 10th renewing your offer of services in the present emergency. I will communicate immediately with you if the occasion arises."

Much to Dr Tucker's disappointment, the occasion did not arise, and his wish to carry on contributing his scientific expertise and experience to the war effort in the crisis days of 1940 was not granted. In his enforced retirement, he returned to the field of academic work he had given up to enlist in the Royal Engineers in 1915. Despite his high level of qualifications and experience, in June 1940 he was offered a very lowly post at Kings College Newcastle, University of Durham. The details are contained in a letter from George W. Todd, M.A., DSc., F.Inst. P., Professor of Experimental Physics, offering him a post as Demonstrator on a temporary basis at £300 per annum from 1 October 1940:

"I understand that you are willing to help us out by accepting a temporary junior appointment of Demonstrator, regarding your action as a contribution to the National call to service. Realizing what it means in expense and domestic upheaval, and remembering your fine record in the world of Physics, we should feel honoured by your acceptance of so junior a post."

Dr Tucker declined the offer, but eventually, for the remainder of the war, he taught Physics at Kings College, Newcastle, travelling there each week, and returning home to London at weekends. His daughter recalled that during those war years, she ferried him around by car on 'secret' work. She also remembered that he was involved with acoustic matters related to the design of air raid sirens.

A sentence in a letter to his old colleague Percy Rothwell in May 1949 reveals Dr Tucker's feelings regarding the end of his career:

"You know it was a bitter disappointment to me not taking an active part in World War II."

On the death of his wife in 1953, Dr Tucker moved to Canada, where he lived with his daughter Beryl on a farm in rural Ontario until his death in July 1955. He left some of his personal papers in an old leather suitcase which was subsequently stored away and lay undisturbed for many years. This valuable archive, which illuminates the life of a largely forgotten scientist, was brought to light again at the farm in Ontario during research for the present account.

CHAPTER THIRTY-EIGHT

RADAR

In the early 1930s, Robert Watson-Watt, a scientist working in radio research and soon to be a leader in the development of radar, was familiar with the work of those attempting to devise an early warning system based on sound detection. On 14 July 1931, he wrote to "Major Tucker DSc" following a visit to the Air Defence Experimental Establishment where he had also met Percy Rothwell. After giving his impressions of the ADEE, Watson-Watt concluded "I am glad to have the opportunity of saying again how much we were impressed by your work there. I hope that you and Rothwell will make any use of us that you can in consultations on matters where you think we may be of use."

In his book Three Steps to Victory, Watson-Watt recorded more thoughts on the acoustic experiments carried out by the Air Defence Experimental Establishment. "By 1932, they had achieved results which were relatively encouraging. But about that date, I was already saying privately 'You are listening up the wrong tree, you should be thinking of radio methods'."

It is remarkable that despite many successes in the field of radio, it was not until the middle of the 1930s that radar emerged. Marconi had sent wireless messages over long distances early in the century, and radio communications between ground based control centres and fighter aircraft were developed during the First World War. During the acoustic years, radio Direction Finding (DF) sets were used to check the performance of sound mirrors. In 1904, a German inventor Christian Hülsmeyer set up a wireless transmitter and receiver, and on transmitting waves towards a ship over a distance of a few hundred yards, he was able to detect the reflected echoes in his receiver. In the 1920s, radio signals were being bounced off high layers in the atmosphere, and directional aerials were well understood.

In January 1931, two Scientists at the Signals Experimental Establishment at Woolwich, Messrs W.S.Butement and P.E.Pollard, proposed a method of locating ships from a shore station "by means of pulsed radio transmissions and the reception of the radio echo received back in the intervals between the transmission pulses." The intention was to use "a high frequency radio beam with a wave length of about 50 cms, and a rotatable aerial system with reflectors to give a narrow beam." Some small scale laboratory experiments were carried out privately by Butement and Pollard, but were not pursued further, partly due to the lack, at that time, of any radio valves of sufficient power output. These proposals of 1931, foreshadow radar developments which were not achieved until the Second World War. It seems possible that Dr Tucker, a member of the Signals Experimental Establishment at Woolwich for many years, was aware of the work of Butement and Pollard, which pre-dates the first RDF experiments at Orfordness by four years.

The birth of radar depended on someone with the insight to grasp the basic ideas from what had gone before, and the development of the technology to make the ideas work in practice.

British radar was sparked off by the gloom of a civil servant, who has already featured in this account, looking through Air Ministry files in 1934. A.P. Rowe, Personal Scientific Assistant to H.E.Wimperis, Director of Scientific Research at the Air Ministry, carried out a systematic review of numerous files dealing with air defence, in particular, the matter of early warning against air attack. He realized that a system based on acoustic devices had many built-in problems, which despite all the work by dedicated scientists led by Dr Tucker, could only give a few minutes early warning. Both Rowe and Wimperis had visited Hythe, and they were aware that efforts to develop an acoustic early warning system were only continued because there was no other way available at the time.

As a result of his depressing studies, Rowe sent a memorandum to Wimperis, on the lines of remarks quoted earlier in this account, that unless some new method of early warning could be discovered, the country was likely to lose the next war if it started within ten years.

Fortunately, Wimperis had an idea with far reaching consequences. In November 1934, he was instrumental in setting up the Committee for the Scientific Survey of Air Defence.

Various references to this committee have already appeared in the story of acoustic defence, but because of its importance in the development of a more sophisticated early warning system, it is relevant to list the members at this point. The Chairman was Sir Henry Tizard, and the members were Professor A.V. Hill, FRS, Professor P.M.S. Blackett, FRS, H.E. Wimperis himself as Air Ministry representative, and A.P. Rowe as Secretary.

It was fortunate that the various players in this story were known to each other, thus smoothing the way for rapid action. In 1918, Major Henry Tizard was serving as Assistant Controller Research and Experiments at the Air Ministry, and during that period he met the young meteorologist Robert Watson-Watt. H.E. Wimperis was also a friend of Tizard, and a fellow serving officer from the First World War. After that war, Wimperis was in charge of an Air Ministry Research Laboratory at Imperial College of Science, South Kensington, where scientist Henry Tizard eventually became Rector. For many years, in addition to that responsibility, Tizard served as a scientific adviser to the Air Ministry. A.V. Hill, a member of the Tizard Committee had also served his apprenticeship in weapons research during the First World War. One feature of the period following the First World War was that, despite economies and other frustrations, civilian scientists were seen to be useful in military circles, and there is no doubt that the involvement of skilled academics made a great contribution to successes achieved by the armed forces in the Second World War. This was particularly true in the case of radar.

The Committee for the Scientific Survey of Air Defence was responsible for the development of British radar. At about the time of the formation of his Committee in 1934, Tizard had asked Robert Watson-Watt, then Superintendent of the Radio Department of the National Physical Laboratory, if there was any possibility of producing a lethal radio beam which could be directed at attacking aircraft. Watson-Watt said that was not feasible, but that it might be possible to transmit radio waves towards an approaching aircraft, and on the waves being reflected, to detect the returning echoes. This was the starting point for radar research, which moved ahead rapidly with the active support of the Tizard Committee.

Events in a muddy field near Weedon, Northamptonshire in February 1935 hastened the end of acoustic research and the birth of RDF - Radio Direction Finding, later known as radar. In the light of the international situation, and the urgent need to press for funds and facilities for radar research, the Tizard Committee required proof that the basic idea would work in practice. As there was a ready source of powerful radio transmissions from the BBC station at Daventry, an experiment was devised in which an RAF aircraft would fly in the beam of that transmitter, and mobile receiving equipment, mounted in a van, would receive the radio echoes from the aircraft. Arnold Wilkins, a radar pioneer and key member of Watson-Watt's research team, was in charge of the van, which was stationed in a field near Weedon. On the morning of 26 February, A.P. Rowe and Watson-Watt arrived at the site to see the 'Daventry Experiment'. As the Heyford bomber flew in the beam, echoes radiated back from the aircraft were detected and displayed as visual disturbances on a cathode ray oscillograph in the van.

Little time was wasted after the Daventry Experiment, and on 1 March 1935, Wimperis and Watson-Watt visited Orford Ness, a place associated with acoustic research in the early days, to choose a site for radar experiments (Map 1 - p.23). Progress was rapid. In June 1935, in a demonstration to the Tizard Committee, an aircraft was followed by radar to a distance of 17 miles (27km), and by July, echoes were picked up at a range of 40 miles (64km).

Members of the Royal Engineers Board were aware in 1935 of the possibilities offered by radar, particularly as an aid to anti-aircraft guns and searchlights. One of the Board members, who had visited Hythe in 1934 to see the acoustic mirrors in action, was Colonel J.P.G. Worlledge. He was a close friend of Robert Watson-Watt, and through this contact, he brought the research work at Orford Ness to the attention of the Board.

Early in 1936, radar experimental work was extended from Orford Ness to a site nearby on the Suffolk coast at Bawdsey Manor, at the mouth of the River Deben, and by May, the team moved there from the exposed site on the end of the Ness (Map 1 - p.23). At about this time, Watson-Watt became concerned by reports that the Air Ministry was considering spending £100,000 on an expansion of the acoustic early warning system, in particular, the building of more 200 foot (61m) concrete sound mirrors. He discussed this point with his colleague Wilkins, and remarked that if they could show that RDF could track aircraft at a distance of 100 km, it would prevent any further expenditure on sound mirrors. In an experimental test flight in March 1936, an aircraft flying along the coast of Norfolk was plotted to a range of 130 km, a result which must have influenced the decision to abandon acoustic mirrors.

The Tizard Committee was successful in stressing the urgency of developing a radar based early warning system, and by 1936, the first station in the radar chain for the defence of the south and east coasts was established at Bawdsey. Four other stations completed the initial chain, at Canewdon and Great Bromley in Essex, and Dunkirk and Dover in Kent. These five stations, of a type identified by the name 'Chain Home' (CH), took part in the Air Exercises in the summer of 1938. The siting of the CH stations is reminiscent of earlier plans for the Thames Estuary sound mirrors. Before the outbreak of Second World War, the chain of radar stations had been extended to cover most of the south and east coasts from Devon to Angus.

An important development in 1936 was the closing down of the Air Defence of Great Britain. This organization, associated with Air Exercises involving the acoustic early warning system in the 1930s, gave way to new Royal Air Force Commands, in particular, Fighter Command, which under Air Chief Marshall Sir Hugh Dowding was to make such effective use of radar in the very near future.

Although the development of RDF as an early warning system against enemy aircraft was carried out by scientists working for the Air Ministry, it is worth remembering that under the War Office, the Air Defence Experimental Establishment was also involved in radar research, some of it carried out by scientists from the acoustic field. For example, a memorandum on

"Trials of RDF Anti Aircraft Gun Set at Bawdsey" from the Royal Engineers Board, dated 12 April 1938 gives details of arrangements for a particular experiment.

"Bawdsey hope now to be ready to begin the Kiné-Theodolite trials on Monday May 2nd. Could you therefore arrange for the K-T and party to be ready to start work at Bawdsey on that date? " There are references to the 'Kiné-Theodolite' in various documents, but there is no description of the device. A likely inference is that it was a type of cine camera used in making a record of such tests. The Royal Engineers Board memorandum includes particulars of accommodation in Landguard Fort, Felixstowe "for one officer, ten other ranks and two listeners from R.E. Experimental Section, Air Defence Experimental Establishment" and under "Transport" arrangements for a "lorry and driver, to take 12 men daily from Landguard Fort to Bawdsey Ferry." Another report of these experiments, headed "SECRET, Trials of Experimental Equipment, Provisional Programme, 1938" using various code words including 'Cuckoo' for radar, contains references to "trials of latest night-dope" (sic) and "Cuckoo - non mobile set (at Bawdsey) with 'Kiné Theodolite'" and also "DF (Direction Finding) accuracy." There are also references to a "Sound Locator" in these papers, with the implication that at the time, the Army was involved in experimental work in both acoustic and radar methods of detection.

In June 1938, the War Office gave a higher priority to radar research work, when the "RDF (War Office) Committee" was established. Committee membership included War Office and Army representatives, Watson-Watt as the radar expert, and the Directors of Scientific Research (DSR) of the Air Ministry and Admiralty.

At this time, a DSR was appointed to the War Office, to bring it into line with the other services. The first holder of the post was Dr H. Gough. The RDF (War Office) Committee was responsible for the provision of the new Army research establishment at Christchurch, Bournemouth, home of the Air Defence Research and Development Establishment which replaced the ADEE Biggin Hill in 1940. The Army radar 'cell' at the Air Ministry research station at Bawdsey, under Dr Tucker's colleague Dr Paris, has already been mentioned, and this work continued on an increasing scale after the ADEE moved from Biggin Hill to Christchurch in 1940.

Various scientists working in acoustic research moved into the radar field in these years of transition. From early 1936, Dr Paris was detached from Biggin Hill to Bawdsey to study ways in which radar could be of use to the Army. Watson-Watt had met both Dr Paris and Dr Tucker during visits to the Air Defence Experimental Establishment in the 1930s. He admired the technical aspects of their work, but thought there was little chance of devising an effective early warning system based on acoustic detection. Dr Paris joined the Bawdsey team permanently on 16 October 1936, leading a small group devoted to Army radar research. As a result of the work of that team, by 1940, searchlights were being fitted with directly mounted radar equipment, enabling the beams to be trained accurately on unseen targets, and radar gunlaying sets were directing the aiming of anti-aircraft guns. These were significant advances over sound ranging methods dating back to the First World War. Subsequently Dr Edward Talbot Paris pursued a scintillating career. During World War II his posts included Deputy Director of Scientific Research, Ministry of Supply, Head of Army Radar and Signals, and Controller of Physical Research and Signals Development. In post war years he became Principal Director of Scientific Defence Research Ministry of Supply and later Chief Scientific Advisor, Home Office. He was knighted in 1954 and died in 1985 aged 96.

By 1940 Percy Rothwell was working at the Air Defence Research and Development Establishment at Christchurch, where in 1941, he was responsible for winding up acoustic research. He subsequently moved into a branch of research which was to lead to dramatic improvements in the effectiveness of anti-aircraft gunnery and bombing, involving experiments with proximity fuses for shells, bombs and rockets. He continued this work during the Second World War, eventually moving to the Radar Research and Development Establishment at Malvern, where he was in charge of the Fuse Group in 1942. In the post war years, he was occupied in the study of German Proximity Fuses, and in the latter part of his career, he was engaged in research at the Armament Design Establishment at Fort Halstead in Kent. In the period after his detachment to the Hythe Acoustic Research Station, Hugh Roberts worked with Rothwell on proximity fuses, and was also closely involved in research into the application of radar to anti-aircraft gunnery. Like Rothwell, he moved from Biggin Hill to Christchurch and later Malvern.

These staff and establishment changes serve as a reminder of the continuity of scientific effort at the time of transition from acoustic to radar methods of aircraft detection. Some of the people worked in both fields, indeed researchers involved in earlier years with sound discs, mirrors and locators, made a significant contribution to radar research and other areas of military science throughout the Second World War and beyond.

The success of radar in the Battle of Britain was due not only to technical advances in transmitting and receiving radio echoes, but also to the setting up of a system of communications between the radar stations, control rooms, and the fighter aircraft. There was a considerable body of experience in this area, dating back to the First World War and the years of attempts to devise an acoustic system. Some of that experience must have been brought to bear in 1936. In that year, a site associated for many years with the Air Defence Experimental Establishment and the sound mirror system, became the base for the Biggin Hill Experiment. Using Gloster Gauntlet aircraft as Fighters, and Hawker Hinds as Bombers, and with the benefit of radar information, practice interceptions were directed from a control room at Biggin Hill. By 1937, this operational system had been adopted by Fighter Command, and it was greatly improved in the short time remaining before being tested in action and found effective against enemy aircraft in 1940. In his memoirs of the Second World War, Prime Minister Winston Churchill described a visit to the underground RAF Operations Room at Uxbridge on 15 September 1940, a decisive day in the Battle of Britain. In his words "all the ascendancy of the Hurricanes and Spitfires would have been fruitless but for the system of underground control centres and telephone cables which had been devised and built before the war by the Air Ministry under Dowding's advice and impulse."

CHAPTER THIRTY-NINE

RESTORATION

The crumbling sound mirrors were still to be seen on their remote sites as the years passed by into a new century. Together with other ruined defence works, they formed part of the historical fabric of Britain, serving as reminders of continuous efforts over many centuries to protect the approaches to the island. A growing interest in military history was reflected in increasing public curiosity about visual remains of defensive structures such as those on the Kent coast. After long years of neglect, features on the sound mirrors appeared in radio and television programmes and the press. Advertised guided walks to the site at Denge on the Dungeness headland were well attended. As a result of many years of commercial gravel extraction, early walkers approached three mirrors almost surrounded by lakes. Visitors were faced with a considerable trek across a shingle causeway and along narrow paths through dense vegetation to reach the site. Many people found the experience very worthwhile, and expressions of amazement on seeing the impressive 200 foot (61m) mirror for the first time were quite common. It seemed that the great curved wall of concrete had aesthetic qualities apart from any scientific or historical appeal.

The fortunes of the Denge mirrors took a dramatic turn for the better in the year 2003 when a restoration project was carried out by English Heritage. The shingle surrounding the mirrors had been quarried extensively, and due to that fact, money became available from the Aggregates

Levy Sustainability Fund, involving a levy used to mitigate the damage caused by the extraction of aggregates. Further funds came from the Historic Fortifications Network, a European Union grant-aided project.

Aerial view at Denge before restoration. The mirrors are almost surrounded by water. In the restoration project, channels were cut through the narrow areas of land on each side to create an island, which was enlarged to fill in the area in front of the 200 foot and 20 foot mirrors to protect their foundations

One main objective of the restoration was to take advantage of existing lakes to create an island site for the mirrors. Contractors began work in July 2003, and the project was completed by the end of November. Heavy machinery was used to cut channels through approach causeways to form the island, and shingle was built up under and around the mirrors to cover exposed foundations. In the process, the 20 foot (6.1m) mirror stood upright again, and shingle was packed under the exposed end of the 200 (61m) foot mirror.

Where water encroached on the mirrors, the island was enlarged. Many tons of shingle were moved in these operations, but as the whole area is a mass of shingle, it was not necessary to import any material to the site. In addition, the edges of the island and the adjacent lakes were given special bank protection using mesh containers filled with gravel known as gabions, allowing speedy re-establishment of natural waterside vegetation.

New island at Denge with restored mirrors 25 November 2003.
Damaged buttresses behind the 200 foot mirror were repaired with new concrete

At the time of restoration, it was hoped that the lakes would eventually become a bird sanctuary under the professional management of the RSPB.

A very special feature of the project was the design and construction of a steel, swing bridge allowing access to the island.

Although there is documentary evidence, previously mentioned in this account, that the War Office intended to destroy the abandoned mirrors in 1940, this was never carried out. However, one aspect of damage to buttresses behind the 200 foot mirror which was something of a mystery was finally solved in 2004 by a letter from Mr Hassall Hanbury Brown. Serving as an army officer, he was stationed at Shorncliffe Camp near

Restored buttresses behind the Denge 200 foot mirror, 25 November 2003

Sandgate on the south-east coast of Kent in May 1940, incidentally just after the time of Dr Tucker's retirement. Hanbury Brown was ordered to take ten men and a supply of explosives to Denge where he was to demolish the 200 foot mirror. The party travelled by truck to the narrow gauge railway station at New Romney where Hanbury Brown met Captain Howey the owner of the Romney Hythe and Dymchurch Railway. From that point, the team travelled over the War Department narrow gauge branch line to the sound mirror site at Denge.

Hanbury Brown planned to begin by destroying the buttresses behind the 200 foot mirror. The job would then be completed by demolishing the wall. In the event, the mirror proved to be a sterner proposition than he had imagined. The first charge was attached to one of the buttresses at the end of the wall. After the explosion, it was evident that although some concrete had been separated from the buttress, the steel reinforcement bars remained in position. Hanbury Brown decided that for further progress, he would need an oxy-acetylene torch to cut through the reinforcement bars. He returned to New Romney Station to borrow the equipment from the railway workshops. He was met on arrival by Captain Howey with a message from Shorncliffe. "You are to get back to camp as soon as possible with all your men and gear." Mr Hanbury Brown was given no reason at the time for the change of plan, and looking back, he referred to the "bizarre eccentricity" of the military mind in giving him orders to blow up an obsolete sound mirror in 1940 bearing in mind the grim military situation in France, only a few miles across the Channel. Before restoration, the damaged buttress could still be seen at the site in the 1990s.

Bank protection, mirror island. New swing bridge under construction,
Denge 25 November 2003

So, seventy-three years after construction, the Denge mirrors were saved from final decay. Perhaps the shades of Dr Tucker and his colleagues look on with approval as visitors cross the bridge to Mirror Island.

New swing bridge to Mirror Island, Denge 25 November 2003
When locked out of use, the bridge forms a barrier across the main
approach causeway. Unlocked and swung over the channel, it provides
access for authorised parties to visit the mirrors. Casual visitors
enjoy a good if distant view of the mirrors over the lakes

*Visitors on Mirror Island, summer 2007. Richard Scarth delivers
one of his talks on the mirrors to an interested audience*

The restored sound mirrors at Denge, 2006

The 200 foot sound mirror on the island at Denge in 2006

CHAPTER FORTY

ANOTHER ISLAND

Late on a cold night in the winter of 1949, twelve years after the abandonment of sound mirrors, two Royal Air Force trucks moved along the road to Sunk Island in the flat landscape of Holderness on the east coast of England. Each truck carried a group of men heavily muffled in greatcoats and gloves against the cold. Continuing over the fens, the trucks eventually stopped at a field gate. From a small guard hut, a Royal Air Force policeman checked passes as the trucks entered the site and halted outside a low brick building. The airmen, mostly National Service personnel, climbed down and filed into the building through heavy steel doors. They exchanged comments with a similar group leaving to board the trucks at the end of their shift. The scene, a real one from the author's experience, was the relief of 'B' Watch by 'C' Watch in the Cold War years, when surveillance of the skies above was carried out 24 hours a day at this place, an RAF Sector Operations Centre.

Passing along a corridor, the men descended into the well of an operations room dominated by a large table displaying a map of the area. Officers looking down on this arena from glass fronted cabins, enjoyed not only a good view of the plotting table, but also a wall at the end of the operations room, completely covered by an information board known as the 'Tote' which was constantly updated to show details of aircraft availability and weather conditions. Several airmen put on headsets and took seats at the table, each one at the map position of a radar station. As information was received from the various stations, aircraft tracks were plotted on the table in coloured arrows, placed according to matching coloured segments on a wall mounted clock. In cabins adjacent to the main plotting room, night fighter aircraft were assisted in the interception of their targets by controllers, working directly from information displayed on radar screens.

Direction Finding stations were controlled from one of the cabins, and a pilot calling by radio for navigational assistance was given a fix of his position, calculated from cross bearings taken from his voice transmission. This system of direction finding, known as DF, was essentially unchanged since it was used in the 1930s to check the bearings of aircraft detected by acoustic mirrors. An overall picture of activities in the operations centre was passed to Group Headquarters by tellers, equipped with headsets, sitting on raised platforms around the main plotting table.

Winter scene, Sunk Island. The low buildings on the right
are the remains of the RAF Sector Operations Centre

Outside, armed airmen patrolled the boundaries of the field. In the quiet of the small hours, apart from the coughing of an occasional sheep, the only sound was the soft humming of electric motors, and the slight swish of air from a large Type 7 radar scanner rotating in the middle of the field. Nearby, a Type 13 height finding scanner nodded up and down as its invisible beam searched the sky. Looking out towards the nearby estuary, on clear nights, the flatness of the landscape created an impression that ships were sailing along the fields.

A Space Age intercontinental radar antenna on the North Yorkshire
Moors. Although much greater in scale, it bears a remarkable likeness to
a sound mirror from the acoustic years

Although the people in the Operations Centre, a mixture of Regular and National Service personnel, were not fully aware of it at the time, they were participating in the final stages of this type of early warning system, operated by men and women of the RAF since the days of the Battle of Britain. As with the preceding acoustic system, the speeds of aircraft, particularly the recently introduced jets, had increased to a point where the system could not keep pace with events. Also, the Operations Centre itself was visible and vulnerable to air attack. By the middle 1950s, this operations room, and others like it, was abandoned and replaced by underground facilities, making use of projected radar information from new and powerful scanners, with direct control of fighter aircraft from radar displays. These changes coincided with the death, far away in Canada, of leading acoustic pioneer Dr W.S. Tucker.

The silence of the fenlands on that cold night in 1949 was briefly disturbed by the sounds of the receding trucks carrying the airmen going off watch. Soon, they passed through a darkened village, with a great church and spire just visible against the night sky. On the coast nearby was a decaying concrete sound mirror dating back to the First World War. It is unlikely that the airmen in those trucks were aware of that relic of a detection system preceding their own which in turn was about to become obsolete. The future, with aircraft movements plotted and controlled not only by sophisticated radar but by computers and satellite technology was unimaginable. Nevertheless, the need for surveillance of crowded skies is a common thread linking air traffic controllers of the computer age with long forgotten acoustic pioneers, manning the sound mirrors and listening for echoes from the sky.

EPILOGUE

FAN BAY

In 2012 the National Trust (NT) acquired land along the cliff tops which flanked the existing footpath, and which forms the Saxon Shore Way and the White Cliffs Country Trail. The path extends beyond Dover, south-west towards Folkestone and north-east towards St Margaret's Bay and on to Walmer. It was known that Fan Hole – also known as Fan Bay – had been the site of a gun battery in the Second World War, and that a system of tunnels had been dug to provide accommodation for 154 men in bunks, with a full complement of gun crews, searchlight operators and various supporting roles numbering some 4 officers and 185 other ranks. It was also known that in the First World War two of the early sound mirrors had been built at Fan Hole, a depression in the cliffs, but their fate was unknown – it was possible they had been broken up, significantly damaged in other ways, or just buried. What was known was that the gun battery, which had consisted of three 6 inch guns, was decommissioned in the 1950s and the portals to the tunnels sealed. Later, in the 1970s, Kent County Council began an initiative to tidy up what many thought were unsightly reminders of the war and the entrances to the tunnels filled in. It was at this time that the still intact sound mirrors were also buried by the simple expedient of pushing some 600 tons of chalk and soil down onto them.

Following the 2012 acquisition of the land, it was decided by the NT that an attempt should be made to re-open the tunnels as part of a tourist experience, and the massive task of digging out the entrances began in earnest. For this a team of fifty volunteers was drawn together and contributed a huge 3,000 hours of free labour on the task; the volunteers being drawn from a cross section of interested groups, local caving clubs, historical research organisations and, of course, members of the NT. On top of this only three specialist contractors were engaged and just £117,000 spent in total – remarkable for the size of the project and a credit to all concerned, and all in eighteen months. The whole scheme was overseen by Jon Barker of the National Trust who admits it was a pretty tough project, and not one he'd easily repeat. Some 30 tons of material was blocking the upper entrance and there was no access for machinery, so it came down to hand digging and manual carrying out of the material which visitors to the site can now appreciate was a huge call on human endeavour.

The mirrors prior to being buried with latrine blocks in front

Plans of the shelter tunnels, drawn in 1940 at the time of construction, indicated that apart from the main entrance, two lower adit entrances led out towards the sea and would have emerged in the vicinity of the mirrors. Once the main entrance was cleared it was possible to inspect the interior which was, on the whole, in good order. Progress down the two adits towards what would have been access to the open air in the Fan Hole depression was halted by infill material; part of which had buried the mirrors. Initially, the clearance was carried out from above the mirror site using a 13 ton tracked excavator with a long reach arm. It was necessary to remove this deposit, as exposure of the mirrors combined with the weight of the material on the slope above them could have had disastrous consequences. An area some 15 metres square, and with an average depth of half a metre, was removed with the added bonus of exposing the original topsoil and potentially regenerating the chalk grassland flora. As the immediate area is listed as a Site of Special Scientific Interest (SSSI) and a Special Area of

Latrine blocks in front of mirror

The northern-most mirror showing damage to the edge and top corner

Conservation (SAC) it was of huge benefit to remove the chalk and soil covering, as well as beginning to expose the lost mirrors.

With the overlay removed, a trackway traversing the 45 degree incline was developed using a smaller 3 ton digger which was eventually able to begin the process of excavating the two entrances to the adits and the mirrors; excavated material being removed up the newly cut trackway by a pair of 3 ton tracked dump trucks where it was tipped and then removed off site. To provide independent observers and to maintain a 'watching brief', members of the Dover Archaeological Group under Richard Hoskins spent many hours on site and prepared a 34 page report on the NT excavation. This records the history of the site and the subsequent excavation in great detail, together with an evaluation of the structures found on site, and an analysis of finds which varied in age, importance and size.

It was during this phase of the excavation work that more positive indications of the sound mirrors were found and it seemed they were still in place and both in good order. When the northern mirror was excavated it was found to be in good condition and comparison with historical photographs indicated that only one crack was new. The southern mirror has evidence of an historic repair which was probably necessitated by damage caused by moisture penetrating to the face of the mirror. A concrete rain cover had been installed and there is still clear evidence of a gutter which was part of this feature. Following excavation it was clear that moisture was once again beginning to permeate through to the face and originates in an impermeable horizontal flint layer which bisects the mirror at about half height, encouraging water to build up behind the mirror and gradually seep through. A temporary rain cover was initially installed after the excavation and the whole structure was repaired to the original specification in November 2015

The substantial remains of some other buildings, situated close to the mirrors, were exposed during the excavation, helping to explain the two passages to the adit entrances, which both extended in a south-easterly direction from the main complex. There was some initial debate whether some of the tunnels predated the Second World War. Were the adit entrances linked to the mirrors and the First World War? However when the inland mirror was excavated, the original trajectory of the tunnel cut though the right hand edge of the northern / inland mirror – so the mirror was damaged when the adit was first cut. It would not have been desirable to damage the mirror if it was still operational which suggests both tunnels were actually cut in the Second World War. These adits would have been used to excavate all the material from the tunnels when under construction. The path outside would have originally had a narrow gauge Hudson track system which transported the spoil to the cliff edge and then dumped it over the side. This would have been the easiest and most discreet way to dispose of the spoil: an important factor as the site could easily be seen by the enemy on the French coast. It was also much easier to cut an adit on the horizontal level on stable ground, so the alcoves from the mirrors would have presented a logical place to start excavation of the tunnel system when suitable sites were being hurriedly identified in 1940. On 3 September 1940 a conference was held at GHQ (Home Defence) and the same day Brigadier Burrowes was dispatched to reconnoitre suitable sites, and by 6 September the site at Fan Hole was selected and confirmed by a War Office Siting Board held at Dover on 30 September, 1940. Once the adits were completed, the alcoves created by the mirrors presented a good site for the latrines. The mirrors and associated structures were camouflaged: many of the pins used to secure camouflage netting were discovered during the excavation. The discovery of another building not shown on the military plan of the site suggests that a large hut was built on the upper side of Fan Hole. The path which connected the mirrors and the hut was probably destroyed when they excavated and built a large generator room during the war.

The primary use of at least one of the tunnels would have been an alternative means of escape; even the smallest Observer Corps bunkers have an emergency raking ladder and hatchway. The other purpose was to provide access to the searchlight installations at the bottom of the Fan Bay depression and also the latrines by each of the sound mirrors. The 1940 plan shows that the latrines by the northern sound mirror were to have piped water and an ablution bench. No such facilities were shown for the latrines by the south mirror. It seems likely in both cases that the latrines themselves took the form of Elsan chemical toilets as no plumbing arrangements were shown on the plan, nor found during the excavation. A water pipe was, however, found where the ablution bench was shown in the plan near the northern latrines.

The excavated (southern) mirror in 2015

The excavated (northern) mirror in 2015

The Fan Bay site relative to Dover Harbour

Richard and Hilda Scarth visit the excavated mirrors in 2014. Left to right,
Pat McMaster, Richard Scarth, Hilda Scarth & Jon Barker

In July 2015 the tunnels were opened to the public and remain a popular attraction. Information can be found on the NT website and at the White Cliffs of Dover Park and other NT information points. Tours of the tunnels and mirrors are guided by volunteers, and hard hats, head lights and other safety equipment are available to visitors. It goes without saying that visitors need to be reasonably fit to walk out to the entrance from a designated meeting point, and to negotiate the stairs and slopes inside. The endeavour of the NT staff and the volunteers has exposed an interesting phase in our history and crucial structures which formed part of the history of acoustic detection.

Material additional to original manuscript by Peter Osborne, Jon Barker and Robert Hall.

The original inland mirror was excavated on 23 October 2014, which coincided with a visit to the site by Richard Scarth and his wife, Hilda. Richard was thrilled to see one of the surviving 15 foot mirrors. He had often visited Fan Bay after the eyesore clearance program and wondered if the Fan Bay mirrors survived. Sadly Richard passed away two weeks after his visit following an accident.

Richard N. Scarth 1930 - 2014

LIST OF PHOTOGRAPHS AND ACKNOWLEDGEMENTS

Page

Archive

PRIMARY SOURCES

Crown Copyright material from the National Archives is reproduced by permission of the Controller of Her Majesty's Stationery Office.
Files consulted:-
AIR1/121/15/40/105;AIR1/146/15/59;AIR1/546/16/15/17;
AIR1/548/16/15/18;AIR2/1195; AIR16 /304, 316, 317,318, 319, 320
ADM116/1430,1431;ADM212/158; ADM245/6;
AVIA7/2761,2762,2763,2764,2765,2767,2768,2792,2799,2809,2907,29
58,2961,2914,2915,2916,2917,2918,2919,2920,2923,2927,2928,2929,293
1,2935,2938,2939,2941,2948,2949,2952,2953,3179,3180,3182,3183,3184
,3185,3186,3187,3188,3189,3190,3254,3258,3528,3551;
AVIA17/3,4,5,6,8,9,10,11,20,22,24,25,26,27, 30,31,37,38,39,40,41,44,47;
AVIA23/1,8,19,54,60,64,70,75,78,82,84,9096,98,105,109,117,121,1
22,124,150,151,152,153,161,162,171,172,176,182,184,199,231,232,253,2
70,277,279,289,295,296.
CAB42/8/5; DSIR23/577; DSIR10/127;MUN4/2009; MUN7/308,309;
WO/662
Thanks are due to Mr A. Williams and Mr P. Sturm, Readers Services Department.
Proceedings of The Royal Engineers Board.
Royal Engineers Journal.
History of the Corps of Royal Engineers.
Theory and Use of Anti Aircraft Sound Locators, War Office 1922, courtesy of Mrs M. Magnuson, Royal Engineers Library, Chatham.
Journal of The Royal Artillery.
The Theory of Anti Aircraft Sound Location and Detection HMSO 1932.
ADEE Reports MD1602.
Sound Locator Handbooks, courtesy of Mrs K.A.Timbers, Librarian of the Royal Artillery Historical Trust, Woolwich.
Thanks are also due to Mr Paul Evans, Librarian Royal Artillery Museum, Royal Arsenal, Woolwich.
M.I.D. Report 46973, Science Museum Library.
Documents from Dover Museum, courtesy of Curator John Iveson.

ACKNOWLEDGEMENTS

The book could not have been written without the help and co-operation of Mrs Beryl Mutton, daughter of Dr W.S.Tucker, and her late husband Lawrence, who not only allowed access to Dr Tucker's private papers, but also made Hilda and myself very welcome at their home in Ontario. That connection was made possible through the help of Dr Peter Draper and his contacts in Canada, to whom very special thanks are due. I am also much indebted to Mrs Sylvia Warren for access to the personal papers of her father Mr Percy Rothwell, a close colleague of Dr Tucker. This account has been greatly illuminated by the reminiscences of Dr Tucker's scientific colleague the late Mr Hugh Roberts.

Interesting details were brought to light in correspondence with many people, including Mr W.G. Allen, Mrs C. Boddington, Senior Archivist, East Riding of Yorkshire County Council, the late Mr Richard Body, Mr M. Bragg, Mr I. Brown, Mr G.A.Dawes, Mr E.F.Cheeseman, Mr David Collyer, Mr T.R.A.Creedy, Sir Edward Fennessy, Mr Hassall Hanbury Brown, Mr J. Harwood, Air Vice-Marshal A.F.C. Hunter, Dr E. Putley, Mr Donald H. Tomlin, Major-General Eric Younson.

Mr R.G.Lewington, Deputy British High Commissioner, Malta, took a personal interest in the research in Malta, and many thanks are due to him and Mr Charles Camilleri, Chief Engineer and his staff at the Telemalta Communications station at Maghtab. Help was also given by Mrs Margaret Dyer, Mr A.R.W.Crowhurst, the late Mr Syd Goodsell, Lieutenant Colonel J. M. Umbers, the Manager of the Castle Keep Hotel, Kingsgate, Broadstairs, Kent, and Halls Aggregates (South Eastern) Ltd. I am particularly indebted to Mr Owen Leyshon of the Romney Marsh Countryside Project for his help in making arrangements for visits to the mirror sites. Over the years, under his leadership, we have been joined by many hundreds of visitors on guided walks to see the sound mirrors, particularly at Denge.

Helpful correspondence was exchanged with librarians and archivists in Redcar and Cleveland, North Yorkshire, Teeside, Sunderland, Newcastle, Hull, and in London the National Physical Laboratory and Imperial College. I am grateful to Consulting Engineers Cameron Taylor Bedford and O & L

Construction Ltd for valuable information and site access during the restoration of the sound mirrors at Denge.

I owe a great debt to my wife Hilda for her help in research and for her patience during the long periods when I was immersed in writing about acoustic matters. We enjoyed travelling together in pursuit of information, including visits to various archives, and overseas to Malta and Canada.

———

Thanks are also due to Robert Hall for his detailed proofreading of the final draft.

BIBLIOGRAPHY

Bragg Michael R D F 1
Paisley Hawkhead Publishing 2002

Churchill Winston S. The Second World War Volume Two Their Finest Hour
London Cassell 1949

Cole and Cheesman The Air Defence of Great Britain 1914 - 18
London Bodley Head 1984

Ronald W. Clarke Tizard
London Methuen 1965

Basil Collier The Defence of the United Kingdom
London HMSO 1957

W.J.K.Davies The Romney Hythe and Dymchurch Railway
Newton Abbot David and Charles 1988

Guilo Douhet - Command of the Air 1921

Max Hastings - Bomber Command
London Michael Joseph 1987

John R. Innes - Flash Spotters and Sound Rangers
London Allen and Unwin 1935

David C. Isby (editor) - Fighting the Bombers, The Luftwaffe's Struggle against the Allied Bomber Offensive
London Greenhill 2003

Alfred Price - Instruments of Darkness
London Macdonald and Janes 1977

Jeffrey Quill - Spitfire - A Test Pilot's Story
London John Murray 1983

A.P. Sayer The Second World War 1939 - 45, Army Radar
War Office 1950.

A. P. Rowe One Story of Radar
Cambridge University Press 1948

Robert Watson-Watt Three Steps to Victory
London Odhams Press 1957

A.F. Wilkins in - Gordon Kinsey - Bawdsey, Birth of the Beam
Lavenham Terence Dalton 1983

Alexander Wood - The Physics of Music
London Chapman Hall 1975

INDEX

THE AUTHOR

Sound is a linking factor in Richard Scarth's experience. He spent his professional life as a musician. His diverse music making included teaching and choral direction in schools, colleges and the university sector of higher education, and practical performance as an organist and keyboard player in dance bands and for musical shows. Along the way he gained various musical diplomas and qualified as an M.A. and Ph.D. from the University of London. Music was not his first choice of career. He began as an apprentice at Blackburn Aircraft, but following the award of a scholarship, he moved into the world of music, although retaining a life-long interest in engineering. During National Service in the Royal Air Force, he worked in a Sector Operations Centre, experiencing at first hand the workings of a radar-based control and reporting system using manual plotting, soon to become history. Although hailing from Yorkshire, much of his working life was spent in the Midlands and the South. He became interested in sound mirrors through a conversation with a fellow lecturer in Canterbury. Subsequently, he wrote about the Kent mirrors for Hythe Civic Society. He later extended his research to cover acoustic aircraft detection in general. He met his wife when they were fellow students in London, and lived until 2014 in retirement on the Kent coast.

OTHER BOOKS AVAILABLE DIRECT FROM INDEPENDENT

BOOKS AND CRECY PUBLISHING
'RAF BIGGIN HILL – THE OTHER SIDE OF THE BUMP'

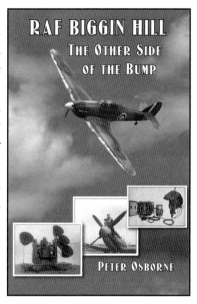

This is a new work exploring the research work which led to the creation of the airfield and the establishment of the Air Defence Experimental Establishment at Biggin Hill. It clearly details the developments in South Camp, the secret War Office area, the history of which has all but disappeared under housing and industrial development.

Key to air defence was the early detection of incoming raiders and, given that RADAR wasn't even the germ of an idea until 1935, it left a vacuum for twenty years which was filled by the science of acoustic detection, tangible remains of which can still be seen along the coast. These huge static 'ears', together with the mobile Sound Locators that were to guide the searchlights and anti-aircraft guns through the night sky during the Blitz, were a product of research and development at Biggin Hill and the all but forgotten scientists and engineers who worked there.

Later the interception tactics, which were to be a key element in the great RAF victory in 1940 were developed during the 'Biggin Hill Experiments', together with radio communications - the reason that the airfield first came to life - were honed to perfection, ready to meet the onslaught. Without the volume of research, development and experimentation undertaken at Biggin Hill there is little doubt that the Battle of Britain would have been lost.

This new work is the product of five years' research and fills a significant gap in the recorded history of the 'Most Famous Fighter Station in the World' and demonstrates that its legacy is much more than its role in the Battle of Britain.

Reviews:

Aeroplane Monthly: The detailed text is nicely written, backed up by an excellent and well produced photo section… a fine addition to existing Biggin Hill literature.

Britain at War: This fascinating and squarely researched title covers RAF Biggin Hill, easily justifiable as the 'most famous fighter station in the world'. However this book offers more on the station's broader history rather than solely concentrating on the station's Battle of Britain role.

FlyPast: This book – which also features hundreds of rarely seen images – is the product of five years research and fills a significant gap in the recorded history of one of the world's most famous fighter stations.

Available by post in Hardback and large format softback, 352 pages with 226 previously unpublished or rarely seen, pictures, plans and illustrations.

Hardback: ISBN 978-1-872836-07-2 - **£19.95**

Softback: ISBN 978-1-872836-12-6 - **£12.95**

'SPITFIRE ON MY TAIL'

Best selling book on the Battle of Britain from the German side. Reprinted for the sixthedition and now available in large format paperback.

On 27 October 1940, having completed over 150 missions, Oberleutnant Ulrich Stein-hilper's fighter was shot down, crashing into the Kent countryside near Canterbury. For Ulrich that was the end of everything for which he'd been prepared in the Luftwaffe since his acceptance in 1936. But there is more than a pilot's story to tell. He shares with the reader what it was like to grow up in Germany as the crippling conditions of the Treaty of Versailles bled away the country's economy; how it was inevitable that the people would succumb to the fatal attraction of Hitler and 'The Party'. More personally, Ulrich relates how the intrigues and politics of a small town were to shape his destiny.

From a mountain village in southern Germany to Berlin swollen with people for the 1936 Olympic Games, we follow Ulrich to the start of his military career and through the rigorous basic training to his first faltering flights as a pilot. Onwards, towards the Battle of Britain and his uncompromising views of the conduct of the battle both by the Luftwaffe High Command and the RAF.

In a fighter group decimated by losses and battle fatigue Ulrich still carries on, but is he really prepared for what has befallen his friends and colleagues? If the Luftwaffe's estimates of British fighter strength were correct, then why are they still facing such determined resistance? Will the Army ever start the invasion of Britain? Will the sacrifice of so many airmen have been for nothing?

Foreword by Stephen Bungay – Author of 'Most Dangerous Enemy'

Hardback:

ISBN (10)	1-872836-00-3
ISBN (13)	978-1-872836-00-3
EAN:	9781872836003

384 pages, hardback
240 mm x 160 mm
Over eighty b&w photographs.

Price: **£19.95**

Paperback:

ISBN (10)	1-872836-79-8
ISBN (13):	978-1-872836-79-9
EAN:	9781872836799

384 pages, paperback
234 mm x 156 mm
Over eighty b&w photographs.

Price: **£12.95**

'TEN MINUTES TO BUFFALO'
The Story of Germany's Great Escaper
Ulrich Steinhilper & Peter Osborne
Non-Fiction Illustrated

ISBN: 978-1-872836-01-0
Hardback only, 431 pages, 45 black & white
illustrations. **Price: £14.95**

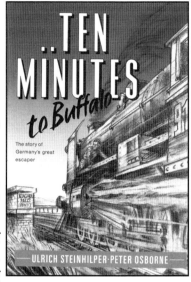

'Ten Minutes to Buffalo' is long-awaited sequel to Ulrich Steinhilper's highly successful first book, 'Spitfire On My Tail'. Unlike the first book, which tells the story of how a young German came to fly in Hitler's Luftwaffe and to fight in the Battle of Britain, 'Ten Minutes to Buffalo' is a catalogue of courage and determination on the ground. In this way it is set to repeat the successful formula by providing a rare chance to witness how things were for 'The Other Side,' this time behind the barbed wire and in Ulrich Steinhilper's case - all too often outside the wire! It relates a story of remarkable courage and perseverance in the most appalling conditions, braving arctic weather and appalling hardship with one thought in mind - to get home.

From his first camp in England away to the vastness of Canada, he and a select few of his fellow officers were to become known as Die Ausbrecherkönige von Kanada (the breakout kings from Canada) and Ulrich was to shine among them. His escapes were innovative and even audacious and it was only bad luck that seemed to keep him from a completely successful 'homerun'.

Very little has ever been written about the conditions of German officers as prisoners of the Allies and practically nothing of their ingenuity and perseverance in planning and executing escape plans so similar to their counterparts in German hands. This remarkable book is entirely written from original hand-written sheets which date from 1942 and which give it a great immediacy and accuracy.

'FULL CIRCLE'

The Long Way Home From Canada
Ulrich Steinhilper & Peter Osborne
Non-Fiction Illustrated
ISBN (10) 1-872836-02-X
ISBN (13) 978-1-872836-02-7

Hardback only, 408 pages, 74 black & white pictures and illustrations.

Price: £17.95

'Full Circle' is the last of three books which record Ulrich Steinhilper's remarkable experiences in the Second World War. From being a front line fighter pilot in the Battle of Britain he becomes a Prisoner of War, but for Ulrich the war is far from over.

In 'Ten Minutes To Buffalo', the story of the first three escapes is told and in 'Full Circle' the story is continued as Ulrich and Hinnerk Waller find themselves back in custody. But that is far from the end of Ulrich's career as an escaper. Nor is it the end of the detailed and fascinating description of life as a POW. Locking up large numbers of bright young men led to the most ingenious schemes to manufacture their own radios, make their own tools and later, on their Ehrenwort (word of honour), to rebuild and run a farm.

Ulrich describes in graphic detail his last attempt to get back to Germany, admitting it was the worst mistake he ever made in his life. From documents, hand-written at the time, and from numerous letters and postcards home he accurately reconstructs what it was like to be a prisoner of the Allies and the hardships that brought at the end.

'Full Circle' completes Ulrich Steinhilper's odyssey and, with, it what is now being described as one of the most important contributions to the broader history of the Second World War to emerge in recent times.

'DON'T TALK – DO IT'

Ulrich Steinhilper

Non-Fiction Illustrated
ISBN (10) 1 872836 75 5
ISBN (13) 978 1 872836 75 1

Hardback only, 272 pages, 40 black & white pictures and illustrations.
Price: 16.95

Word Processing is a term which most people understand today, but fifty years ago there was only one voice using it, a young typewriter salesman who was working for IBM Germany. Ulrich Steinhilper had the idea to use Textverarbeitung (Word Processing), a new concept, so that office products could be marketed in the same way that Data Processing equipment was sold by IBM. It was not as we might recognise it today; it was more a holistic approach to the diverse skills which are needed to improve office efficiency and to bring streamlined factory production line techniques to the office. Fortunately he submitted his thoughts as a Staff Suggestion and was duly paid 25 German Marks for his trouble, but he had registered it and had proof of it. When others tried to claim that it was they who had first conceived the name 'Word Processing' Ulrich fought for recognition and, finally, IBM committed it to paper and sent him on a trip around the world in recognition of his work.

Over and above being the story of the evolution of Word Processing, 'Don't Talk - Do It!' is a fascinating record of the development of post-war business. It is also an intriguing illustration of how one man made his contribution in the true pioneering spirit, helping Germany rise from the ruins of World War II to one of the world's most successful industrial nations.

REPRINTED FOR POPULAR DEMAND

'TARGET DRESDEN'
Alan Cooper

Non-Fiction Illustrated
ISBN (10): 1-872836-60-7
ISBN (13): 978-1-872836-60-7

 Paperback: 256 pages, 43 b&w photographs
and illustrations.

Price: £10.95

On the night of 13-14th February 1945, 796
Lancasters and 9 Mosquitoes of RAF
Bomber Command, dropped 1,478 tons of
high explosive and 1,182 tons of incendiaries on the city of Dresden. A
firestorm developed, which led to large areas of the city being burned out.
At the time of the attack, Dresden was crowded with refugees fleeing the
advancing Soviet Army resulting in between 40,000 and 50,000 casualties.
On the morning of the 14th a second attack was carried out by the United
States Army Air Force followed by two further US attacks.
Target Dresden chronicles the development of bombing from the earliest
days through the tactical and strategic bombing of WWII and gives the story
behind these controversial raids.

'TEST PILOTS'
Wolfgang Späte

Non-Fiction Illustrated
ISBN (13) 978-1-872836-80-5
Paperback: 304 pages 102 b&w photographs
and illustrations. **Price: £10.95**

This is an exciting new book relating the firsthand experiences of predominantly German Test Pilots. Including over one hundred photographs and illustrations, the majority of which have never been seen before, it is full of refreshingly new material. The collection of anecdotal accounts covers such varied flying tests as those of the Natter, a manned, rocket-launched interceptor designed to release a salvo of missiles at Flying Fortress formations; and the DFS 228, arguably the forerunner of the Lockheed U2, with a service ceiling calculated at eighty thousand feet and a range of nearly a thousand miles. There are also vivid descriptions of the first trials of the ejector seat; towing aircraft on a one metre long rigid tow; the beginnings of air-to-air refuelling, and even the plans for a bomber which would tow its own fighter escort across the Atlantic to engage the USAF over their home ground. Test Pilots is essential reading for all aviation enthusiasts and historians.

Foreword by Captain Eric 'Winkle' Brown
C.O. Enemy Aircraft Flight, RAE Farnborough (1945–47)
Author of 'Wings On My Sleeve'
'Although Wolfgang Späte never became an established test pilot himself, he has opened the door into some fascinating scenarios which caught his imagination. The reader should eagerly share these.'

Captain Eric Brown, CBE, DSC, AFC, RN

'BLUE SKIES AND DARK NIGHTS'
Bill Randle

Non-Fiction Illustrated
ISBN (10): 1-872836-40-2
ISBN (13): 978-1-872836-40-9

Hardback only, 352 pages, iillustrated with
over 90 black & white photographs.
Price: **£19.95**

'Blue Skies and Dark Nights' is the autobi-
ography of Group Captain Bill Randle. From
his initial flight training in the United States
on the fledgling Arnold scheme, to the
bombing of Germany, through a remarkable evasion and successful 'home
run', to MI9 and the formation of post-war Escape and Evasion policy with
the Americans, to learning to fly helicopters with the US Marines, then on
to taking part in search and rescue missions in Korea; this is a honest and
straightforward account of a unusual career in the RAF and beyond.

Those with an interest in the RAF and world affairs will find Bill Randle's
story fascinating as he describes what it was like to be at the centre of many
world events. It also clearly illustrates the frustrations implicit in a service
life, as well as the great humour and tragedy which go with the acceptance
of the responsibilities of rank.

'MY WAR'

Behind Enemy Lines with SOE in Europe and the Far East

Harry Verlander

ISBN: 9781872836850
Binding: Hardback
Dimentions: 240mm x 160mm
Pages: 368
Photos/Illus: Over 80 b&w photographs and illustrations.

Price: £19.95

The Special Operations Executive (SOE) French section, Jedburgh teams, and Special Air Service (SAS) sent into west and south-west France, helped the French Resistance liberate the whole area without assistance from any other ground forces.

Having been deeply involved behind the lines in France, Harry Verlander volunteered to serve once more, but this time in the mountains and jungles of Burma. No more the rolling countryside of rural France but the brutal uncompromising hand-to-hand fighting against the Japanese. This very personal story gives a detailed account of both the campaign in France and that vicious time in Burma.

'SHARK SQUADRON PILOT'
Author: Bert Horden

ISBN: 9781872836454
Binding: Hardback
Dimentions: 234mm x 156mm
Pages: 193
Photos/Illus: Over 80 b&w photographs

Price: £19.95

A graphic illustration of the realities of the air war in the Western Desert, Shark Squadron Pilot describes Bert Horden's service with 112 'Shark' Squadron and the ground attack role of the 'Kittys'. With their garish shark's mouths painted on their aircraft 112 Squadron wreaked havoc on the German Afrika Korps inflicting terrible damage with machine gun fire and under-slung bombs.

Using his diary and flying log book to preserve the accuracy and immediacy of the events Bert Horden presents a superbly graphic account of desert flying.

AVAILABLE FROM:

INDEPENDENT BOOKS
3, Leaves Green Crescent
Keston
BROMLEY
BR2 6DN

Tel: 01959573360
Email: mail@indbooks.co.uk
Web: www.indbooks.co.uk

CRECY PUBLISHING
Unit 1 Ringway Trading Estate
Shadowmoss Road
Manchester
M22 5LH

Tel: 01614990024
Email: enquiries@crecy.co.uk
Web: www.crecy.co.uk